The W6SAI HF Antenna Handbook

The W6SAI HF Antenna Handbook

By William I. Orr, W6SAI

CQ Communications, Inc.

Fourth Printing 2005

Library of Congress Catalog Card Number 96-084315
ISBN 0-943016-15-0

Editor: Terry Littlefield, KA1STC
Managing Editor: Gail M. Schieber
Editorial Assistant: Nancy Barry
Technical Advisor: Lew Ozimek, N2OZ
Layout and Design: Edmond Pesonen
Illustrations: Hal Keith, K & S Graphics
Cover art: Janine Perry

Published by CQ Communications, Inc.
25 Newbridge Road
Hicksville, NY 11801 USA

Printed in the United States of America.

CAUTION: Working on antennas and towers can be dangerous. All warnings on equipment and all operating and use instructions should be adhered to. Make sure that the antenna is disconnected from the station equipment before you begin to work on it. Make sure that your antenna is not close to power lines, and that it cannot drop onto a power line if wires or supports fail. Do not attempt to climb a tower without a safety belt. It is best to work on your antenna with someone who can assist you with tools and who will be able to help in the event of a problem or emergency.

Table of Contents

Preface

My interest in ham antennas started at an early age. For my tenth birthday, my dad gave me a Philmore crystal set and a pair of genuine Brandes headphones. The set had a tapped tuning coil, and I could clearly hear three or more fellas talking back and forth when I moved the tap just so. The voices were very weak. Who were they? Was I eavesdropping on local telephone calls? My dad said no, the stations I heard were radio hams.

Radio hams? I talked to my friends about this new discovery and we figured out that fellas like us could talk on the radio, if we just knew how to do it. It was obvious that a transmitter and an antenna were required, and probably a license of some sort—and call letters. If we had all of this, then we could be real radio hams.

Putting up a good antenna seemed a fine way to get things started. A nifty place to erect a transmitting wire was from my second-story bedroom window out to an old tree at the back of the lot. It was nearly 100 feet away. Attaching the antenna to the house took but a moment one warm spring day. I reeled the wire out across the yard and climbed up into the tree with a length of clothesline to make a tie-off point. I climbed up to a large vee, about 25 feet above ground. There I was able to stand steady in the tree. This seemed a good place to hook the antenna. By chance, I happened to glance to the right into the next-door neighbor's yard. There was his daughter lying on a blanket taking a sunbath! Starkers! Holy Smoke! I nearly fell out of the tree! I must have made a slight noise, as she unshaded her eyes, saw me, and grabbed a blanket, running for the house, yelling that she would "fix me" when she caught me. (She was about two years older than I.) She caught me for sure the next day on the way to school and planted a hard fist right in my face. I concluded that I definitely would have to be more circumspect when I again attempted to hook my sky-wire in the tree.

I was making progress. In a few months the back-yard was littered with scraps of copper wire from experimental antennas. It was amazing! I could snatch signals out of the air from all over the world and hear them on my new two-tube receiver. Once I got my ham ticket, I could be on the air and talk to these fellas! One of the keys to success was a good antenna

and I was going to find out all I could about these fascinating devices!

I soon met some of the local amateurs. W2DOM had an "end-fed Zepp" antenna. I carefully wrote down the specifications of this awesome device. W2DRH had a "delta match" center-fed wire, with a transmission line spaced with wooden dowel rods. W2OA, the DX king, ran a monster kilowatt transmitter with a Windom antenna. "I can melt the head off a hammer when I touch it to my feedline," he said modestly. I was impressed.

Once I got my ticket and got on the air, I quickly picked up some more antenna lore. When I migrated to 20 meters, I discovered the "Johnson-Q" antenna. That was a dipole of magical properties with a heavy aluminum matching system hung from the middle of the wire. I bought one, erected it with some difficulty, and it worked very well until I found out that some of the DX operators had beam antennas! How could my dipole compete with a beam? I didn't have the space to erect all the poles and wires that were required for a big beam. Alas. The famous antenna expert, John Kraus, solved my problem with his famous W8JK rotary beam. John's beam was small and easy to build. It was a killer! I could compete with the big boys! I quickly won an early WAC on 20-meter phone in 1937 and was ready for the big time.

Meanwhile, out in California, hams were experimenting with rotary Yagi beams. W6APU and W6PKK built 3-element Yagis for 10 meters that quickly established the supremacy of this type of antenna. At last! Here was the ultimate antenna for the DX-minded radio ham (me)! But where could I buy aluminum tubing? The lucky W6s lived near aircraft manufacturing plants, and surplus tubing was cheap. Not so in the New York area.

That problem was solved after World War II. We moved to Los Angeles, and by 1947 the surplus stores were full of aluminum tubing at two bucks a length. In 1948, W6TEZ, W6VFR (now W6FR), W6WKU (now W4BAA), and I built an all-aluminum 3-element Yagi for 14 MHz (described in *QST*, February 1949). This unique design quickly became the standard of comparison for 20-meter DX chasers.

Since those early days, the ham magazines have presented a lot of information covering antennas, which are just about the last field of experimentation available to the DX-minded ham with a modest pocketbook. In this handbook I have compiled some of the antenna types with which I've experimented over the years. These are good antennas. They work. They are easily built and don't cost very much. Build one of these designs and have a lot of fun.

And so it goes. I've been fascinated with antennas since those early days in New York when I found out what fun it was to build and erect sky wires. However, I never again had the thrill of looking over the fence and seeing the neighbor's daughter sunbathing—starkers! You certainly don't get that opportunity every day!

Acknowledgements

This book is the product of many individuals. The basic material was derived from my monthly columns in *CQ* magazine, but it is a long adventure from a series of short articles to a completed book.

I owe special thanks to Dick Ross, K2MGA, Publisher of *CQ* magazine, who encouraged this project and who lent it his enthusiastic support. I certainly owe special thanks to Terry Littlefield, KA1STC, Editor of CQ Communications' *Communications Quarterly* magazine, and Gail Schieber, Managing Editor of *CQ* magazine, for their help and cooperation and uncanny ability to straighten out my tangled syntax. John Dorr, K1AR, and Nancy Barry of CQ Communications were of important assistance in the initial stages of producing this book. My thanks also go to Ed Pesonen, Hal Keith of K & S Graphics, and Janine Perry for their artistic talents in producing the layout, illustrations and cover art, respectively. I thank them all for their technical help and their support and cooperation.

Finally, this book is dedicated to my dear wife, Natalie (Sunny), who departed this life during the final preparation of this work.

About the Author

Bill Orr became interested in radio at a very tender age when he dismantled his dad's Radiola IIIA to find the little men inside who were talking and making music. His father was not amused, and Bill's career as a would-be ham was put on ice for several years, during which time he contented himself with building crystal receivers.

Finally, in 1934 Bill was licensed as W2HCE. He started out on 160 meters with the popular homemade "46 job" transmitter and a simple three-tube superhet receiver. The best DX was Florida—not bad. During the summer months he built a one-tube transceiver for 5 meters. It was mostly ineffective.

The DX bug had bitten W2HCE badly, however, and in 1935 he migrated to 20 meters. Using a dipole and 120 watts he achieved the coveted "WAC Phone" award, which was not an easy task in those early days.

Reading articles by John Kraus, W8JK, on his compact rotary beam in the old *Radio* magazine, Bill was inspired to build one. The amazing performance of this beam fueled his interest in antennas, which remains to this day (with Bill's thanks to John).

Moving to California in 1938, Bill was relicensed as W6SAI when he was an undergraduate at the University of California. Bill's grandiose plans for a super-DX station came to a quick halt with the advent of World War II. Bill was in the Radio Test Department of Douglas Aircraft Co., and while he worked with radios for the duration, his "on the air" experience was limited to only military circuits.

Back on the air after the war, Bill was one of the first hams with a full-size, 3-element, 20-meter rotary beam. He quickly earned DXCC #17 and WAZ #4.

After a stint in the Missile Division of Hughes Aircraft Co., Bill and his family migrated to the San Francisco area. There he joined Eitel-McCullough, a pioneer manufacturer of high-power vacuum tubes. He retired from this work after 28 years, gaining a good working knowledge of transmitting tubes and transmitters.

Bill was active in Project Oscar (now AMSAT) and attended the launch of Oscar 1 at Vandenburgh AFB. He has been licensed as FP8AC, 3A2AF, KH6ADR, and ZL0SAI. He is the author of over 100 technical articles and many books, including the *Radio Handbook,* the *Beam Antenna Handbook,* and *All About Cubical Quad Antennas.* Bill's colleague on many of the books is his life-long friend Stu Cowan, W2LX, whom he thanks.

Bill operates mostly on 18 and 24 MHz, phone and CW, with some experiments on 1296 MHz FM ("the undiscovered band"). He lives in Menlo Park, California, and has six grown children and four grandchildren. Bill doesn't chase DX like he used to, but he does enjoy building antennas and chatting on the air with his many friends worldwide—and writing an occasional article or handbook. That's pretty good for a fella who sat at the back of his English class in high school and threw spitballs at the girls!

Introduction

This is a "hands on" handbook. It's long on methods for building practical antennas and short on abstract theory. Theory you can find in other handbooks. These are inexpensive, practical antennas that work! They are easy to build, provided you keep your wits about you. No special expertise is needed.

You'll need a few good tools, instruments, and accessories to do the job. Here's a handy list of things I have around for antenna work:

• **Safety belt.** You need a belt if you're going to do serious antenna work. There's no use breaking your neck unnecessarily. Many good belts are advertised in ham magazines. Your friendly ham equipment distributor probably has one or two types in stock.

• **Tools.** In addition to the usual run-of-the-mill tools, you'll need some specialized ones. I'll give you the RadioShack catalog numbers of some helpful gadgets. No doubt you can find a lot of this stuff at other places: automotive outlets, ham equipment distributors, and maybe even the corner drugstore.

Soldering tool. Your best bet is a rechargeable, cordless soldering gun. Get rid of the dangling line cord. You might trip over it scrambling around on your roof. Try RadioShack's cordless gun (64-2194) with a 40-watt blade (64-2197). If you insist on a regular gun, RadioShack no. 64-2193 will do the job. I don't recommend gas-powered butane torches. These are far too dangerous to use while clambering around in trees, etc.

Solder. The new soldering tape is very handy (RadioShack no. 64-010). The 60/40 solder formula is more traditional. You'll find a 1-pound roll very useful (64-008).

Other gadgets. You'll also need diagonal cutters, long-nose pliers, an assortment of screwdrivers, and a sharp jackknife. A good tape measure and a yardstick are essential. Gone are the days when you could build an antenna with a rusty Boy Scout knife and a broken screwdriver!

• **Instrumentation.** You'll be flying blind in your antenna work if you don't have at least one good instrument to tell you what's going on with your antenna. The most popular device is the SWR meter. Some fellas use a laboratory-grade through-line wattmeter that has plug-in power/frequency heads.

SWR can be computed from the forward and reverse power readings. One popular plug-in is rated at 100 watts over the 2–30 MHz range.

A less expensive SWR meter is the dual-needle device that registers both forward and reflected power simultaneously. It is less expensive than the plug-in style meter and is satisfactory for most ham use. Stay away from cheap, CB-type meters, as their accuracy is poor.

Investigate the newer instruments, such as the SWR Analyzer (sometimes called an Antenna Analyst). These nifty, pocket-size instruments combine a signal generator, a frequency counter, and an SWR readout. More on these instruments in Chapter 10.

A few experiments make interesting measurements with a signal generator, a receiver, and an RF bridge. The venerable General Radio bridge can sometimes be found in surplus stores that handle instruments. The measurements are accurate, but time-consuming. The bridge readings can be plotted directly on a Smith Chart, if you like that kind of thing.

• **Rope.** For light-weight, temporary antennas, good old 9/64-inch diameter sash cord (sometimes called "mason line") is ideal. It will last about a year before it gradually rots out. It's great stuff for experimental or Field Day antennas. Some fellas use ordinary clothesline, which also seems to last about a year before it goes kaput.

The 3/16-inch diameter, solar-resistant Dacron double-weave line is the best grade of rope to use. Nylon rope is next best, although it has a tendency to stretch. Sometimes it is helpful if your antenna is tied to a swaying tree!

• **Pulleys.** Galvanized awning and clothesline pulleys are cheap. Even when oiled, they only last a year or so. If it's easy to get to the pulley, it can be replaced when necessary. Otherwise, you'll have to go to a higher quality marine pulley, or a wood-sheathed pulley of the type used in construction work (expensive!).

Living in a mild climate, I got away with sash cord and galvanized pulleys for years. The extreme winter of 1995, however, finished off my cheap-and-dirty antennas, and the following spring I had to replace all the antenna hardware.

• Finally, a good dose of **common sense** is absolutely invaluable. Don't attach your antenna to a power pole! Don't run your antenna over or under utility lines! Don't do anything foolish! Watch yourself when you climb trees or work on a rooftop. Use rubber-soled shoes.

A well-known DXer once put up a 40-foot, guyed tower on his roof. He stepped back to admire his work—right off the edge of the roof! Luckily, he landed in a large bush and escaped alive, with only scratches and plenty of bruises, including a bruised ego. Don't pull a stunt like that! Use your head. Good luck, and go to work!

Bill Orr, W6SAI

Chapter 1

A Quick Look at Coax, Ground Loss, Antenna Height, SWR, Radiation Resistance (and all that jazz)

In the mid-thirties, the military standardized its transmission systems around a newly developed coax line with a polyethylene, low-loss dielectric. The cable had a characteristic impedance of 52 ohms. This means that for a given power level, a properly terminated cable had an input voltage-to-line-current ratio at any point along its length of 52-to-1 (52:1). It was called RG-8/U (for Radio-guide #8/utility cable).

About twenty years later, the cable impedance was changed to 50 ohms to conform to international specifications, and a whole family of new cables was produced for this modern system. Today's amateurs use either cable, although the older type is still popular among many enthusiasts. In Europe and other parts of the world, some coax cable is standardized on 75 ohms impedance. This family of cables is currently used overseas, but isn't popular in the United States, aside from TV, video, and computer installations.

Antenna Matching and SWR

A properly matched 50-ohm coax has a source (transmitter) with a 50-ohm output port, and has an antenna at the other end of the line adjusted for a 50-ohm feedpoint. In this ideal case, the applied voltage-to-line-current ratio at any point along the cable is 50:1.

If, for some reason, the antenna feedpoint is other than 50 ohms, a mismatch occurs and some of the RF energy reaching the antenna is reflected back along the cable toward the source (**Figure 1-1**). At the

source it is re-reflected back to the antenna. The reflected power may, in some instances, pass back and forth along the cable a number of times, before eventually being accepted by the antenna.

The forward-going and reflected waves react upon each other, much as ripples in a pond when two pebbles are tossed in. The resulting combination wave pattern is called a standing wave. Thus, on a mismatched coax line, the voltage and current ratio isn't constant along the line. However, aside from a slight decrease in power due to cable loss, the power passing through the line remains constant when a standing wave exists.

All of this happens in the merest microsecond, and

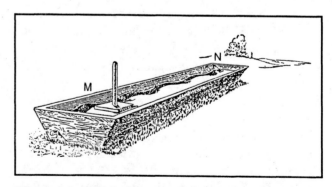

Figure 1-1. Wave reflection may be visualized in a water trough. When energy is applied at M by a flat paddle, a water wave travels toward the opposite end, N. A wave of water splashes up on the end board, and as it falls it delivers energy to a new wave, which travels back again toward M. Both the water wave and electrical wave are known as reflection. The resultant wave pattern is called a standing wave.

the only way an observer will notice it is by means of an instrument designed to detect forward and reverse energy flowing in the coax. One such instrument is the SWR meter. This device monitors the voltages in the coax, and the result is presented in terms of the standing wave ratio (SWR).

SWR is a representation of the amplitude of cable voltage, frozen in time (**Figure 1-2**). The reference is the 50-ohm line impedance. If the SWR is unity (represented as 1:1), there is no reflected voltage because the antenna feedpoint exactly matches the cable impedance. If, however, the ratio is higher (say, 2:1), an impedance mismatch exists.

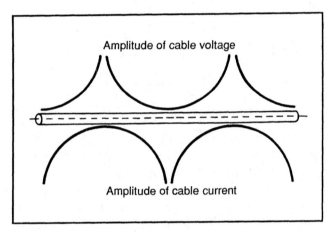

Figure 1-2. Although amplitudes of voltage and current vary along the line, the product of voltage and current (watts) is constant along the line. The SWR meter monitors the forward and reverse voltage flowing in the line.

Transceiver Shutdown

Coax cables, and amateur antennas, can work efficiently with SWR values as high as 5:1, but the modern solid-state transceiver protects the expensive output transistors from destruction by high SWR by reducing power output in relation to the SWR level (**Figure 1-3**). The shutdown effect is noticeable on any band where high SWR occurs, and the degree of shutdown depends upon the transceiver design.

The average ham antenna shows unity SWR only at the resonant frequency (the design frequency); operation off this frequency results in a higher SWR level. As a result, maximum transmitter power can't be obtained across most amateur bands from a solid-state rig unless some kind of impedance matching network is placed either at the antenna or the transmitter. Sometimes networks are used in both places to achieve wideband transmitter loading.

Trimming the Coax Line

Remember my mention of the 50:1 voltage to current ratio in a matched coax line? Well, if the line is mismatched to the antenna, different ratios will be found at different points along the line. The upshot is a standing wave on the line. Transceiver shutdown is a direct result of high SWR. You can compensate for this situation by adjusting the length of the line, so that an appropriate impedance is presented to the transmitter. You haven't changed the SWR, but you have changed the voltage-to-current ratio at the transmitter end of the line (see **Figure 1-2**). If you're lucky, you can find a line length that provides a termination the transceiver will accept.

I have a collection of short line sections, with PL-259 plugs on each end. The sections are 2-, 4-, and 8-feet long. I can splice one or all of them in the line with PL-258 couplers. I watch the power output indicator on the transceiver. Presto! A certain line length permits proper transmitter loading! I haven't changed the SWR on the line; I've merely found the spot that the transceiver accepts for maximum power output.

Changing frequency can screw up this scheme, but it's better than a poke in the eye with a stick. It gets you on the air with a minimum of hassle. For a more elegant solution, read next about the antenna tuner.

The Shutdown Problem Solved with an Antenna Tuner

The annoying shutdown problem can be solved permanently with an antenna tuning unit (ATU). The

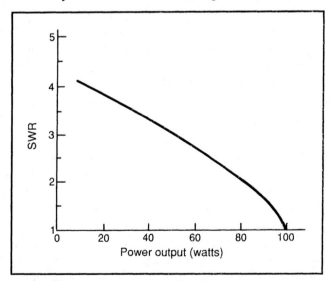

Figure 1-3. The transmitter shuts down when SWR becomes excessive. A solution to the problem is to use an antenna tuner (ATU).

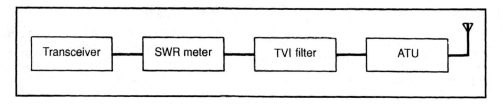

Figure 1-4. Place the ATU after the SWR meter and the TVI filter.

ATU really doesn't tune the antenna; it transforms the SWR at the transceiver end of the coax line to unity, or near unity, so the transceiver can deliver maximum power output.

Some transceivers have built-in ATUs that automatically match the SWR and make the appropriate internal circuit adjustments. Transceivers that lack this feature require an external, add-on ATU as additional station equipment.

Older, tube-type transceivers had panel controls ("tune" and "load") that compensated for the SWR of the coax line—provided the SWR figure wasn't excessively high. This convenience is lacking in today's solid-state equipment, and confirms the saying that "newer is not always better."

The LCL, CLC, and Z-match Antenna Tuners

The ATU is a network that provides a unity match for the transmitter. It's connected as shown in **Figure 1-4**. Note that the TVI prevention filter and SWR meter are inserted in the line before the ATU and that the SWR meter is placed before the filter for best results.

There are a few popular types of ATUs on the market. All accomplish the same function, but they differ in circuitry (**Figure 1-5**). Two types have three main controls. One design has a tapped inductor with a rotary switch and two variable capacitors. This is described as a capacitor-inductor-capacitor (CLC) tuner. The second type has two adjustable inductors and one variable capacitor (inductor-capacitor-inductor, or LCL, tuner). Some amateurs prefer the LCL design, as the capacitor to ground provides a degree of harmonic attenuation that isn't present in the CLC network. Either the LCL or the CLC design does the

job of matching the antenna circuit to the transmitter.

The "Z-match" unit is another popular tuner. It has no switches and tunes the range of 3.5 to 30 MHz, with only tuning and loading controls. (More on this interesting device later.)

Some expensive ATUs have a built-in SWR meter. Just twist the controls for the lowest SWR reading! In this case, an external SWR meter isn't required.

The Line Isolator

It's a happy world when everything works as it should. Your antenna is a real DX-getter, the SWR on the line is low, and you don't need an antenna tuner. Let me know when this nirvana arrives.

It's a problem to keep the RF where it belongs, especially since it's radiated into space by the antenna. The radiated field is picked up by nearby antennas. One such antenna is the shield of your coax line! Even if you have a balun at the antenna feedpoint, RF can travel along the outside of the coax, bypassing the SWR meter and the TVI filter, and ending up in your transceiver, or perhaps on the chassis of your TV or stereo gear.

On 10 meters, this can result in a "hot" mic that will "bite" you when you touch it. You also might get audio feedback on transmit, or perhaps pop up in your telephone line. Great stuff, eh?

It is possible to isolate the amateur station from undesired line current by using a line isolator. This device is a short section of transmission line loaded with ferrite rings to increase the inductance of the outer conductor. It works in the manner of an RF choke—choking off current flowing on the outside of the coax, while leaving the current within the line undisturbed. A

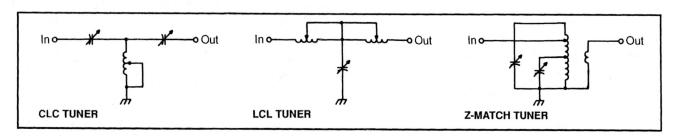

Figure 1-5. Shown here are various forms of antenna-tuning units.

line isolator is a handy thing to have. You can never tell when you'll need it. When you do, place it in the coax line. You may need to experiment to find where it works best. I put mine at the point where the coax left the vertical plane and ran horizontally along the roof of the house. (I chose this point because it was easy to reach!) No engineering talent is required.

Radiation Resistance

One term that continually emerges in antenna talk is *radiation resistance*. Energy supplied to an antenna is radiated in space or lost in the form of heat in the antenna conductors. Think of the radiated energy as energy dissipated in a resistor of a value that consumes the actual amount of power radiated by the antenna. This "resistor," which is not real, is called radiation resistance, designated R_R. Ohmic resistance is real and dissipates energy in the form of heat. The total power taken by the antenna is a function of the ohmic resistance and the radiation resistance. In most cases, ohmic resistance is very low compared to the radiation resistance and can be ignored.

Look at the radiation resistance as the load for the transmission line. Radiation resistance varies with the antenna type, antenna length and height above ground, antenna element diameter, and proximity effect of nearby objects. If the radiation resistance is known, it's possible to determine the best way to couple the antenna to the coax line and the line to the transmitter.

Antenna Reactance

Antenna reactance at the feedpoint occurs when the antenna is operated off the resonant (design) frequency.

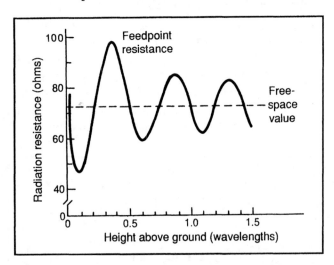

Figure 1-6. Feedpoint or radiation resistance of a horizontal dipole is influenced by ground loss.

Because amateur operation encompasses bands rather than discrete frequencies, antenna reactance is usually present in the antenna circuit. There's no power lost in antenna reactance; it merely complicates the antenna matching problem. Solid-state transmitters dislike a reactive load, and one job of the ATU is to compensate for antenna reactance. Reactance varies with antenna characteristics, just as does radiation resistance.

The combination of antenna radiation resistance and reactance is lumped together as feedpoint impedance by some amateurs, although the term *radiation resistance* is used more often. The latter term assumes the experimenter is describing a resonant antenna.

Ground Loss

Ground loss is a factor that influences antenna characteristics. Most antennas are designed and analyzed in a "free space" environment. That is, the effect of the nearby earth is removed from the investigation. Once the antenna design has taken shape, the antenna is then modeled with respect to the earth. In this case, the earth is assumed to be a perfect conduction plane of copper.

The next step is to model the antenna over "real earth"—an imperfect conductor, the conductivity (and loss) of which varies from location to location. This is where the fun begins. The relatively poor conductivity of the earth results in absorption of the inductive field of the antenna and represents a loss in usable energy. This is especially noticeable in antennas for the 80- and 160-meter bands that are placed close to the ground. "Close to the ground" means less than 0.25 wavelength at the operating frequency. This is equivalent to about 140 feet on 160 meters and 70 feet on 80 meters. Not many hams can get their horizontal antennas that high in the air!

Figure 1-6 tells the story. Antenna radiation resistance is influenced by antenna height. Assume the antenna is an 80-meter dipole. A common height for this antenna is about 25 feet, which is approximately 0.1 wavelength. Theory shows that the radiation resistance for this example should be about 20 ohms. Actual antenna measurements above "average ground" often reveal a radiation resistance of about 45 to 55 ohms—a nice match for a coax line!

The extra 25 to 35 ohms is a result of ground loss, and is equivalent to placing a resistor of this value in series with the antenna feedpoint. In this instance, over half the transmitter power is dissipated in ground loss. The situation is even worse on 160 meters, as it is difficult to elevate an antenna to a point where ground loss is insignificant.

Most hams can't do very much about ground loss. It should be realized, however, that this loss is an important factor in antenna performance, particularly on the lower frequencies.

Is there any benefit to be obtained from ground loss? Can anything be gained from losing a large percentage of transmitter power output in heating the ground? There is one benefit: the SWR bandwidth of the antenna increases as ground loss rises (**Figure 1-7**). This isn't a very efficient way of improving bandwidth, but there it is, and you might as well take advantage of something you can't easily change! Swapping overall antenna efficiency for bandwidth is something done every day, but most hams don't think about ground loss. Some even are surprised when they learn about it.

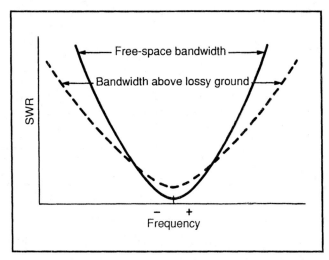

Figure 1-7. The effect of lossy earth upon the bandwidth of a horizontal dipole.

Recommendations

Raise your antenna as high in the air as you can, within reason. Low antennas are a direct invitation to television, stereo, and telephone interference, as the strong antenna field encompasses the wiring and circuitry of these devices. Heights below 25 or 30 feet should be avoided because of this problem, and also because of high ground losses.

How high is high enough? Installation costs, esthetics, and local ordinances or deed restrictions often determine maximum antenna height. For all-around operation, plus the ability to work DX, heights of 45 to 60 feet are generally popular. Many amateurs settle for antenna heights in the 35- to 45-foot range and achieve excellent results on all bands—provided they are not in the DX race or contest enthusiasts. In these cases, they'll get trampled underfoot by serious operators with large arrays and high towers. It boils down to how seriously you take your hobby.

You can work plenty of great DX with 100 watts and a simple wire antenna mounted well in the clear. For serious competition, though, that may not be enough. Starting out with a modest antenna is a good idea. Then, after a period of operation during which you get the "feel" of your favorite band, you may decide to build a larger and more imposing antenna.

Erect one of the antennas shown in this handbook. Experience extended operation with it. Try another antenna, if you wish. You'll soon decide for yourself how seriously you wish to compete as far as "antenna power" goes!

Operational flexibility requires complete coverage of several amateur bands. Modern transceivers can change bands at the flick of a switch. Many antennas, however, are basically one-band, narrow-frequency devices that can only be operated over a complete ham band, or many bands with the addition of auxiliary tuning circuits. This calls for an antenna tuner—either built-in or as an add-on accessory. It is indispensable for the modern station, providing the operator with the tuning and loading required for multi-frequency operation.

The best bet for the gregarious operator is a multiband antenna—that is, one that can operate efficiently on more than one band. Later chapters discuss many multiband antennas. Build one and enjoy!

Chapter 2

Feedlines, Antenna Hardware, and Accessories ("Little Things Mean a Lot")

The success or failure of your antenna installation depends to a large extent upon the hardware you choose. If you use bolts and brackets that rust, cheap coax, or skimpy hardware, you'll regret it in the days to come.

This chapter discusses often overlooked antenna details—the smaller components that make up an antenna system. This is the area where the beginner (and the Old Timer, too) can get into big trouble.

The Wire Antenna

There's much to be said for a wire antenna. A large number of amateurs favor this time-proven "sky wire." It's cheap, easy to construct and erect, and less likely to lead to problems with neighbors than a more expensive and more visible Yagi beam. On the other hand, a practical wire antenna has less gain than a good Yagi, but in many cases the difference in signal strength between the two antennas is small compared with differences between one signal and another. The ionosphere is a great leveler of signals, regardless of antenna type!

You can work plenty of DX with a wire antenna. Sometimes it's the only type of antenna one can put up on a residential lot saddled with deed restrictions and surrounded by vigilant neighbors. The wire antenna isn't obtrusive and doesn't attract attention. That's a big consideration for many operators.

Listen to the DX signals on your favorite band.

You'll find many loud ones coming from stations using simple wire antennas. Many of your fellow hams are working DX with a wire antenna, and you can, too! Here are some pointers that will help you build a good one.

What Wire to Use?

In a pinch, you can use almost any wire for an antenna. Insulated hookup wire will work well for a small, temporary type. For general use, the ideal antenna wire is copper—strong enough to avoid breakage due to climate and weather conditions, and able to resist elongation (stretch) caused by wire tension. For example, you can build a light-weight 14-MHz dipole supporting a small-diameter coax feedline (RG-58) from no. 16 AWG soft-drawn, solid-conductor, enamel-insulated wire.

A more rugged and weather-resistant installation uses no. 12 AWG wire, and a storm-proof installation calls for no. 18 or no. 14 AWG solid, copper-clad steel wire for the flat-top. This wire is also recommended for 160- and 80-meter antennas where the wire length and weight may lead to stretching over time. The wire tends to be springy and will coil up into a mess if you don't have it firmly stretched out and tied down when working with it.

Soft-drawn wire should be prestretched before use, or it will gradually stretch when you get it up in the air. I hook one end of a length of wire I intend to use

2-2   THE W6SAI HF ANTENNA HANDBOOK

to a fence post, wrap the other end around a screwdriver handle, and give the wire a slow, hard pull, putting all my weight into it. I can feel the wire stretch. A little practice, and you'll be an expert at prestretching wire, too! Bare, stranded wire isn't recommended because it oxidizes rapidly in the open air. Also, it's difficult to solder because each strand must be cleaned individually to make a good connection.

What Coax to Use?

A wire catalog will reveal a bewildering number of different 50-ohm coax lines at varying prices. The more expensive coax is labeled "Mil Spec" (meets military specifications). Terms such as "Mil Type" or "Mil Spec Type" were coined to imply the cable is made to specifications that adhere to military standards. This assertion may or may not be true, depending upon the manufacturer's conscience.

For medium power (up to 200 watts peak transmitter output) and runs up to 100 feet, the RG-58 family of coax is popular. The best types have 95- to 97-percent braid coverage and solid polyethylene dielectric, and are PVC jacketed. RG-58/U has a no. 20 AWG bare-copper center conductor and a nominal impedance of 53.5 ohms (not so good). RG-58A/U has a tinned center conductor and a nominal impedance of 50 ohms (better). RG-58C/U is similar; it has a noncontaminating, long-life jacket (best). Each succeeding type costs a few cents more per foot than the previous one. Many hams settle for RG-58A/U. It's easy to work with and has the right impedance value.

The next larger cable size is the RG-8X (or RG-8/M) type. It has a power-handling capability of up to 600 watts peak transmitter output. The advantage of this particular 50-ohm cable is that it's light and flexible, handles more power, and has about 15-percent less RF loss per unit of length than the RG-58 types. The cost, naturally, is a little higher.

The "workhorse" of amateur radio is the RG-8/U family of cables. However, the military classification for this cable has been discontinued and this designation may mean anything. Caveat emptor! The classic RG-8/U cable, now made only on industrial demand to meet JAN-C-17A specifications, is a 52-ohm line with 97-percent shield coverage. Its power capability is in excess of the amateur legal limit. It is not cheap. The cable is also made to conform to MIL-C-17D specifications with a noncontaminating jacket. This stuff is hard to find in stores. Sometimes individuals can purchase it as surplus military stock.

Of more interest to the average amateur is the "RG-8/U type" cable made by reputable manufacturers. Be cautious when buying this cable, as various versions exist. For example, RG-8/U type cable (Belden 8214) has a 50-ohm impedance and 97-percent shield coverage. Such cable isn't bad at all and is suitable for general amateur use.

On the other hand, another RG-8/U type cable (Belden 9208) has a 57-ohm impedance and only 80-percent shield coverage. Use it with caution. The cable's higher than normal impedance will result in erroneous readings on an SWR meter designed for a 50-ohm line, and the skimpy outer shield makes it difficult to solder the braid to a coax plug because the heated inner dielectric tends to squirt out the shield interstices during the soldering process.

Other manufacturers make similar cables, and sometimes the cable distributor sells an unknown product as "RG-8/U"—but no longer pins down size, capacity, shielding, stranding, dielectric, or jacketing. The description indicates only that it's a cable of nominal 50-ohm impedance. An honest description of "RG-8/U" would require a listing of specifications for the above parameters. Many catalogs, such as Belden's, clearly specify the differences between the 8214 and 9208 style cables. Some manufacturers ignore this important distinction.

One solution to this perplexing cable problem is to forget "RG-8/U" and buy RG-213/U, a newer military-approved type. It's a 50-ohm line with the power capability of RG-8/U, 97-percent shield coverage, and a noncontaminating jacket. This cable has about half the power loss of RG-8X and is the premium choice of smart DX operators. After all, coax cost is a small percentage of the dollars spent on your station. Why not get the best?

All of this information, and more, is summarized in **Table 2-1**.

Cable	OD	Belden	RadioShack
RG-58/U	0.195 in.	8240	278-1314
RG-58A/U	0.195 in.	8259	—
RG-8/M	0.242 in.	9258	278-1313
RG-8/U	0.405 in.	8214	278-1312
RG-213/U	0.405 in.	8267	—

Notes:
1. All center conductors stranded except RG-58/U.
2. Belden coax is named RG-8X instead of RG-8/M.
3. Coax plug is PL-259 (RadioShack no. 278-188).
4. Adapter for RG-58/U is UG-175/U (RadioShack no. 278-206).
5. Adapter for RG-8/M is UG-176/U (RadioShack no. 278-204).

Table 2-1. Fifty-ohm coax and connectors.

Shop note: Cutting large-diameter coax is a messy job unless you have the proper tool. Coax cutters are expensive, but a hedge shear with a cutting notch in the base of one blade is a good substitute. Place the coax in the notch, and you'll get a clean cut!

Twinlead Feedline

Some wire antennas are designed to be fed with two-conductor balanced line (variously known as twinlead or window-line). A few amateurs use open-wire line (two no. 18 AWG conductors spaced four inches apart by homemade, waterproofed dowel spacers). "Twinlead" refers to heavy-duty TV-type ribbon line. The transmitting-type twinlead can be obtained in either 75- or 300-ohm impedance levels. Insulation is a PVC web. This stuff is okay for power levels up to 200 watts peak transmitter output, or so.

"Window-line" is a form of heavy-duty twinlead that has square holes, or windows, punched through the insulation to decrease the RF loss. Depending upon conductor spacing, the line may have an impedance of 300 or 450 ohms. These lines work best when twisted once every few feet. Use silicone spray on the line to bead the water during a rainstorm.

You can make a twinlead standoff insulator from a short section of PVC pipe. Just drill a hole through the walls to pass a mounting screw (**Figure 2-1**). Twinlead is used with special antenna types and with some center-fed, multiband antennas. More on these antennas later.

Coax Plugs

The majority of ham equipment and antenna accessories make use of the so-called "UHF" family of coax hardware developed about 1938, when ultra-high frequency (UHF) meant anything above 10 meters! The antenna receptacle mounted on your transceiver, SWR meter, or ATU is a UHF-type SO-239. The popular PL-259 coax plug mates with this receptacle.

The PL-259 comes in many forms. It may have phenolic or Teflon™ insulation, and may be either nickel- or silver-plated. Many hams consider the less-expensive phenolic-insulated plug satisfactory for any legal power level. Most knowledgeable operators opt for the silver-plated plug, as it's very hard to solder to the nickel-plated one. Here's why:

In order to solder a nickel-plated plug, the plating must be filed away from the soldering area, and the solder holes run through with a drill to remove the plating from the sides of the holes. Otherwise it's almost impossible to solder the coax braid to the plug shell. The silver-plated plug makes soldering easier, provided you use a soldering tool large enough to do the job. A 250-watt soldering iron or gun is recommended to attach the plug to the coax line. Soldering speed is important; too much heat over an extended period melts the inner insulation of the cable. It takes a bit of expertise to perform the job, but once learned, you can make a cable termination that won't fail in use.

Crimp-on coax plugs that require no soldering are available. It's tempting to use these, but they have a bad record for reliability and often work loose—usually when you're getting ready to call a choice bit of DX!

Before attaching the coax plug to the receptacle, fill it with a nonconducting lubricant such as Dow Corning 3145 sealant. You may use other lubricants, but make sure they don't contain acetic acid, or the plug will quickly corrode.

The PL-258 splice, used to join two PL-259 plugs, and the M-359 right-angle adapter are other handy coax accessories. To use the RG-58 size cable with a PL-259 plug, you must add a UG-175/U reducer. A UG-176/U reducer is required for RG-8X cable. Other exotic adapters and splices are available, but these common ones are encountered every day in HF amateur radio.

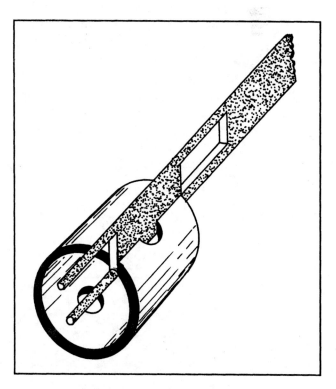

Figure 2-1. A short section of PVC pipe makes a cheap standoff insulator for ladder line. This is a brainstorm of Press Jones, N8UG, "The Wireman."

Aluminum Tubing

Tubing takes the place of wire in the Yagi beam antenna. Long gone are the days when you could buy a 12-foot length of aluminum tubing for a dollar. The stuff is now expensive, but it's the material of choice for construction of an all-metal HF Yagi beam.

In general, small beams for the 20- and 15-meter bands use a 2-inch diameter boom with a wall thickness of 0.065 inch. A 12-foot length weighs about 7 pounds. The 6061 alloy commonly is used because it has good strength and is relatively corrosion resistant. Ten- and 6-meter beams can use a 1.5-inch diameter boom with the same wall thickness. Weight for a 12-foot section is about 4 pounds.

Except for 6-meter beams (the elements of which can be made from a single length of tubing), Yagi elements are made of short sections of telescoping tubing. This saves weight and reduces wind resistance. If the element tubing has a 0.058-inch wall thickness, the next smaller size tubing will telescope into it, with a clearance of 0.009 inch.

It's easy to join element sections having this clearance. Slit the larger element for two or three inches with a hacksaw and secure the joint with a stainless steel, screw-type hose clamp (**Figure 2-2**). Sheet-metal screws aren't recommended.

Before you secure the joint, it's wise to coat the overlapping section of the inner tube with a conducting grease used with aluminum electrical wiring, such as Penetrox, Cual-aid, Ox-guard, or equivalent. This will prevent the joint from corroding over time. Element U-bolt clamps and small hardware should be stainless steel, or you might be in trouble when the time comes to take down the beam! It isn't pleasant to wrestle with a rusted bolt or bracket when you're atop the tower on a cold, windy day!

Antenna Rotors

A great advantage of the Yagi is that it may be turned to aim the maximum signal at your contact. This requires an antenna rotor. Several heavy-duty rotors are available for amateur service. A TV rotor isn't recommended, except for a small 6-meter beam. The rotor is exposed to heavy torque when the wind gusts and the antenna whips about. Accordingly, the rotor should have a brake that locks the shaft when the power is removed. Ham-style rotors have this brake. Various rotor sizes are available. Choose the one that will accept your antenna weight and wind-load factor. Unless you have a monster beam, most medium-priced rotors work okay with the popular mid-sized beams on the market.

Once you've chosen your rotor, your next job is to choose the rotor cable. Rotor cable comes in various wire sizes, and the proper size is usually specified in the rotor manual. The longer the cable run, the larger the wire size required to do the job. If the wires are too small for the length of run, the rotor will be starved for power. It may turn very slowly, or in some cases, the safety brake may not retract enough to let the rotor turn. Saving pennies on rotor cable is bad economics. Many rotors require a 6-wire cable with two heavy no. 18 AWG leads for the brake and motor, and six lighter no. 22 AWG leads for the direction indicator and limit switches.

Splice a disconnect plug in the rotor cable at the base of the tower or antenna support. This will come in handy when you're testing the rotor or doing work on the antenna. You can place a temporary control box at the tower base in case antenna rotation is required during work. A nice 8-connector breakaway plug is available from auto supply stores. This plug set is designed for house trailers; however, it can be used for rotor service provided it's wrapped with waterproof material.

Shop note: RF connector sealant tape (Coax-seal®, RadioShack no. 278-1645, or equivalent) can be used to keep moisture out of coax plugs. Moisture is the number one killer of coax lines. Mold the sealer around the plug with your fingers. Wrap splices and connections with electrical tape. I highly recommend 3M Scotch™ Super 33-plus vinyl tape. Other tapes tend to unwrap themselves when exposed to heat and cold. This brand doesn't have that annoying characteristic. As mentioned before, the coax plug should be filled with silicone lubricant (Dow Corning 3145, or equivalent) to seal the joint between plug and line from moisture. To sum it up: use silicone lubricant in the plug-receptacle area, seal the plug with coax-sealant goop, and wrap the whole mess with Scotch Super 33-plus tape. Get it? Got it! Good!

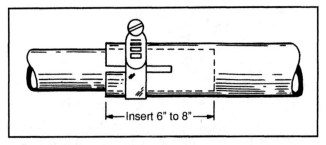

Figure 2-2. Slit the larger element section and hold the smaller section in place with a stainless-steel hose clamp.

Antenna Insulators and Baluns

A minimum of two end insulators and one center insulator (or balun) is required for a wire antenna. RadioShack carries a nice end insulator (278-1336); Alpha-Delta type CIN end insulators are excellent. Equivalent insulators can be obtained from various amateur supply houses. The center insulator (or balun) should have an SO-239 coax receptacle built in, plus a hook to support the center of the antenna, if need be.

In most cases a balun isn't required on low-band dipole-type antennas (160 and 80 meters). A simple center insulator will suffice. For the higher bands a current-type 1:1 balun is recommended. Steer clear of voltage-type baluns; they don't work well in this type of service. You can make a simple line isolator (incorrectly called a balun) by stringing a number of ferrite beads on the outer shield of the coax. Various distributors carry ready-made ferrite-bead baluns and isolators, or you can build your own from kits sold by antenna-parts distributors.

Antenna Supports

The cheapest support for a wire antenna is a nearby tree. The antenna can be slung between the peak of your roof and the tree. The idea is to get the antenna at least 25 or 30 feet in the air. If you have no tree handy, or live in a one-story dwelling, you might consider various forms of guyed, slip-up masts, like those used for TV antennas. DON'T run the antenna near, over, or under a power line!

Here's an example. The RadioShack 36-foot telescoping mast (15-5067), plus ground mount and guy wires, makes a substantial support for the far end of your wire antenna. Some surplus distributors sell Army MS-44 mast sections. These are 6-foot, heavy aluminum pipes that join together to form a 36-foot mast. The MS-44 is more rugged than the RadioShack mast, but the assembly is heavier and harder for one person to erect. Guy wires and hardware aren't usually supplied with the sections.

The beam antenna requires a tower support, as opposed to a simple mast. Fixed, guyed towers are available, as well as self-supporting telescoping towers and tilt-over towers. It's wise to spend time studying various tower types and sizes available, as any tower installation is a serious financial undertaking. In addition, many communities require a building permit to erect a tower, where a TV-type mast may be erected with no problem.

Before you buy a tower, study the building ordinances for your town and read the deed restrictions for your lot or subdivision. Too many hams have erected a tower and then fallen into a dispute with the local Planning Commission or Building Department as to the tower installation, placement, or legality of the tower itself. Even if you win such a dispute, it will take a toll on your nerves and pocketbook!

Chapter 3

Single-Wire Antennas That Work

O ne attribute of a wire antenna is that it's nearly invisible! Made of no. 14 or no. 16 wire, with pale-gray insulators, it blends in nicely with the background. That's a great advantage in an urban area where many neighbors equate a transmitting antenna with telephone or TV interference.

The Invisible Windom Antenna for 160, 80, or 40 Meters

The antennas described in this chapter are easy to build and get working. Some of them have been around for a long time. Others are brand-new, but new isn't always better. One of the oldest wire antennas, still in use today, is the single wire-fed Windom antenna first described in amateur literature in 1929 by Loren Windom, W8GZ.

The single-wire feed system was developed by Frank Conrad, 8XK, of Westinghouse, who used it in 1926 in the broadcast band to feed a vertical Marconi antenna. Operation is based on the fact that the reactance at any point on a half-wave antenna is zero. The radiation resistance, however, goes from a nominal 72-ohm value at the center to infinite ohms at the end. In practice, antenna current doesn't actually drop to zero at the ends; the resistance doesn't become infinite, but reaches a very high value.

If the impedance along a single-wire feeder is between 72 ohms and "very high," it should be possible to find a point on the antenna that will match the feedline characteristic impedance with a resistive termination.

Simple as it seems, mathematical determination of the impedance of a single wire feeder is quite complex, and it wasn't until computer-driven antenna analysis programs became available that antenna operation was completely understood.

The single-wire Windom is a great antenna for Field

Day and is useful in difficult situations where a visible antenna draws unwelcome comments from the neighbors. Finally, it's cheap and easy to erect.

Figure 3-1 shows an 80-meter Windom. It's about a half-wave long and is tapped by a feeder-wire at an off-center point. The tap point is chosen to present a feedpoint impedance of about 500 ohms—a value that's easily matched by most ATUs. At antenna resonance, feedpoint reactance is zero.

The dimensions shown for the 80-meter antenna are usable over a range of about 200 kHz. Thus, the antenna should be cut to 3.6 MHz for CW work, or 3.9 MHz for phone operation. Operation over the complete 80-meter band is possible with either set of dimensions, provided the ATU has sufficient operating range. Trimming the length of the feed wire helps to establish proper loading, in some cases.

Harmonic Operation

The Windom is capable of operation on even-order harmonics. If multiband operation is required, an ATU is a necessity, as the harmonic resonances do not exactly fall in the amateur bands. In addition, the tap point isn't correct for harmonic operation. Nevertheless, the Windom operates as a random-length, sin-

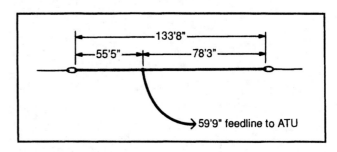

Figure 3-1. The invisible 80-meter Windom antenna. For the 40-meter version, divide the dimensions by two.

gle-wire antenna, with the feeder serving as part of the radiator on harmonic frequencies.

(Some of the above material was obtained from a private communication from John Nagle [SK], formerly K4KJ, who performed extensive experiments on the Windom antenna. These were described in the May 1978 issue of *Ham Radio* magazine.)

The 40-meter Windom works on the harmonic frequencies (the 20-, 15-, and 10-meter bands) and can also be operated on the 10-, 18-, and 24-MHz bands with a good ATU. On bands other than 40 meters, the antenna functions as a random wire, but the feedpoint impedance still remains around 150 to 700 ohms. Finally, the 40-meter antenna can be operated on 80 meters and the 80-meter antenna can be operated on 160 meters—if your ATU has the tuning range to compensate for the off-tune condition of the antenna.

The Ground Connection

Ground return current with the Windom is low—lower than a Marconi antenna, for example. Thus, ground losses are relatively minor; however, they shouldn't be ignored. Make the best ground return connection you can. Four 2-foot ground rods parallel-connected will do the job in most cases. Make sure the earth is well-packed around the rods (**Figure 3-2**). Cut the ground wire as short as possible for best results.

The Coax-fed Multiband Windom Antenna

In the early 1950s, some amateurs resurrected the Windom (**Figure 3-3A**), substituted a 300-ohm ribbon line for the single-wire feeder, and used a balanced antenna tuner at the station to achieve multiband operation . The idea worked, but bringing the feeder into the shack was a direct invitation for TVI!

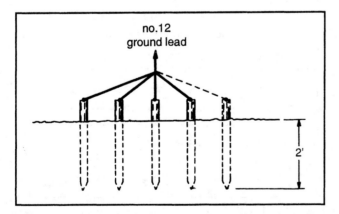

Figure 3-2. Military experiments have shown that multiple ground rods (four or more) are more effective than a single 8-foot rod.

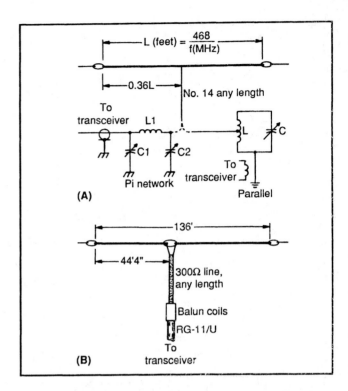

$$L \text{ (feet)} = \frac{468}{f(MHz)}$$

Figure 3-3. The OCF antenna was featured for many years in ARRL publications. (A) The original Windom antenna. (B) The coax-fed version of the Windom. (Original drawing appeared in the *ARRL Handbook*.)

The Early Days

It was thought that coax feed might clean up the TVI, so the next variation on the off-center-fed (OCF) antenna was to shorten the ribbon line and add a 4:1 balun and a 75-ohm coax line running station (**Figure 3-3B**). Again the scheme worked, and this version of the antenna appeared in both the *ARRL Handbook* and the *ARRL Antenna Book* for almost ten years. The editors of these publications, however, warned readers, "it is claimed that the antenna offers a good match for the 300-ohm line on four bands, and although this is more wishful thinking than the actual truth, the system is widely used and does work satisfactorily."

The use of 75-ohm coax with the antenna was a handicap, as very few 75-ohm SWR meters existed at that time. Meaningful information on real-life OCF antenna operation was skimpy and mainly based on hearsay, as accurate RF measuring techniques and equipment were generally unavailable to the amateur fraternity.

OCF Antenna Mysteries Are Solved!

Finally, in 1954 William Wrigley, W4UCW, a Research Engineer at the Georgia Institute of Technology, provided in detail the analysis of an off-center-fed dipole antenna. He gathered and organized the avail-

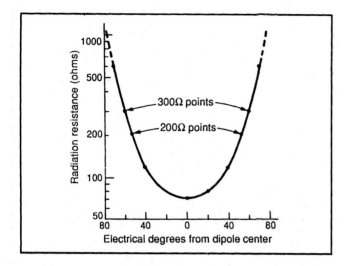

Figure 3-4. W4UCW's graph of radiation resistance of a dipole in free space as the feedpoint is moved away from the center.

able information on the subject and added additional data that he had derived. He investigated harmonic operation of the antenna and provided meaningful numbers concerning the feedpoint resistance (radiation resistance) of a dipole in free space as the feedpoint is moved away from the center (**Figure 3-4**).

The plot shows that two points exist along the dipole where a 300-ohm termination is possible—one on each side of the center point. In this example, the points are about 60 electrical degrees from the center of the antenna (30 degrees from each end). This is equivalent to a distance of 16.6 percent from either end of the dipole.

Wrigley showed, however, that when the dipole is mounted 0.1 wavelength above ground, the 300-ohm tap point is 23 degrees from one end, which is equivalent to 12.7 percent of the total antenna length. Obviously, the tap point varies with respect to antenna

height above the earth. Either amount is much less than the tap distance shown in the handbook illustration (**Figure 3-3B**). Next Wrigley showed that this point or any other feedpoint along the dipole is resistive and has no reactive component at antenna resonance.

Wrigley now examined harmonic operation of the half-wave antenna. **Figure 3-5** shows the relationship, illustrating that for good harmonic operation on the higher frequency amateur bands, an 80-meter antenna should be cut to resonate below the low edge of the band. He suggested that a length of 136 feet is an acceptable compromise for multiband operation (80, 40, 20, 15, and 10 meters). This length resonates at about 3.45 MHz.

As a whole, Wrigley's data agrees closely with that derived by modern computer antenna analysis.

The Wrigley OCF Antenna Design

As his theoretical example, Wrigley chose a 136-foot, 80-meter OCF dipole placed 25 feet above ground (0.1 wavelength at 80 meters, 0.2 wavelength at 40 meters, 0.4 wavelength at 20 meters, etc.). The resonant frequencies of this antenna were 3.42, 7.10, 14.27, and 28.75 MHz. The calculated bandwidths for a 2:1 SWR were 51 kHz on 90 meters, 88 kHz on 40 meters, 194 kHz on 20 meters, and 214 kHz on 20 meters. Not very encouraging!

W4UCW then computed results when antenna height was boosted to 65 feet (0.25 wavelength at 80 meters). He concluded that the best compromise feedpoint position for harmonic operation was at a 150-ohm point on the antenna. Bandwidth was improved on the two lower bands, but the problem of obtaining a 150-ohm line was difficult.

Wrigley reasoned that the use of a coaxial pair of 75-ohm lines was impractical, as the coupling effects

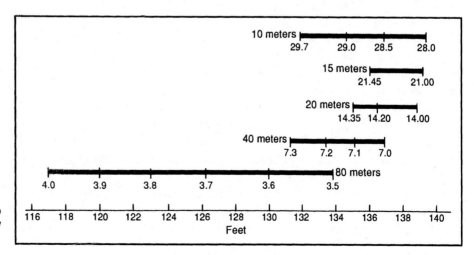

Figure 3-5. Harmonic relationship of HF bands as illustrated by W4UCW. (See text for details.)

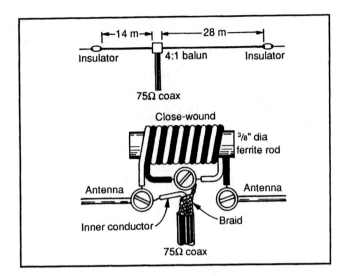

Figure 3-6. The "FD4 Windom" with a balun placed at the feedpoint. This version was used by GM3MXN. The "m" refers to meters, whereas 14m = 45 feet, 11-3/16 inches, and 28m = 91 feet, 10-5/16 inches. (Drawing courtesy of *Radio Communication*.)

due to the induced currents in the outer surface of the shields would produce unpredictable distortions in impedance, and that these distortions would vary on different harmonics.

Wrigley's conclusion was that the OCF antenna, tempting as it might seem, was impractical. He could not find a feedpoint position that would match a 300-ohm feed system and permit multiband operation, and even if one were found, antenna bandwidth was too narrow for everyday use.

And there the matter stood for 17 years.

The OCF Antenna Lives!

It must be remembered that Wrigley's studies were theoretical, and based upon an infinitely thin dipole in free space. Imponderable things such as end effect, wire diameter, and the presence of imperfect earth below the antenna couldn't be taken into account. Of course, these parameters enter into the design of a real-life antenna, but the data supplied by Wrigley formed the basis upon which to build a practical OCF antenna. He pointed the way. It remained for someone to build the antenna and make meaningful measurements.

In 1971, Spillner, DJ2KT, built a modified form of the OCF antenna. It was described in the German magazine *QRV* in December of that year. The antenna gained popularity in Europe under the name "FD4 Windom." **Figure 3-6** shows a version of this antenna, which made use of a simple voltage-type 4:1 balun built by Sorbie, GM3MXN.[2] Sorbie also found

that he could load this simple antenna on the 18- and 24-MHz bands, as well as on the harmonic bands of 80 meters.

In 1983, Scholle, DJ7SH, and Steins, DL1BBC, connected two OCF dipoles in parallel for coverage of all amateur bands between 160 and 10 meters. SWR plots of the installed antennas revealed exceptional bandwidth. Was W4UCW wrong in his pessimistic bandwidth predictions? Or, was this the ultimate multiband HF antenna, at last?

The DJ7SH/DL1BBC antenna was described in a 1990 *QST* article and created quite a stir.[3] Several commercial versions of this design promptly hit the market. One such antenna was reviewed in *QST* with mixed results.[4] Bandwidth seemed very good, but the antenna was especially susceptible to parallel mode currents flowing on the outside of the coax shield. This made exact measurements difficult.

All of this information was intriguing, so I decided to use a computerized antenna modeling program to examine an OCF. If it looked promising, I decided I'd build one myself and try it out.

An Examination of the OCF Antenna

The antenna feedpoint data provided by Wrigley and others can be checked quickly using a modern computerized antenna-modeling program such as the one produced by Brian Beezley, K6STI (3532 Linda Vista Drive, San Marcos, California 92069). Operation of the program is interesting. It divides an antenna into segments. The program user chooses the number of segments for his analysis. The computer then uses the wire segmentation to model conductor current in sections called *pulses*. Current is uniform within each pulse. In my case, I chose 68 pulses, as each pulse is equivalent to a foot distance on a 7-MHz antenna. This made computation easy. By iteration, the feedpoint may be moved along the antenna from the center toward one end. A readout of antenna resistance and reactance at each specified point is created, enabling the user to compute the SWR for a match to a 200-ohm feed system. The simulation is for a height above ground of 40 feet.

Why choose a 200-ohm feedpoint? Because a 50-ohm line and a 4:1 balun can provide this termination. Europeans and others who use 75-ohm line and a 4:1 balun can select a 300-ohm feedpoint. The user then carefully chooses the number of segments in the antenna file to duplicate the physical dimensions of the antenna and the requirements of the feed system.

Once I found the 200-ohm point, I scanned the antenna on the harmonic frequencies—20, 15, and 10 meters. I quickly found that Murphy's Law was in full flower. The optimum tap point was different on each band and also varied with height above ground. In addition, if the shorter section of the flattop approached a half-wavelength on 10 meters (about 17 feet), the antenna presented a high feedpoint impedance and was useless on that band.

The only practical solution was to find a compromise point that provided a reasonable feedpoint impedance on all bands. I chose a practical antenna height of 40 feet. Otherwise, I could spend the rest of my days juggling height, versus feedpoint, versus SWR, versus wire size. I settled on no. 14 wire, and my goal was a maximum SWR limit of 2:1 on 40 meters and the harmonic bands.

The W6SAI Compact OCF Antenna

It isn't readily apparent to me that any feed system by itself can alter the intrinsic bandwidth of a dipole antenna. A computer run on a sample antenna to check bandwidth seemed like a good idea. Using the computer program, I chose a 7-MHz dipole 40 feet high as the guinea pig. It, in turn, was first fed at the center, then 31 percent from one end, and finally 19 percent from the other end. Inputting these data to the computer and making a frequency run from 6.7 to 7.4 MHz revealed that in all cases the bandwidth of the dipole, taken between the 2:1 SWR points, was about 420 kHz—identical within the measuring tolerances of the experiment. This cast doubt in my mind that dipole bandwidth is a function of feedpoint placement.

Space limited me to a 40-meter OCF dipole. Accordingly, the computer model was configured for that band. I chose a tap point that was 20.5 percent from one end. This point was based on data gathered on an 80-meter computer model, and was one which would provide a reasonable match to a 200-ohm source on all bands.

I fed the dimensions into the computer file, and made a run across the 40-meter band and its harmonics. The results looked good enough to warrant construction of a real antenna to hang from a yardarm on my tower.

Building an OCF Antenna

The next step was to build an OCF dipole and make direct impedance and SWR measurements. Perhaps the amazingly broad SWR curves exhibited by the German

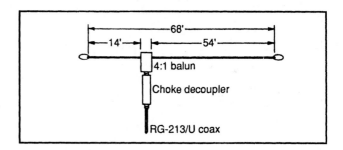

Figure 3-7. The OCF multiband antenna at W6SAI for 40, 20, 15, and 10 meters.

antenna were a result of ground loss caused by the low height of the test antennas. AT DL1BBC, the antenna was only about 22 feet above ground at the center, rising to 26.25 feet at the ends. The DJ7SH antenna was only 16.4 feet above ground and partially passed over a garage roof. The antenna was in an inverted-V configuration. I was curious to see what my OCF antenna would do at a reasonable height above ground, when checked with reliable instrumentation.

My real-life 40-meter OCF antenna was 68 feet long and fed 14 feet from one end. I used a 4:1 current-type balun (Radio Works B4-2KX) along with a ferrite choke decoupler (W2DU design) to "cool off" the coax line and permit accurate measurements. (Radio Works can be contacted at Box 6159, Portsmouth, Virginia 23703; the owner is Jim Thompson, W4THU.) A 50-ohm transmission line connected the antenna to the test equipment (**Figure 3-7**). The antenna was placed in an inverted-V configuration, with the balun and decoupler at the 40-foot elevation and the antenna ends at a height of about 30 feet.

Antenna Measurements

The first step was to check antenna R (resistance) and X (reactance) at various frequencies. I used an HP-606A signal generator and a calibrated General Radio 916 RF bridge. A Kenwood R-2000 receiver served as a null detector. After these tests, I repeated measurements with an SWR meter.

Alerted by the *QST* review citing transmission-line problems, I placed ferrite sleeves along the coax line to decouple it from the antenna field and to increase the common-mode impedance. Each sleeve consisted of six ferrite beads (Amidon FB-43 1020) placed close together and held in position by plastic cable ties. (Amidon Associates can be reached at Box 956, Torrance, California 90508.) The coax line was RG-213/U. I ran the line down to ground level (at which point I placed a sleeve) and then took it away from the

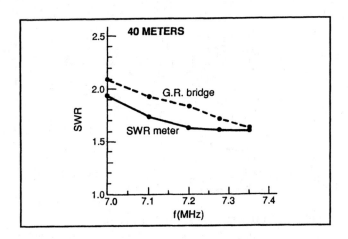

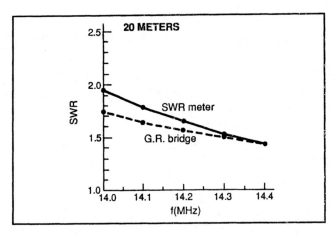

Figure 3-8. The OCF dipole showing measured SWR curves for 40 meters.

Figure 3-9. The OCF dipole showing measured SWR curves for 20 meters.

antenna at right angles.

I took the R and X figures derived from the RF bridge and converted them to SWR measurements. The resulting curves are shown in **Figures 3-8** through **3-11**. Operational bandwidth on each band exceeds the values predicted by W4UCW, and in fact, are comparable to figures previously predicted by the computer program. It seemed as if the multiband antenna was at hand.

Line Current Problems

My last step was to add an additional 50 feet of coax to cover the distance to the operating position. Then I ran SWR measurements on all bands using the station transceiver, a Bird 43 directional wattmeter, and a Daiwa model CN-720 SWR meter. Curves for the General Radio Bridge measurements may be compared with those made with the SWR meter.

On 40 meters, the operational SWR was approximately 2:1, dropping to about 1.6:1 at the high end on the band. Antenna resonance was near 7.35 MHz (**Figure 3-8**). On 20 meters, the highest operational

SWR was at the low end of the band, being about 1.7:1 (**Figure 3-9**). At the high end, SWR ran close to 1.4:1. SWR response on 15 meters was very good, running from about 1.4:1 at the low end to 1.35:1 at the high end (**Figure 3-10**). The 10-meter curves were quite flat, running from about 2:1 at the low end to about 2.4:1 at the high end (**Figure 3-11**).

Why the difference in readings between the instruments? There are several reasons. First, common-mode current tends to flow on the outer surface of the coax shield even with extensive ferrite suppression. Second, it's difficult to decouple the line running to the transceiver, as it runs parallel to the antenna, near the ground, for some distance. Ferrite sleeves along the line help a lot. Finally, neither the SWR meter nor the Bird wattmeter can be classified as a precision instrument. It would take a lot more line decoupling and a network analyzer (costing many kilobucks) to obtain more accurate SWR readings. Unfortunately, even with the best isolation possible, it's still possible for unwanted parallel currents to flow because the line is asymmetrically coupled to the antenna. Current

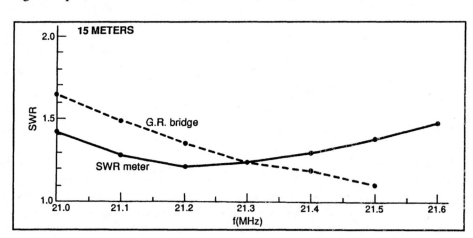

Figure 3-10. The OCF dipole showing measured SWR curves for 15 meters.

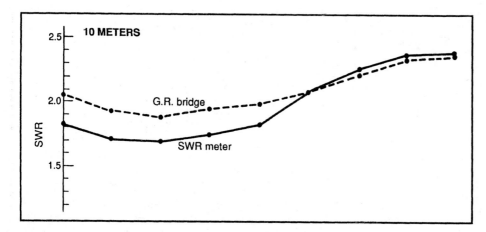

Figure 3-11. The OCF dipole showing measured SWR curves for 10 meters.

induced from the short leg probably won't be equal to that induced from the long leg. The currents will not cancel completely. Hence, some parallel current is bound to flow on the outside of the coax shield.

Given the choice, I believe the RF bridge measurements to be the more accurate of the two sets because of the residue shield current. In any event, the curves looked good. It was easy to load the antenna directly with a tube-type transceiver. A solid-state job required the service of the built-in antenna tuner to achieve the full output when the SWR approached 2:1.

The General Radio Bridge told me that operation on the 18- and 24-MHz bands would be difficult, as SWR on those bands would be very high. However, SWR measurements run at the station indicated SWR values less than 3:1 on those bands! To date, I've worked plenty of DX on 18 MHz, and a few stations on 24 MHz, in spite of the band sounding "flat." Operation on 24 MHz wasn't as good as I had hoped. All of this bears future investigation.

The Final OCF Antenna

The conclusions I reached from these interesting tests are that the OCF concept is practical, and a suitable antenna can be designed for harmonic operation provided antenna length and feedpoint are chosen properly. For 80-meter fundamental and harmonic operation the OCF antenna should be about 136-feet long. For 40-meter fundamental and harmonic operation, I recommend a length of 68 feet. For a 50-ohm line with a 4:1 current balun, the tap point lies about 20 percent from one end, depending upon antenna height and location. I chose a tap point of 20.5 percent. A good current-type balun is needed for proper antenna operation.

A ferrite line decoupler is required just below the balun. Additional ferrite decouplers along the line and at the transmitter are recommended if the line runs parallel to the antenna for any distance.

Either antenna will operate with reasonably low SWR on the harmonic bands, plus provide operation on the higher WARC bands.

If you use a tube-type transceiver with pi-circuit output, you probably won't need an ATU (antenna tuning unit) at the station. If you use a solid-state transceiver, you'll find it less forgiving; consequently, an ATU (built-in or auxiliary) will be required. If you don't use an ATU, power output of the transmitter will drop as coax SWR rises.

The Bottom Line

The OCF antenna seems particularly susceptible to common-mode currents flowing on the outside of the coax shield. The effect of these currents can be reduced by use of decoupling sleeves. If you take the proper precautions, the OCF will prove itself to be a workable multiband HF antenna that is an asset to the modern amateur station.

There are still unanswered questions: Why does the antenna seem to work on 18 and 24 MHz? What is the effect of the ferrite balun on overall operation? What is the effect of antenna height above ground? Would a sleeve-style W2DU 4:1 balun be more effective than a ferrite toroidal balun? Can the tap point be placed at a more advantageous position? I'm sure other experimenters will enjoy playing with this intriguing antenna and finding the answers to some of these questions.

For more information, I suggest reading "How to Design Off-center Fed Multiband Wire Antennas Using That Invisible Transformer in the Sky," by Frank Witt, AI1H, in *The ARRL Antenna Compendium*, Vol. 3.

The OCF antenna? Well, as for me, I'll take a 6-element Yagi on an 80-foot boom at 125 feet for 20 meters any day.

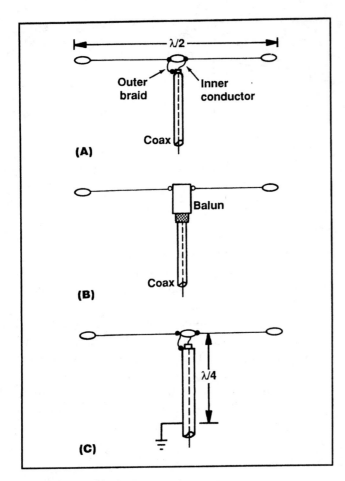

Figure 3-12. (A) Direct coax feed, (B) balun feed, and (C) quarter-wave grounding.

Controlled Feeder Radiation

As every amateur knows, connecting a balanced, center-fed antenna to an unbalanced feedline results in some degree of feeder radiation. A good example is a coax line feeding a dipole (**Figure 3-12A**). And as every amateur also knows, this hookup will work, so why worry about it?

As far as the dipole goes, there's no big problem. One outcome of feeder radiation is that the classic figure-8 radiation pattern of the dipole is filled in by feedline radiation, so the result is a nearly omnidirectional pattern. That can be a big help for general all-around operation.

Since the coax outer shield is coupled to the antenna (directly at the feedpoint and indirectly by means of coupling between coax and the antenna field; **Figure 3-13**), loading problems may develop. A modern, solid-state transmitter may not load properly unless the feedline is trimmed to a critical length. Moving the feedline about with respect to the antenna may help, too.

When the unbalanced coax is attached to a balanced beam (a Yagi, for example), the indirect feedline-to-

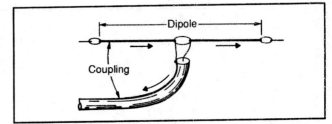

Figure 3-13. Outer braid current can be induced in the coax if the line does not come away at right angles to the axis of the antenna.

antenna inductive coupling tends to ruin the otherwise good front-to-back ratio of the beam on transmit and receive. This all is due to radiation and pickup from the outer shield of the line.

What to do? One solution is to use a balun between the feedline and the antenna (**Figure 3-12B**). Another solution is to make the coax line act as a sort of balun by grounding the shield of the line a quarter-wavelength below the antenna feedpoint (**Figure 3-12C**).

Use Feedline Radiation to Your Advantage

It's possible to make use of feedline radiation, as B. Sykes, G2HCG, pointed out in the May 1990 issue of *Radio Communication*, an RSGB publication.[5] He notes that using feedline radiation to fill in antenna pattern nulls can easily be achieved by moving the balun down the feeder a quarter wave from the antenna feedpoint. This permits radiation from the top part of the feedline, while the balun stops the radiation from the rest of the line (**Figure 3-14**). Sykes calls this technique "controlled feeder radiation" (CFR) and notes that it depends upon radiation from the outer shield of the coax, which doesn't occur with balanced feeders, or from a feeder-

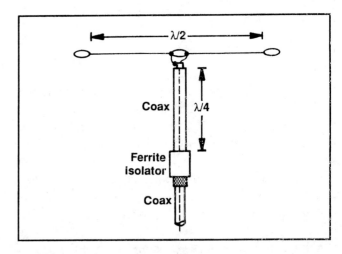

Figure 3-14. The G2HCG adaptation of Figure 3-12C for controlled feeder radiation. Use a 1:1 balun.

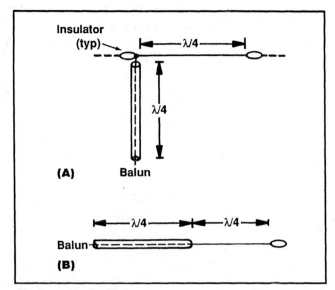

Figure 3-15. (A) End-fed quarter-wave wire plus controlled radiation feeder. (B) End-fed half-wave dipole antenna.

balun combo such as that shown in **Figure 3-12B**.

G2HCG's antenna is shown in **Figure 3-14**. It's a dipole with the balun placed 0.275 wavelength below the feedpoint. This provides an omnidirectional, vertical polarized pattern radiator combined with the standard figure-8 pattern of the dipole. The low-angle, vertical radiation is a considerable bonus because it is achieved without the need for an expensive and complicated system of ground radials.

A simple variation of this idea is shown in **Figure 3-15A**. This consists of a horizontal, end-fed quarter-

wave element combined with a vertical CFR section. The antenna radiates vertically and horizontally polarized energy to produce a virtually omnidirectional signal. Straightening the antenna results in a very useful low-impedance end-fed dipole (**Figure 3-15B**), which may be strung conveniently from the upstairs window of your station to a nearby tree.

Other amateurs, principally in Europe, have tried CFR with success. At least one U.S. manufacturer features wire antennas with controlled feeder radiation (The Radio Works, Inc.) and interest in this novel idea is growing.

It is instructive to examine controlled feeder radiation with an antenna analysis program. I used the K6STI version to see what, if anything, feeder radiation contributes to a dipole antenna pattern. I chose a dipole cut to 14.2 MHz, 40 feet above the ground, as my guinea pig, and input the data to the antenna program. With no feeder radiation, the dipole exhibited the classic figure-8 pattern. Maximum radiation was at right angles to the wire. Radiation off the end of the antenna was absent.

I added a vertical radiator about a quarter-wave long to the dipole in the manner shown in **Figure 3-14**. The length of the vertical section was varied to see what the results would be.

If the vertical section was very short (an eighth-wave, for example) it accomplished little. As the length was increased, vertical radiation increased, and

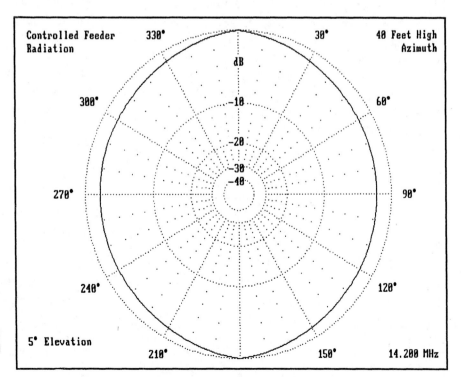

Figure 3-16. Nearly omnidirectional pattern of a dipole with controlled feeder radiation.

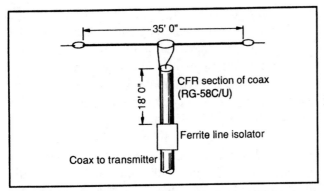

Figure 3-17. Dimensions for the CFR dipole. Height above ground is 40 feet. Feedpoint impedance is about 40 ohms.

the nulls of the figure-8 pattern started to fill in. When the vertical section was about a quarter-wave long, the combined radiation pattern was nearly omnidirectional (**Figure 3-16**). Finally, when the vertical section was longer than a quarter wave, the pattern started to revert back to the figure-8 dipole plot.

I noted that as the vertical section was increased in length, the feedpoint impedance of the antenna and the resonant frequency changed. When a nice, nearly circular pattern was obtained, antenna length was slightly longer than normal. The length of the radiating section of coax was very close to a quarter wavelength. Dimensions for the 20-meter band are shown in **Figure 3-17**.

The Line Isolator

The line isolator is the key to controlled feeder radiation. It provides a very high impedance to outer shield current, effectively choking it off from the rest of the feedline.

Note that the RF on the outside of the coax at the choke point can be quite high, as the end impedance of this section of the antenna can be several thousand ohms. The RF voltage drop across the choke is therefore high. Proper operation of the antenna depends

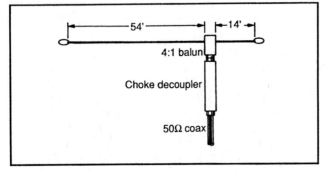

Figure 3-18. The W6SAI experimental OCF multiband dipole. The balun is the B4-2KX by Radio Works.

upon the isolation provided by this choke.

I would be pleased to hear from experimenters who try this simple antenna. Let me know your operating results.

More About the W6SAI Compact OCF Antenna

My OCF antenna is shown in **Figure 3-18**. It's designed for 40-, 20-, 15-, and 10-meter operation. As a nice bonus, I found that it also works on 18 MHz. Operation on 10 or 24 MHz is marginal due to extremely high SWR on the balun and feedline.

After a six-week trial period, I found that the antenna had performed very well. It took a little effort to remove RF from the outside of the coax line. However, once that was accomplished with ferrite isolators, I could vary the line length without a change in the SWR reading. I've worked plenty of DX with the antenna, and it provides a modest amount of gain on the higher bands (see **Table 3-1**).

GAIN OVER λ/2 DIPOLE	
Band	**Gain**
40 m	0 dBd
20 m	0.4 dBd
17 m	0.6 dBd
15 m	0.9 dBd
10 m	1.4 dBd

Table 3-1. Gain of the OCF antenna on the HF bands.

The only direct comparison I could run was on 18 MHz, where I compared the OCF against a ground-plane antenna, well located, with the base about 10 feet above ground. In the great majority of cases (including contacts in Europe and Asia), the OCF dipole was at least a good S-point better in both transmission and reception than the ground plane. On the other bands I had no comparison antenna.

On 40 meters during my weekly sked with W6GNX (about a mile away from me) and W6FR in Fullerton (about 380 miles away), W6FR reported no difference in signal comparisons between my signal and that of W6GNX, as judged against previous contacts when I used a 40-meter, center-fed dipole.

I could work DX on 20 meters, but it was often difficult in the face of competition from high-power stations with big beams. If I had a good shot at the DX, I usually raised the station. Ten meters was generally dead, so the reports were few. However, the OCF was a hot antenna on 18 and 21 MHz. It was easy to break the pile-up on F6BLQ/D2 (Angola) on 18 MHz, and on a good opening on 21 MHz I worked ten Euro-

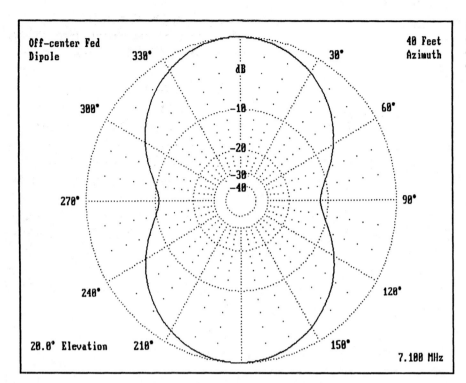

Figure 3-19. Azimuth plot of the OCF dipole on 7 MHz. Note on the 270-90 degree axis the pattern is slightly canted to the left.

peans on the first call in less than 30 minutes. All of these contacts were made with 100 watts.

Pattern Plots of the OCF Antenna

The computer-derived pattern plots for the HF bands are shown in **Figures 3-19** through **3-22**. On 40 meters, the classic dipole pattern exists with a slight unbalance in the plot (see the 90- and 270-degree points).

At an elevation of 40 feet, the main lobes are maximum at an elevation of 50 degrees above the horizon.

On 20 meters, a clover-leaf pattern exists with a slight cant to the longer wire. Angle of elevation of the lobes is at 25 degrees. On 15 meters, the lobes split again, with a decided advantage to the directions off the longer wire. Even so, the difference in pattern symmetry is only about 2 dB. The angle of elevation

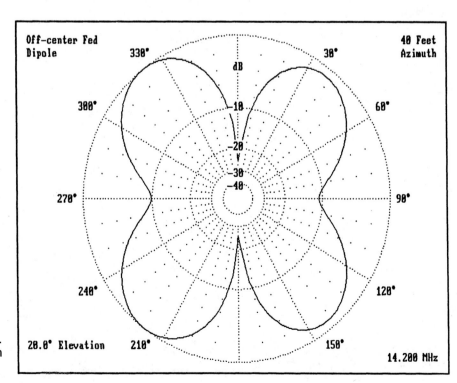

Figure 3-20. Azimuth plot on 14 MHz. A slight cant on the clover-leaf pattern can be seen.

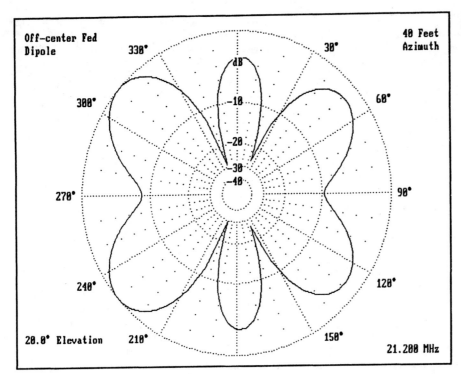

Figure 3-21. Azimuth plot on 21 MHz. The cant amounts to about 2 dB on the major lobes.

for the main lobes is approximately 15 degrees.

On 10 meters, there's further lobe splitting, with maximum radiation at an angle of about 30 degrees to the axis of the wire. Elevation of the main lobe above the horizon is about 10 degrees.

The elevation plots are controlled by antenna height above ground. In my case, antenna height is about 40 feet. Note that in real-life, the deep nulls shown in the patterns probably are washed out because the imperfect ground beneath the antenna blurs the reflection pattern.

Bandwidth Response of the OCF Antenna

I still haven't determined why the antenna exhibits such good SWR bandwidth. It's possible that the

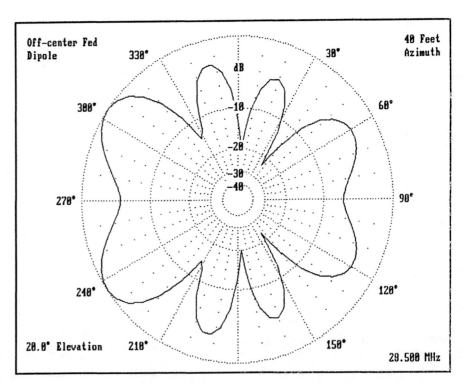

Figure 3-22. Azimuth plot on 28 MHz. The cant is 3 dB on the major lobes.

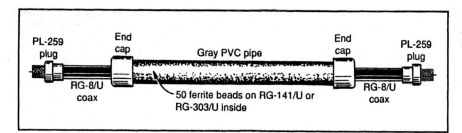

Figure 3-23. Ferrite line isolator. Use Amidon FB-2401 beads. The kit is available from The Wireman, Inc.

interaction between the antenna and the 4:1 balun has a nullifying action on system reactance. It would be interesting to try a W2DU-style ferrite-bead balun in place of the ferrite-core balun I currently use. This begs investigation, but I doubt if I'll get around to it!

The computer program suggests that the antenna provides a good match on 50 MHz! I have no gear for that band, but someone, someday, will try the antenna on 6 meters and determine if the computer projection is correct.

Transmitter Loading

Although SWR is quite reasonable on the harmonically related bands, it's higher than I like on 18 MHz (about 3:1). In addition, solid-state rigs don't like to work into even a modest SWR, and protect themselves by cutting power in response to the SWR level. Since this or any other multiband antenna exhibits SWR levels detrimental to operation of such transmitters, an antenna tuner is mandatory for optimum transmitter operation. The built-in tuners in some modern rigs do the job; if not, you should use an external antenna tuner. In my mind, a low-loss, multiband antenna that doesn't require an antenna tuner hasn't been invented yet. Perhaps some more experimental work on off-center-fed systems may solve that problem. Oh happy day!

Building a Ferrite Line Isolator

Building a line isolator isn't a big deal. The Wireman, Inc. (261 Pittman Road, Landrum, South Carolina 29356; Press Jones, N8UG) furnishes an isolator kit that consists of 50 ferrite beads and a length of Teflon™ coax (kit no. 833). It's easy to assemble an isolator from this kit (**Figure 3-23**).

You'll need a 12-inch length of gray PVC pipe—the 3/4-inch outer diameter type used in sprinkling systems. This is available with threads at both ends. You'll also need two end caps of white PVC, schedule 40 type, used for plumbing. You can thread the gray pipe into the white end caps.

To build your isolator, you first need to thread the

beads onto the Teflon coax and anchor them in position with small plastic cable ties. Twist the coax shield ends into pigtails and tin. Next, drill the end caps to pass RG-8 size cable. Use a 3/4-inch drill and enlarge the holes, if necessary, to pass the cable. This should be a tight fit. Strip the ends of the RG-8 cables, make pigtails of the braid, and splice them to the ends of the Teflon line—after passing the line through the PVC pipe. Wrap the inner conductors with electrical tape, and connect the pigtails together with a short length of tinned wire.

The assembly sequence is as follows:

1. Place the beads on the Teflon cable and anchor them in position.

2. Prepare the ends of the Teflon cable.

3. Drill the end caps.

4. Pass lengths of RG-8 through the end caps.

5. Prepare the ends of the RG-8 with pigtails.

6. Pass the Teflon coax (with the ferrites) through the 3/4-inch PVC pipe.

7. Solder the connections between the Teflon coax and the RG-8 coax.

8. Tape and insulate the connections.

9. Pour a small amount of PVC cement into each end cap.

10. Press the end caps onto the pipe ends.

11. Put PL-259 plugs on the ends of the RG-8 cable.

The 4:1 Balun

You can build a 4:1 balun from a kit (item 835) from The Wireman. Press also sells an assembled balun (item 824). The Radio Works sells a 4:1 balun, too; ask for catalog number B4-2KX.

So there you are. You can save money and build your own isolator and balun, or you can spend some more bucks and get them ready-made. The choice is yours.

The G5RV Multiband Antenna

The concept of the famous G5RV antenna has been around for a long time. The original design was conceived by Art Collins (SK), ex-W9CXX. It was packaged as a kit and died a quick death, as the matching

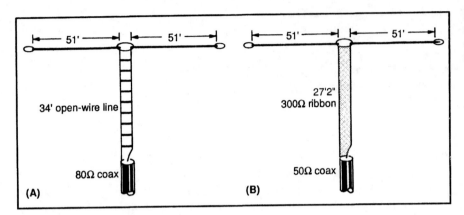

Figure 3-24. (A) The original G5RV antenna with open-wire line and 80-ohm coax. (B) The revised G5RV with ribbon line and 50-ohm coax.

section (hung from the center of the antenna) was composed of copper tubes!

The idea resurfaced in the 1950s, when the design was revamped to eliminate the tubes, and was popularized by R. Varney, G5RV. Varney also modified the antenna for coax feed, instead of the original two-wire transmission line.

The basic G5RV design consists of a 102-foot flat-top (three half waves on 20 meters) center-fed with a 34-foot, 450-ohm impedance transformer (**Figure 3-24**). This closely matches the antenna to an 80-ohm source on 20 meters. (Remember, the British generally use 75–80-ohm coax.) Various articles on the G5RV confirm the belief that for "all-band" operation, a balanced antenna tuner (ATU) is helpful.

Multiband with the G5RV

Although designed for 20 meters, it was quickly found that the G5RV antenna would function quite well on other bands if an antenna tuning unit (ATU or Transmatch) was used at the transmitter. No one worried much about SWR in those days.

By the time the antenna crossed the Atlantic, the antenna was modified to use a 300-ohm ribbon matching line (no one built open-wire lines anymore) connected to a 50-ohm coax transmission line (80-ohm coax wasn't available in the USA). That's when problems developed, aided in part by the widespread use of the SWR meter.

A lot of amateurs built and used the modified G5RV (**Figure 3-24B**). Some of them reported good results, while others couldn't get the antenna to load properly. No one was sure what the SWR readings meant, as they varied from shack to shack for supposedly the same antenna design. What did all this mean? What was going on?

Various versions of the G5RV have been described in the amateur magazines, and different designs are

advertised for sale. Some use a balun transformer to match to coax, while others do not. No specific make of 300-ohm line is universally used, and there are as many different types of line as there are fleas on a dog. It all depends upon the economics of the manufacturer who builds the line—and there is plenty of bad line available.

There doesn't seem to be a single design I can point to and say, "That's the real G5RV antenna!"

Checking a G5RV Antenna

The antenna I bought had conventional dimensions plus an "in-line transformer" (balun) which went between the ribbon line and the coax (**Figure 3-25**). The instructions stated the antenna covered 3.5 through 30 MHz, except 10 MHz. It suggested the antenna be mounted one full wavelength above ground on the lowest frequency on which the antenna is to be used. For 80 meters this is about 270 feet in the air! The instruction sheet modified this suggestion, saying that this height is impractical in most installations, and urged the user to put the antenna as high in the air as he can. It also recommended that the feedline be

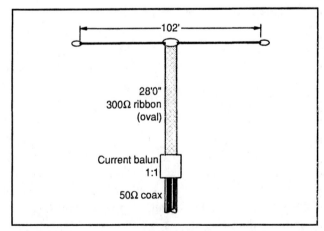

Figure 3-25. The revised G5RV with current balun and modified ribbon line.

brought down vertically to the ground before leading it away at an angle, or parallel to the antenna.

My installation of the G5RV was typical—almost 45 feet high at the center and about 30 feet high at the ends. I brought the feedline down vertically as directed and then ran the coax a few dozen feet to my test instruments. At no point did the line run parallel to the antenna. A little extra coax was coiled up into a simple RF choke to suppress extraneous currents that might flow on the outside of the shield.

My test equipment consisted of an HP-606A signal generator, GR-916A precision RF bridge, and a Kenwood R-2000 receiver which acted as a null detector. The G5RV was checked on all bands (including 10 MHz) and the results are given in **Table 3-2**.

REPRESENTATIVE G5RV ANTENNA

Band	Freq. (MHz)	SWR
80 m	3.5	6.3
	3.6	4.98
	3.7	4.47
	3.8	4.66
	3.9	4.76
	4.0	5.67
40 m	7.0	2.65
	7.1	3.05
	7.2	3.67
	7.3	4.50
20 m	14.00	1.83
	14.10	2.15
	14.20	2.64
	14.35	3.28
15 m	21.00	5.98
	21.10	5.86
	21.20	5.71
	21.30	5.66
	21.45	5.69
10 m	28.0	4.83
	28.2	4.81
	28.4	4.42
	28.6	3.99
	28.8	3.64
	29.0	3.34
	29.2	2.58
	29.4	2.29
	29.6	1.94
	29.7	1.88
WARC Bands		
30 m	10.1	8.50
17 m	18.11	1.84
12 m	24.95	4.52

Table 3-2. Results of the G5RV checks on all bands (including 10 MHz).

Interpreting the Results

The RF bridge gives its readout in terms of R (resistance) and X (reactance) at the instrument end of the coax line. A computer program changes these figures into SWR values. My coax line was about 50 feet long, and to simplify matters I assumed there was no signal loss in the coax. I made measurements every 100 kHz across the bands (every 200 kHz on 10 meters). I had available a separate program for my computer that would determine the feedpoint impedance at the antenna—provided the line constants and length were known—and also translate R and X into SWR.

On 80 meters the measured SWR across the band was quite high, but the G5RV worked well when used with my station equipment and auxiliary ATU. ATU tuning was very sharp, and the unit required readjustment when the operating frequency was over a few tens of kHz. Reports for the G5RV roughly corresponded to those received when a dipole was used. On this band, a portion of the flat-top is folded back into the 300-ohm line. It's possible that heating of the line may be experienced with the use of high power. I only ran 150 watts, so I had no such difficulty.

On 40 meters, the SWR was much lower but the ATU was required on the high end of the band. Reports were excellent. However, no comparison antenna was on hand. Stations on my weekly sked into southern California noticed no discernible difference from my signal of earlier contacts using a dipole, as compared to another amateur a few miles from my location. Not very scientific, I agree, but meaningful in the long run.

SWR on 10 MHz was very, very high. No wonder operation on this band wasn't recommended! I crossed it off the operating list.

As for 20 meters, the SWR started out at less than 2:1 on 14.0 MHz and increased slowly as I raised the operating frequency. The ATU proved necessary at the very high end of the band. I worked plenty of overseas DX with the G5RV, and it seemed as good as a dipole. Maybe slightly better.

Eighteen MHz operation was quite good, with a low value of SWR. No ATU was required. Again, I noted no long-term difference between this antenna and a good dipole, except that the G5RV pattern was better than the dipole in the directions near the ends of the wires. Theoretical gain over a dipole in the favored direction is about 1.2 dB.

SWR was high on 21 MHz and an ATU was required. Even so, the antenna sounded "flat" on this band and signal reports received were poor. Operation was passable, but not as good as my quarterwave vertical. I'd give the G5RV a grade of "D" on this band.

Twenty-four MHz also showed a high value of SWR. It seemed that the antenna was a poor performer on this band, too. I did work a few stations, but the reports were mediocre.

Ten meters exhibited a very high SWR at the low end, which gradually decreased as the frequency was raised, until it fell below 2:1 at the high-frequency end of the band. The band was poor, so it was difficult to evaluate the antenna. Theory says the antenna is quite directional off the ends on this band. Theoretical gain is about 2 dBd. An ATU is recommended for general operation.

What Does It All Mean?

The bottom line is that the G5RV design functions on all amateur bands between 80 and 10 meters, with the exception of 10, 21, and 24 MHz. SWR isn't really low on any band, despite some claims.

I found that the SWR on any one band could be improved at the expense of the SWR on other bands by shortening or lengthening the 300-ohm ribbon matching section. I also noted that the SWR could be changed for the better on a particular band by moving the coax about with respect to the plane of the antenna. Finally, I found that an "isolation transformer" or 1:1 current-type balun is a necessary requirement at the point where the ribbon line meets the 50-ohm coax line, or SWR readings will change drastically with changes in coax-cable length. Again, running the coax parallel to the antenna resulted in odd-ball SWR readings.

SWR readings at the station proved puzzling. On 20 meters, they correlated nicely with the measurements made with the RF bridge. On 10 meters, the readings were higher in the station; on 40 meters, they were lower. On 80 meters, they were higher at the high end of the band and lower at the 3.5 MHz end.

All this was very perplexing. The SWR readings seemed to be a function of coax-line placement and length of line. I believed the RF-bridge readings more than the SWR readings, as they were made under the best possible conditions (short coax line running at right angles to the plane of the antenna), whereas I doubted the reliability of the SWR readings taken with a traditional wattmeter at the far end of a long, randomly placed coax line.

I finally was able to reproduce the bridge measurements to a good degree on the wattmeter, after I placed

the ferrite cores along the line to the shack. A group of cores were moved along the coax until they seemed to isolate the line from the antenna field (**Figure 3-26**). Readings settled down after that and generally resembled the readings made by the RF bridge.

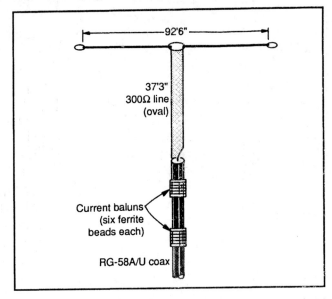

Figure 3-26. The W6SAI version of the ZS6BKW version of the G5RV antenna! Normal details covering waterproofing of coax to ribbon connection apply.

Lessons Learned Regarding The G5RV Antenna

1. A current-type 1:1 balun should be used to connect the ribbon line to the 50-ohm coax.

2. Placement of the coax feedline with relation to the antenna is critical, and SWR will change with line position.

3. If the G5RV is slung from a yardarm on a metal tower, the ribbon line should be spaced at least 3 feet clear of the tower.

4. A good match on any one band can be made by shortening or lengthening the ribbon line a few inches at a time. However, this advantage is only achieved by a poorer match on some other band.

5. The SWR cannot be altered by changing coax length if the line is properly decoupled from the field of the antenna, but the impedance at the station end of the line can be altered by varying line length to provide the best match to the transmitter. If the SWR at the transmitter changes when line length is changed, it's an indication that there's coupling between the outer shield of the line and the antenna. Groups of ferrite slugs placed along the line at intervals will help reduce this effect if it annoys you.

6. Tube-type rigs with an adjustable output circuit have greater loading range than do solid-state transmitters. In many cases, the tube-type rig can be used with the G5RV without requiring an auxiliary ATU.

7. It's a good idea to decouple the outside of the line at your transmitter. Do this by slipping six ferrite beads over the coax shield before you place the plug on the line. Type 43 beads (Amidon no. 43-1024 for RG-8 coax) will do the job. (Use Amidon no. 77-1024 for RG-58 coax.)

8. Finally, the G5RV functions as an "all-band" antenna (less the 10-, 12-, and 21-MHz bands), but an ATU is usually necessary unless a lot of time-consuming pruning and trimming of the ribbon are done. Even then, transmitter matching at the station will only improve one band at the expense of another.

Bottom line: The G5RV is a popular antenna, and with it you can work a lot of DX. It has a little gain over a dipole on the higher bands, but not much. If you have a modern rig, be prepared to buy an ATU to make the antenna work properly (unless your rig contains one).

A Different G5RV Design

Can the G5RV antenna be improved to reduce the SWR on the transmission line and/or provide better SWR bandwidth? The G5RV has been around a long time, and many attempts have been made to make it a better performer on the HF bands. The most promising results I know of are those of Dr. Brian Austin, ZS6BKW, of the University of Edinburgh, Scotland.[6] Aided by a computer program and field tests, he varied dimensions of the G5RV design, trying to achieve a reasonably low value of SWR response on all major HF bands.

The ZS6BKW design uses a 50-ohm coax line and either a 400-ohm open-wire line or a 300-ohm ribbon line. Unfortunately, the design doesn't incorporate a balun between the coax line and the balanced line transformer, so the SWR measurements run on this design may be open to question.

Alas, I couldn't buy a ZS6BKW antenna, so as a last resort I built one. As I went along, I discovered that the velocity of propagation of 300-ohm ribbon line varies from the accepted figure of 0.82, depending upon who manufactured the line and the physical shape of the cross-section of the line. I found I had to add 6 inches to the original BKW line dimension to get the best results. Also, a 1:1 current balun at the bottom of the line is a necessity. My final dimensions are shown in **Figure 3-26**. The SWR data for 40-, 20-, and 10-meter bands are shown in **Table 3-3**. The

SWR on both the 18- and 24-MHz bands is very good, but the SWR response on the 80-meter band is about the same as with the G5RV, and an ATU is required. Use ferrite beads to "cool off" the coax line.

As with the earlier G5RV design, physical placement of the coax line and its length can determine SWR at the transmitter. For those amateurs wishing a slightly shorter antenna, or those dissatisfied with the generic G5RV design, this antenna may be an acceptable alternative. The ribbon line can be trimmed for best results on one band. Once the dimensions are adjusted for your particular installation, you'll find this a very satisfying antenna.

REPRESENTATIVE W6SAI ANTENNA		
Band	**Freq. (MHz)**	**SWR**
80 m	3.5	7.68
	3.6	6.26
	3.7	5.25
	3.8	4.43
	3.9	4.36
	4.0	4.60
40 m	7.0	1.72
	7.1	1.95
	7.2	2.77
	7.3	3.00
20 m	14.0	2.50
	14.1	2.20
	14.2	1.76
	14.3	1.38
	14.35	1.42
15 m	21.00	4.96
	21.10	4.94
	21.20	4.72
	21.30	4.70
	21.45	4.70
10 m	28.0	4.38
	28.2	3.49
	28.4	2.92
	28.6	2.53
	28.8	2.11
	29.0	1.69
	29.2	1.48
	29.4	1.68
	29.6	2.40
	29.7	2.55
WARC Bands		
30 m	10.1	8.11
17 m	18.11	1.11
12 m	24.95	2.75

Table 3-3. SWR data for the 40-, 20-, and 10-meter bands for the W6SAI version of the ZS6BKW version of the G5RV.

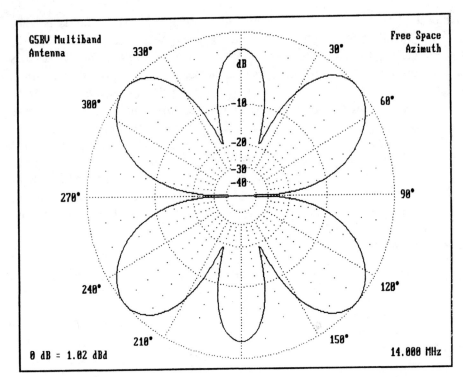

Figure 3-27. Pattern of the G5RV on 14 MHz.

Polar Plots of the G5RV Antenna

Polar plots of the G5RV antenna are shown in **Figures 3-27** through **3-29**. The field patterns of the original G5RV and the ZS6BKW version are the same for the most part. On 80 meters, the pattern is the familiar figure-8 of the conventional dipole. The pattern is the same on 40 meters, but slightly narrower, and exhibiting a

gain of about 0.5 dB at right angles to the antenna wire.

The 20-meter pattern has the main lobes at an angle of about 45 degrees to the wire. These lobes exhibit a gain of 1.02 dBd. The lobes at 90 degrees to the wire are down about 2 dB from the main lobes. In real life, the deep nulls of the pattern will tend to be filled in to a great extent.

The 15-meter pattern shows the main lobes displaced

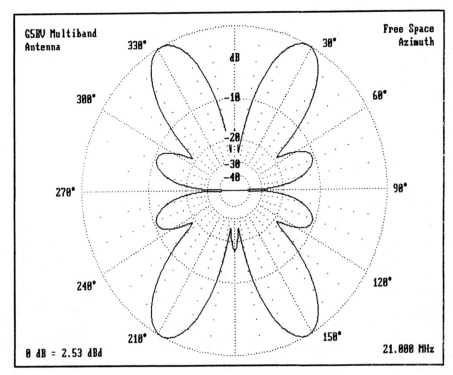

Figure 3-28. Pattern of the G5RV on 21 MHz.

Figure 3-29. Pattern of the G5RV on 28 MHz.

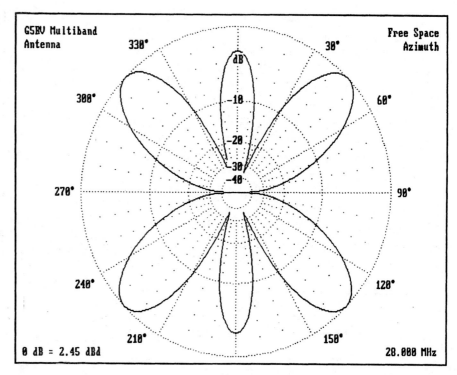

above 65 degrees from the wire, with a large null at right angles to the wire. Four minor lobes exist, each down about 10 dB from the main lobes. It isn't a very exciting pattern, as radiation in-line with the wire and at right angles to it is largely suppressed. Hopefully, the nulls will be filled in by virtue of the antenna environment.

The 10-meter pattern shows even more lobe splitting. Gain of the main lobes is about 2.45 dBd. Again, there are a lot of gaps in the plot.

Summing it up, the G5RV antenna operates like an ordinary random-length, center-fed wire with no special properties other than it can be matched reasonably on most amateur bands with little effort.

Analysis of the G5RV Antenna

The IEEE (Institute of Electrical and Electronic En-

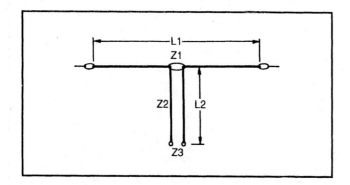

Figure 3-30. The basic G5RV antenna adapted for 50-ohm feed by GØGSF (ZS6BKW). (See text for details.)

gineers) colloquium digest No. 1992/181 (Great Britain) presents a simple method of analyzing the performance of the G5RV antenna. **Figure 3-30** is a drawing of the generic antenna. Dr. Austin claims that when Z2 is greater than 275 ohms and less than 450 ohms, an acceptable impedance match will occur at a number of frequencies in the HF range. The optimum value of Z2 lies between 325 and 400 ohms.

Dr. Austin further states that for any minimum operating frequency and a given value of Z2, there are specific lengths for the flat-top (L1) and the transformer-line (L2) which provide the best impedance match. The frequencies that provide the best match are related by the following series (which varies slightly for different values of Z2): 1, 1.99, 2.53, 3.49, 4.07, 5.62, and 7.18. That is, if the fundamental frequency is taken as 3.6 MHz, the next resonance point is:

$$3.6 \times 1.99 = 7.164 \text{ MHz}$$

followed by:

$$3.6 \times 2.53 = 9.108 \text{ MHz}$$
$$3.6 \times 3.49 = 12.564 \text{ MHz}$$
$$3.6 \times 4.07 = 14.652 \text{ MHz}$$
$$3.6 \times 5.62 = 20.232 \text{ MHz and}$$
$$3.6 \times 7.18 = 25.848 \text{ MHz}$$

(I'll call this antenna design #1.)

Dr. Austin built and tested a number of G5RV-type antennas. One design, of interest to amateurs, provided resonant frequencies just outside amateur bands, with the dimensions shown in **Figure 3-31**. The design frequency was 7.32 MHz, and the theoretical harmonic resonance series was 1, 2.01, 2.55, 3.54, and 4.10. Measured resonance with VSWR less than 2:1 was achieved at 7.32 MHz, 14.68 MHz, 18.63 MHz, 25.88 MHz, and 30.027 MHz. (I'll call this antenna design #2.)

A ferrite-sleeve balun (W2DU-type) consisting of 40 ferrite beads (73 material) was used between L2 and the 50-ohm coax line, and the effect on the SWR was minimal. Dr. Austin concluded that the use of a balun wasn't justified.

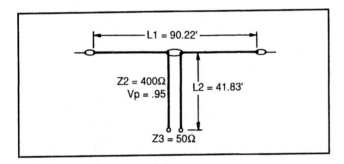

Figure 3-31. The GØGSF design for a multiband antenna. The design frequency is 7.32 MHz.

A GØGSF Antenna For the Amateur Bands

The Austin design #2 provides resonance points just outside the high-frequency ends of the 40-, 20-, 17-, 12-, and 10-meter bands. The first design (#1) provides resonance in the 80-, 40-, and 20-meter bands with close-resonance near the 30-, 15-, and 12-meter bands. As-is, either design would seem to work well with a transceiver equipped with an antenna tuner. Indeed, design #1 seems to be the long-desired "all-band" antenna if higher values of SWR are accepted for operation on the 30-, 15-, and 12-meter bands.

Dr. Austin provided a chart that would assist in designing a particular multiband antenna (**Figure 3-32**). The variables are L1; L2; the minimum operating frequency f_{min}; and the impedance of the transformer-line, Z2, which is limited in impedance to the range between 275 and 400 ohms. For any given values of f_{min} and Z2, there are specific lengths of L1 and L2 that satisfy the impedance match. Note that dimensions are in meters.

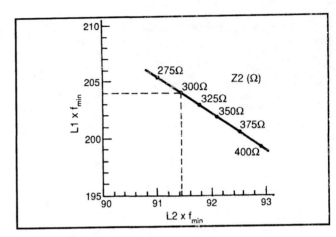

Figure 3-32. A copy of "Design Line" for the multiband antenna derived by GØGSF.

To design a specific antenna using the chart, it's necessary to first choose the impedance of Z2. A convenient value is 300 ohms, as transmitting-type ribbon line is readily available in this impedance. Velocity factor of the line is about 0.8.

From the 300-ohm point on the chart, draw a horizontal line to the y-axis to determine the quantity ($L1 \times f_{min}$). This is about 204. Choose the minimum operating frequency—say, 7.1 MHz. Dividing 204 by 7.1 gives an L1 value of 28.732 meters, or 94.26 feet. (Meters divided by 0.3048 gives feet.) This is rounded off to 94 feet, 3 inches.

Now from the 300-ohm point on the chart, drop vertically down to the x-axis to find the product ($L2 \times f_{min}$). This is approximately 91.5. Divide this by f_{min} (7.1 MHz), which gives an L2 value of 12.887 meters, or 42.28 feet. This is rounded off to 42 feet, 4 inches.

This completes the antenna design shown in **Figure 3-33**. The theoretical resonant frequencies are 7.1 MHz, 14.13 MHz, 17.96 MHz, 24.78 MHz, and 28.9 MHz. Band coverage is 40, 20, 17, 12, and 10 meters. The 30- and 15-meter bands are missing.

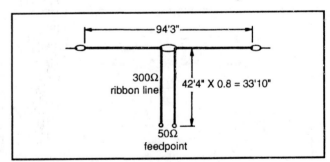

Figure 3-33. The final design of a multiband antenna for 40, 20, 17, 12, and 10 meters. The 300-ohm line is cut short to compensate for the velocity factor (0.8).

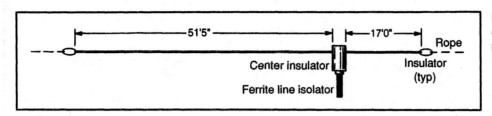

51'5"   17'0"   Rope

Center insulator

Insulator (typ)

Ferrite line isolator

Figure 3-34. The full-wave dipole for 20 meters. Azimuth plot is a cloverleaf. The feedpoint impedance is about 86 ohms.

A Full-wave Dipole

I desired a simple wire antenna that would place a main lobe into Europe. Unfortunately, my home was cleverly placed on a lot in such a position that any simple dipole antenna I could squeeze onto my property would plop its main lobe into central Africa, an area remarkably devoid of amateur radio operators. My chosen band was 20 meters, although this antenna can be cut for other bands, as I'll explain later.

Computer Analysis of the Problem. My antenna analyzer program quickly told me that given the direction in which I could erect a wire antenna, my best bet was a full-wave job with a cloverleaf pattern. One of the leaves would be aimed directly at Europe. The problem was if the full-wave antenna was fed at the center, as is the general case, it instantly would become two half-waves in phase and provide a narrow beam at right angles to the wire. That wasn't what I was looking for.

How about feeding the full-wave antenna at a point of maximum current in one of the half-wave sections? That would provide the proper current relationship in the antenna, with the appropriate pattern.

The first run of the computer program produced a wire about 68 feet long, fed about 17 feet from one end (**Figure 3-34**). At the design frequency of 14.2 MHz the feedpoint impedance is about 86 ohms. This configuration looks suspiciously like a multiband, off-center-fed antenna, but it is not. It is a one-band job with a pattern quite different than that of a dipole.

Building the Antenna. It was easy to build the antenna. I had an old klystron magnet coil (courtesy of the scrap pile at a local electronics outfit) that had thousands of feet of no. 16 enamel wire on it. I wound off about 70 feet. I used an Alpha-Delta model Delta-C antenna hardware kit consisting of a center insulator and two end insulators. The light-gray color of the devices blended nicely with the smoggy atmosphere. Below the center insulator, I placed a Radio Works C1-2K ferrite line isolator.

Everything went together in about an hour, and I eagerly checked out the antenna with my MFJ-259 analyzer—resonance at 14,200 kHz, just where I wanted it. I had erected it at a height of 40 feet. The

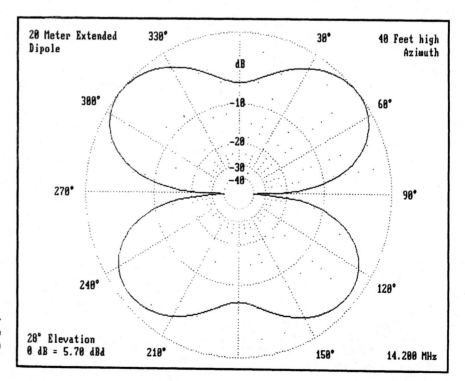

20 Meter Extended Dipole   330°   30°   40 Feet high Azimuth

dB

300°   -10   60°

-20

-30
-40

270°   90°

240°   120°

20° Elevation
0 dB = 5.70 dBd   210°   150°   14.200 MHz

Figure 3-35. The azimuth plot of a full-wave dipole. North is at the top of the screen. The gain figure (lower left) represents ground reflection gain.

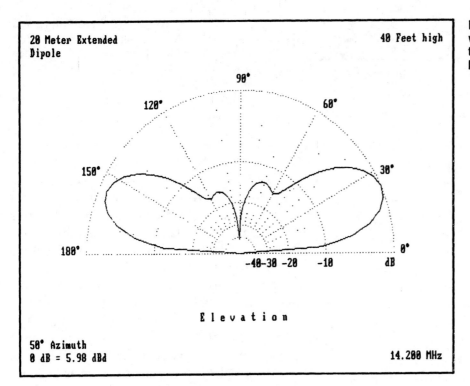

20 Meter Extended Dipole

40 Feet high

Elevation

50° Azimuth
0 dB = 5.98 dBd

14.200 MHz

Figure 3-36. Elevation plot of a full-wave dipole at 40 feet. The angle of the main lobe depends upon the height of the antenna above ground.

results matched the computer program very closely, so it looked as if it was time to try the antenna on the air.

The Computer Analysis. I used an analysis program of Brian Beezley, K6STI. The azimuth plot of the antenna is shown in **Figure 3-35**. Lobe maxima are at an angle of about 50 degrees to the wire, and large nulls appear at 90 and 180 degrees. In real life, over an imperfect ground, I doubt if these nulls are as

deep as they look, or as wide as they appear to be. Time will tell.

I next ran an elevation plot (**Figure 3-36**). The pattern is not quite a mirror image, as the feedpoint of the antenna is off-center, but it looks as if the pattern difference is only about one dB.

The elevation angle of the main lobe is about 28 degrees, and that is a function of antenna height above

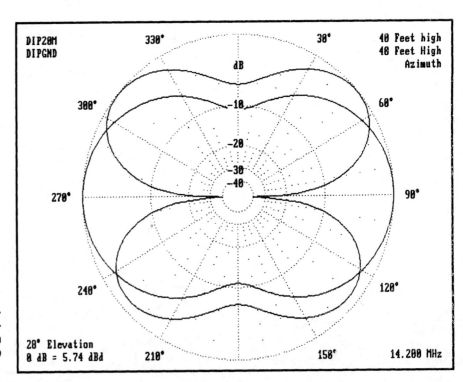

DIP20M
DIPGND

40 Feet high
40 Feet High
Azimuth

20° Elevation
0 dB = 5.74 dBd

14.200 MHz

Figure 3-37. Elevation plot of a full-wave antenna compared to a half-wave dipole. Note the increase in gain at azimuth angles near the line of the antenna—about 3 dB!

Figure 3-38. Low-angle gain of a full-wave dipole shows up in comparison with a half-wave dipole.

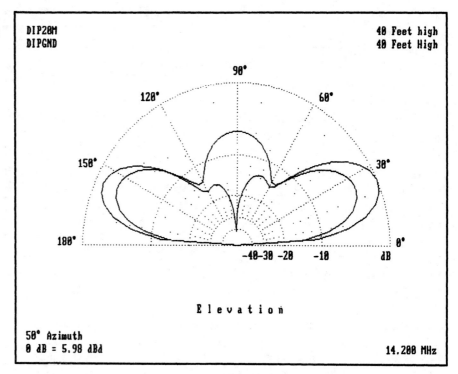

ground. I'm stuck with that! Even so, the lobe exhibits energy at a 10-degree angle that is only about 4 dB below maximum.

What have I gained over a simple center-fed dipole placed in the same position? Look at **Figure 3-37**. At a 28-degree elevation angle it looks as if I picked up about 3 dB at an azimuth angle of 45 degrees—the direction of Europe! Not bad for a few extra feet of wire.

At a 50-degree azimuth angle, the increase in gain of the extended antenna clearly shows up (**Figure 3-38**). And down at about a 10-degree angle it looks as if the improvement is on the order of 3 dB.

The last check was to observe the elevation patterns at a 10-degree azimuth angle, almost in line with the antenna (**Figure 3-39**). Here the extended dipole shows its worth. The 4-dB advantage is clearly appar-

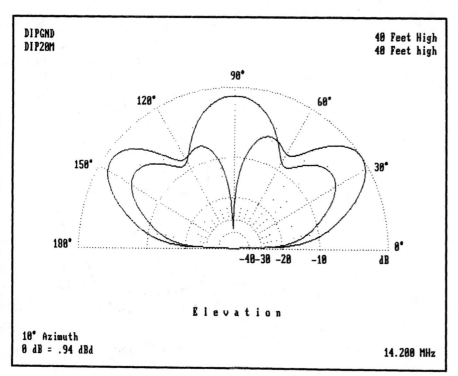

Figure 3-39. An end-on view of the antenna plot. Note the pattern improvement at take-off angles below 30 degrees.

ent at 10 degrees, and carries through up to the angle of maximum power.

Where does the gain come from? Well, the antenna takes power from where I don't want it (straight up) and directs it to where I do want it. The actual power gain of the antenna itself over a dipole is less than one dB. It is merely that the antenna takes advantage of ground reflection and provides enhanced, low-angle radiation where it will do some good.

Feeding the Antenna. The input resistance at resonance of this antenna provides pause for thought. It is about 86 ohms. If a 75-ohm transmission line were used, the SWR would be very low. However, no one I know uses such a line, nor are there any SWR meters easily available that work with a 75-ohm line. The solution? Use a 50-ohm line.

This is not as bad as it seems. SWR at antenna resonance is about 1.7, slowly rising as the antenna is operated off-resonance. Since every red-blooded ham has either an auxiliary antenna tuner or a tuner built into his transceiver, the SWR poses no problem. If you have time and various short lengths of coax, I'll bet you could arrive at a feedline length that would permit proper transceiver loading without a tuner! Those of you with a memory like a steel trap will realize this scheme doesn't change the SWR; it merely provides an impedance that is more satisfactory to the

transceiver (akin to taking a journey around the perimeter of a Smith Chart!).

Results. When I finally connected the antenna to my transceiver, I had to go outside to see if it was really up in the air, It was. With my usual luck, I had landed in the midst of a solar fadeout! I was able to get an encouraging report from an amateur across town who heard me with a fine signal. The band gradually came back to life, and in a short time I worked a 4X4, a UA3, and a ZP6 with good reports both ways. It therefore looks as if the antenna is working. Since that lucky day, I've worked a bunch of Europeans and other DX at random places around the globe.

Other Bands. There is no reason why you can't build this full-wave antenna for other bands. (See **Table 3-4** for dimensions.) A cloverleaf pattern will be provided on each band.

References

1. William Wrigley, "Impedance Characteristics of Harmonic Antennas," *QST*, February 1954, pages 10–14.

2. Tom Sorbie. See "Technical Topics," Pat Hawker, *Radio Communication*, December 1990, page 31.

3. John Belrose and Peter Boulaine, "The Off-Center-Fed Dipole Revisited," *QST*, August 1990, pages 28–34.

4. James Healey. See Product Review, "Garant Enterprises GD-8 'Windom Antenna,'" *QST*, September 1990, pages 30–32.

5. B. Sykes, "Controlled Feeder Radiation, *Radio Communication*, RSGB, May 1990.

6. Dr. Brian Austin, ZS6BKW, "Computer-aided Design of a Multiband Dipole," *Radio Communication*, RSGB, August 1985, pages 614–617.

FULL-WAVE ANTENNA DIMENSONS		
Band	Long Leg	Short Leg
18 MHz	40' 4"	13' 2"
21 MHz	34' 4"	11' 4"
24 MHz	29' 4"	9' 6"
28 MHz	25' 9"	8' 4"

Table 3-4. Dimensions of the full-wave antenna for the 18-, 21-, 24-, and 28-MHz bands.

Chapter 4

Multiband Dipole Antennas

The center-fed dipole is as old as radio itself. Today, it's the most widely used antenna in amateur radio. Even though it's a single-frequency antenna, it has been modified for multiband operation.

The multi-frequency dipole was invented and perfected by Howard K. Morgan, Superintendent of Communications, Transcontinental and Western Airline, Inc. The requirement of the airline (the grandfather of TWA) was for a simple multi-frequency antenna that would provide good reception of various aircraft frequencies at ground communication stations. The antenna devised by Morgan was described in the August 1940 issue of *Electronics*, and the original drawing from that article appears as **Figure 4-1**. The Morgan antenna consisted of a center-fed dipole with the end insulators replaced by parallel-tuned circuits. Extra wire sections were added beyond the circuits so the dipole was again resonant at a lower frequency.

As an example, if the center dipole section is cut for 21.2 MHz and the parallel-tuned circuits (commonly called *traps*) are tuned to 21.2 MHz, the dipole works in a normal manner; the very high impedance of the resonant trap acts as an insulator. Wires added after the traps have little, if any, effect on antenna operation at or near 21.2 MHz.

If wire sections added after the traps are cut to the proper length, the overall antenna system will resonate at a lower frequency—say, 14.0 MHz. The presence of the tuned circuits affects the length of the antenna, so resonance is obtained at 14.0 MHz with an overall antenna length somewhat shorter than normal. A typical antenna is shown in **Figure 4-2A**. The traps act as electrical switches that are either open or closed, depending on the frequency of operation of the antenna.

Morgan's article pointed out that antennas for operation on as many as four different frequencies had been built successfully. Finally, the article provided detailed information concerning adjustment of the traps for proper antenna operation.

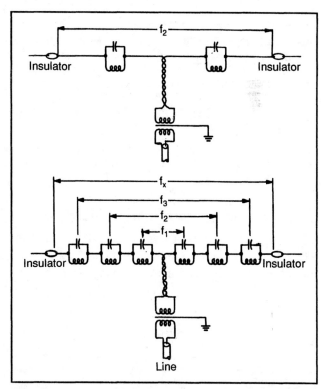

Figure 4-1. The original rendition of this illustration appeared in *Electronics* magazine. It depicts the trap-dipole scheme evolved by Howard K. Morgan. The multi-frequency antenna was designed for ground-station reception in the aeronautical service. Parallel-tuned trap circuits served as insulators at the resonant frequency of the trap and antenna.

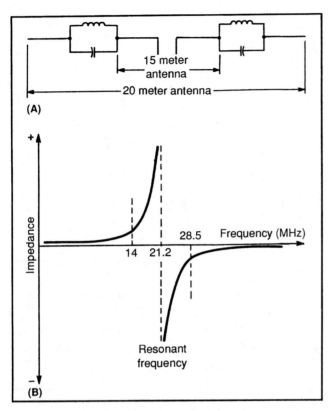

Figure 4-2. Operation of the tuned trap for a 20–15 meter, two-band dipole antenna. (A) At trap resonance, the trap displays very high-impedance characteristics, the equivalent of an insulator. Examples given are for a trap tuned to 21.2 MHz (15 meters). (B) Impedance chart of a 15-meter trap showing reactance curve through the 14–28 MHz region. At 14 MHz the coil is the dominant component of the trap, and at 28.5 MHz the capacitor is dominant. The antenna is resonant at 14 MHz, but isn't resonant at 28.5 MHz. An extra set of traps is required for 10-meter operation, as shown in Figure 4-3.

Resurrection of the Multiband Dipole

Morgan's multi-frequency antenna died a quick death. Here was the perfect antenna for operation on the various amateur high-frequency bands; the traps were easy to build and adjust and low-impedance transmission line was readily available, yet nobody carried the idea forward. With the coming of World War II and the ban on amateur radio, the multiband-antenna principle fell by the wayside.

It wasn't until after the war that the concept of multiband operation surfaced again, in a design by Chester Buchanan, W3DZZ, shown in the December 1950 issue of *Radio and Television News*. Buchanan described a dual-band beam for 10 and 20 meters using trapped elements. He also provided the first complete description of how the trapped antenna worked. His final beam design, known to many DXers as the "W3DZZ beam," was fully described in *QST* in March 1955.

How the Triband Antenna Operates

Frequency-sensitive "switches" are the operating secret of the triband antenna. The switches consist of a capacitor and inductance connected in parallel. This is a simple parallel-tuned circuit, which provides a very high impedance across the terminals at the resonant frequency.

The actual value of the impedance is the reactance of the coil times its Q ($Q \times Q_L$). If the value of Q is high (Q being the electrical excellence of the coil), the circuit works as a high-impedance insulator at the circuit resonant frequency.

The curve in **Figure 4-2B** shows that the off-frequency reactance of the circuit is quite small—inductive at frequencies lower than resonance and capacitive at frequencies higher than resonance. When the trap is placed in an antenna, the equivalent circuit of the antenna above and below resonance is as shown in **Figure 4-2A**. On 15 meters, the center portion of the antenna works as a dipole with trap "insulators" tuned to 15 meters. When the antenna is used on 20 meters,

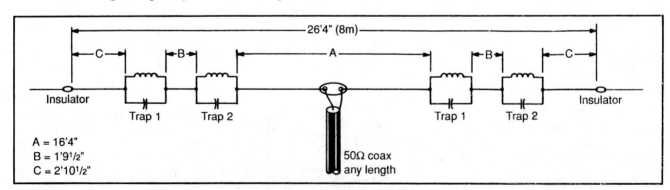

Figure 4-3. A triband element for 20, 15, and 10 meters. Dimensions are given for no. 16 antenna wire size (not critical). Each trap is resonated to the design frequency before installation in the antenna. The length of each trap is about 2 inches. A small ceramic or mica ceramic, rated at 3 kV, is used, which should have zero temperature coefficient.

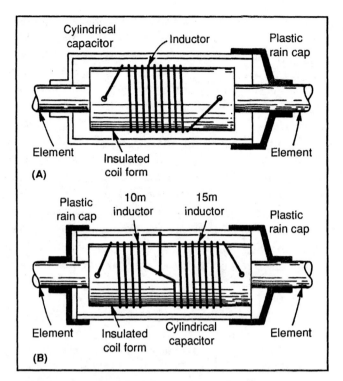

Figure 4-4. Typical trap construction. (A) Single trap composed of an inductor connected in parallel with a cylindrical capacitor. The capacitor serves as an outer shield for the inductor and provides capacitance between the cylinder and coil. The end of the assembly is sealed against weather with a plastic rain cap. (B) Dual, two-band trap composed of two coils mounted within a single cylindrical capacitor. The number of turns on the coils and their placement within the cylinder determines effective capacitance. The ends of the assembly are sealed with plastic rain caps. Connection between the coils and the cylinder is made at the center junction of the inductors.

the inductive reactance of the traps is quite low, and they act as loading coils. The wire length between the traps is cut so the wire, plus the loading coils, is resonant at 20 meters, in conjunction with the center section. Thus, on 20 meters, the trap dipole is considerably shorter than normal because a portion of the antenna is duplicated by the series inductance on the traps; the antenna is *nonresonant* on 10 meters unless extra traps are added.

To put it all together, in a triband element, the inner section and inner traps are resonant at 10 meters, the middle portion of the antenna and associated traps are resonant at 15 meters, and the whole antenna assembly is resonant at 20 meters (**Figure 4-3**).

Trap Performance

The trap is the heart of the triband antenna. A good trap will have reasonably high Q and must be waterproof. Many amateurs make their own traps for tri-

band dipoles[1] from an airwound inductance and a transmitting-type ceramic capacitor. The trap is placed in a waterproof housing.

Commercially-made traps for triband antennas are more sophisticated and are designed for mass production. The two traps in one section of an element may be combined into one structure, as shown in **Figure 4-4**. This arrangement provides a compact and rugged assembly. As far as I know, no reliable information exists as to the actual gain of a triband beam compared to a full-size antenna. Admittedly, the perfect trap hasn't yet been built, so some power is lost in each trap. Also, on the two lowest bands, power is lost in the inner traps, which act as loading coils.

On the whole, the tribander design is good. The triband antennas on the market *work*, and work well, judging from the number of DXers who use them and the robust signals they put out.

Triband Beam Bandwidth

One specification in which the tribander suffers is bandwidth. On 10 meters, where the inner set of traps acts as insulators, the bandwidth of the tribander compares favorably with that of a conventional 10-meter dipole. On 15 and 20 meters, operational bandwidth is somewhat restricted, because a portion of the element on each band is made up of the trap (or traps) for the higher-frequency band.

A set of representative SWR curves for a triband Yagi and a full-size 20-meter Yagi is shown in **Figure 4-5**. Both beams are built on 20-foot booms. Observe that

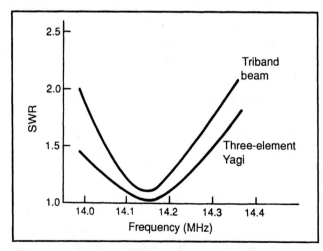

Figure 4-5. SWR bandwidth curve of a typical triband Yagi beam is quite sharp on 20 meters, approaching 2:1 at band edges. A three-element, full-size Yagi exhibits a more moderate SWR curve for the same frequency span. On 15 meters, tribander bandwidth is somewhat improved and is essentially equal to a full-size Yagi on the 10-meter band.

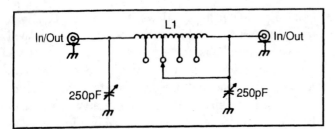

Figure 4-6. Simple ATU for coaxial line. Capacitors are single-spaced receiving types for powers to 250 watts. Mica compression units can be used for low power. The inductor consists of 15 turns, 1-inch diameter and 2 inches long. Tap to the coil is through a ceramic, single-pole rotary switch, such as Centralab 2501 (two to six positions, nonshorting). The coil is tapped every other turn. A wire tap can easily be soldered to the coil by depressing the turn on either side of the tap with a screwdriver to allow the tap wire to pass around a turn of the coil (coil may be a B&W miniductor or equivalent). The network is symmetrical; either terminal may be used for input or output.

the 20-meter bandwidth of the tribander suffers in comparison with the full-size 20-meter beam, but bandwidth improves on 15 meters, and is equal for both antenna designs on 10 meters. This is of little consequence to the amateur who has a tube-type final-amplifier stage with an adjustable output network, but it poses a problem to those who have a solid-state output stage that requires an antenna with a low standing-wave ratio.

One way around this problem is to build an ATU that will reduce the SWR at the transmitter end of the line (**Figure 4-6**). This simple matching network is placed between the coaxial line to the antenna and the station SWR meter. The capacitors and number of coil turns are adjusted for lowest SWR on the operating band. It can easily be adjusted for near-zero SWR at any point in the 10-, 15-, or 20-meter bands by tuning the controls for minimum SWR as observed on the meter. The settings can be logged for future use.

Is a Triband Yagi Beam Practical?

Based on personal observations over the years, the answer to this question is *yes*. With a well-made

tribander, you have the tremendous advantage of three-band operation with one relatively small antenna. I've used a triband Yagi for years, alternating with a full-size 20-meter beam on occasion. As far as working DX goes, I can do equally well with either antenna, and I notice no difference between the three-band design and the single-band beam.

Common sense and measurements made on the triband Yagi tell me that it isn't as efficient as the full-size beam. The bandwidth is somewhat restricted, and the front-to-back ratio isn't quite up to snuff, particularly on 15 and 10 meters. However, these complaints fade away when I consider the convenience of working *three bands*, and the fact that I can compete in DX work and get reports that are just about equal to those of others in the area.

Tests. Before I installed the tribander—and I wouldn't have believed this—I took the traps into the company laboratory and measured the Q on a precision meter. A trap I made out of the best materials available (air-wound, silver-plated, copper coil, and a transmitting-type ceramic capacitor) provided a Q of over 300 at 30 MHz.

The Q of a commercial trap, measured at 30 MHz, was only about 180. This so discouraged me that the triband beam sat in my garage in the original box for about a year. Finally, deciding to see for myself how the antenna performed, the 20-meter Yagi came down, and the tribander went up in its place. Despite my misgivings, the tribander worked, and worked well. Some of my engineering colleagues sniffed in disdain at my unscientific test and were unmoved when I beat them out in a DX pileup. "Pure luck," was their conclusion. Well, I don't know about that. Luck and operating skill are surely factors to be reckoned with, but if the antenna doesn't work, all the operating skills in the world are to no avail.

Power transfer. It's true that some transmitting power is lost in the traps. I have a telescoping tower and can reach the traps in my antenna from the garage

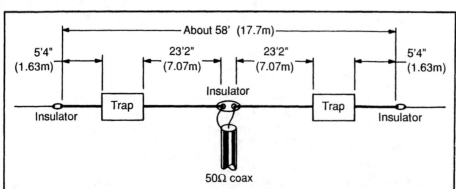

Figure 4-7. The 30/40-meter dual dipole. SWR is below 1.2 on the 30-meter band and below 1.7 on the 40-meter band. Forty-meter resonance is about 7.13 MHz.

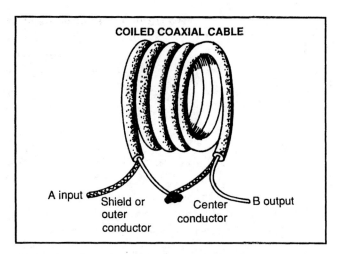

Figure 4-8. Single-element trap winding detail.

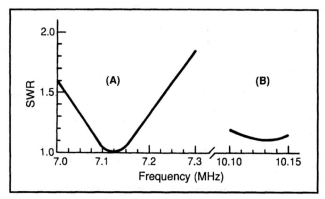

Figure 4-9. SWR plot of a 30/40-meter dipole. (A) is the 40-meter plot; (B) is the 30-meter plot.

roof when the tower is retracted. Running a kilowatt input for 10 minutes, key down (when the band is dead!) leaves the traps slightly warm to the touch. Obviously, some RF power is being converted to heat in the traps. Other hams (having more ego than common sense) have attempted running excess power to a trap Yagi beam and have damaged the traps.

In conclusion, then, a good trap Yagi beam is an acceptable compromise for the amateur who wants three-band operation. If a solid-state transmitter is used, an ATU will prove helpful in making the transmitter perform at top efficiency.

A Trap Dipole for 30 and 40 Meters

Figure 4-7 shows a trap dipole designed for operation on 30 as well as 40 meters. Simplified traps, such as those shown in N3GO's article in *Ham Radio*[2], are used. These simplified traps can be built in minutes and will work as well as the more complex, discrete-component designs that use separate inductors and capacitors. Trap design is shown in **Figure 4-8**. If built as shown, they need not be adjusted for frequency. Overall length of the trapped antenna is about 58 feet, making the design smaller than that for a full-size 40-meter dipole. This is very convenient for the ham with a small lot.

The traps are wound on a short section of 1-1/4 inch outside-diameter, clear-PVC water pipe. Lengths of RG-58A/U are used for the inductors. Exactly 9-5/8 turns are required for trap resonance at 10.075 MHz. Each trap requires only about 56 inches of coaxial line, nuts and bolts for termination points, and a length of PVC pipe. What could be cheaper?

When the traps are completed, they may be checked with a dip oscillator. Self-resonance between 9.9 MHz

and 10.2 MHz is okay. Resonance at 10.125 MHz (or thereabouts) is achieved by pruning the center sections of the antenna, and resonance at 7.15 MHz is achieved by pruning the tip sections. SWR curves for the antenna described are shown in **Figure 4-9**.

A word of caution: The traps should be protected from the weather. My original traps were exposed and I noticed that the SWR curves shifted when the traps became wet with rain. This was probably caused by an increase in the distributed capacitance between the turns of the trap coil caused by the film of water. The transmission line and ends of the trap windings should be protected from moisture, because water can be sucked into the line by capillary action along the braid wires of the shield.

I first tried to seal the traps by using a tube of so-called RTV, bought at an auto supply store. This was a disaster. After a few days the metal hardware on the traps turned a nasty green color. I examined the tube of goop and found the words "contains acetic acid" among the small print on the back of the tube. I then got a tube of the right stuff, *General Electric* RTV, and noted that no acetic acid was mentioned on the label. I cleaned the traps and slathered the new RTV over the connections and ends of the RG-58/U coaxial cable coil. That did the job.

As an alternative, *Dow-Corning* 3145 sealant can be used. It doesn't have the acid component in the mixture. (**Warning!** Dow Corning 732 Silastic Sealant, widely available, gives off an acid as it dries out. This, like the cheap so-called RTV, will damage metallic parts.) One learns something new every day.

Practical Two-band Dipole for 18 and 24 MHz

Here's a simple antenna you can build for the 18- and 24-MHz bands. Important antenna dimensions are

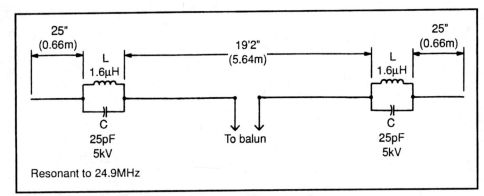

Figure 4-10. Trap-dipole antenna for 18- and 24-MHz bands. The trap is held in position by a 4-inch long ceramic insulator. The antenna is fed from a 1:1 balun and 50-ohm coaxial line.

shown in **Figure 4-10**. The traps are made of a coil-capacitor combination, as discussed previously, and mounted to a small ceramic insulator which serves to take the pull of the antenna.

Before the traps are installed, they must be frequency-checked with a dip oscillator and a calibrated receiver. Place the trap in an area free of nearby metallic objects and loosely couple it to the dip oscillator. When resonance is indicated, note the frequency of the oscillator on the nearby receiver. The traps should show resonance within ±100 kHz of 24.9 MHz. One end turn on each trap should be broken free of the coil bars so it can be moved about to set the exact resonant point of the trap. You'll find that when you attach the trap across the supporting insulator, the resonant frequency will drop a bit because of the capacitance across the insulator. It's best to shoot for a resonant trap frequency about 24.9 MHz; the insulator capacitance will then place your trap "right on the nose." You also can run your checks after assembly. Take your choice.

The length of the tip sections is critical for proper operation on 18 MHz. Varying the tip length by as little as one inch per end will change the resonant frequency about 150 kHz. Since the band is only 100 kHz wide, this means tip dimensions are critical to about an inch to establish antenna resonance within the band.

The tip dimensions shown in **Figure 4-10** are quite accurate. If you want to frequency-check the whole antenna, suspend it in the air, in the clear, about six feet above the ground. Place a 1/2-turn inductor across the center insulator, and measure the 18- and 24-MHz frequencies of the complete antenna with a dip oscillator coupled to the inductor.

When I made my antenna, I cut the tip sections about a foot longer than necessary and then folded them back and twisted the wires around the active antenna wire. That provided plenty of extra wire in case I had to lengthen the tip sections. Once I reached the correct length, I cut off the excess wire. After

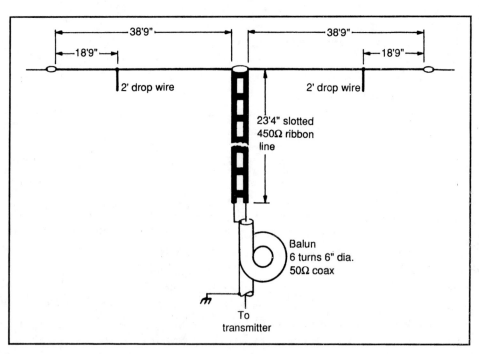

Figure 4-11. The G3TKN multiband antenna for 10, 18, and 24 MHz. The length of the slotted ribbon line shown is adjusted in length to compensate for the velocity factor (see text).

making some minor adjustments, I found out that removing one inch at each end of the center dipole raised the resonant frequency of the antenna 100 kHz/inch at 24.9 MHz. (Since the length of the 24.9-MHz dipole affects the resonant frequency of the 18.1-MHz dipole, the 24.9-MHz dipole must be pruned before the tip sections are adjusted.) When the antenna was completely tuned, it was hauled up my tower and anchored in a V-configuration at the 45-foot level, with the ends dropping down to the 25-foot level and tied to two nearby trees. SWR measurements revealed that the maximum figure on either range was under 1.3:1, with near-unity SWR at the design frequency on each band.

Note: More information on multiband antennas and trap antennas can be found in the 22nd edition of the *Radio Handbook*, published by Howard W. Sams & Co., a division of MacMillan, Inc.

A Multiband Dipole for 10/18/24 MHz

Have you operated the WARC bands? If you don't have an antenna that will do the job, consider the simple and effective design by V.C. Lear, G3TKN/VO1XG, shown in **Figure 4-11**. It was described in *Radio Communication* magazine, a publication of the Radio Society of Great Britain (RSGB). This sky-wire is inexpensive, is easy to build, and shouldn't require an antenna tuning unit (ATU) in most instances. (Placement of the antenna and the height above ground

affect SWR, as is the case with other antennas.)

The G3TKN antenna consists of a dipole with the center portion folded upon itself to form a balanced feedline. The length of one half the flat-top plus one half the open-wire feedline is 64 feet 7 inches. This is equal to 5/8 wave on 18.8 MHz, very close to 7/4 wave on 24.9 MHz, and reasonably close to 3/4 wave on 10.12 MHz.

On the 10-MHz band, the antenna operates as two half waves in phase, providing a figure-8 pattern slightly narrower than a dipole, with about 0.75 dB gain over a dipole (**Figure 4-12**). On 18 MHz, the antenna is nearly three half waves, center-fed, showing six lobes, with about 0.5 dB gain over a dipole oriented with respect to a pair of major lobes (**Figure 4-13**). The stub acts as a 1:1 transformer providing a low-impedance feedpoint.

On 24 MHz, each antenna leg is about one wavelength long. Short loading wires are added to the flat-top to bring resonance within the band. The wires are placed at high-impedance points for 24 MHz, which turn out to be low-impedance points for the other two bands. As a result, the effect of the wires is minimal on 10 and 18 MHz. The radiation pattern shows four lobes, with a power gain of about 1.7 dBd for each lobe (**Figure 4-14**). The loading wires provide a means of pruning the antenna for a compromise match, if required, depending upon the antenna height above ground, nearby objects, etc.

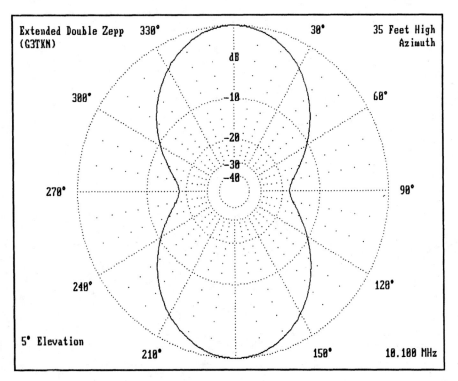

Figure 4-12. Pattern of the G3TKN antenna at 10 MHz.

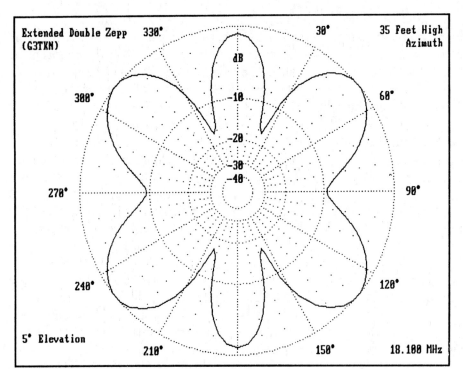

Figure 4-13. Pattern of the G3TKN antenna at 18 MHz.

The Matching System

The two-wire stub can be built with homemade open-wire, but it's a lot easier to use slotted "ribbon line," provided the velocity factor of the line is taken into account. Either a 450-ohm slotted line (Saxton 1562, or equivalent) or a TV-style, 300-ohm slotted line (Saxton 1563, or equivalent) is satisfactory. The veloc-ity factor of both lines is 0.9. Thus, an open-wire line, spaced two to four inches, is 25 feet 10 inches long, but the equivalent ribbon line is only 23 feet 4 inches long. Solid dielectric ribbon line isn't recommended, because it can be adversely affected by the weather.

An RF choke balun is required to isolate the shield of the coax feedline. Simply wind the coax into a

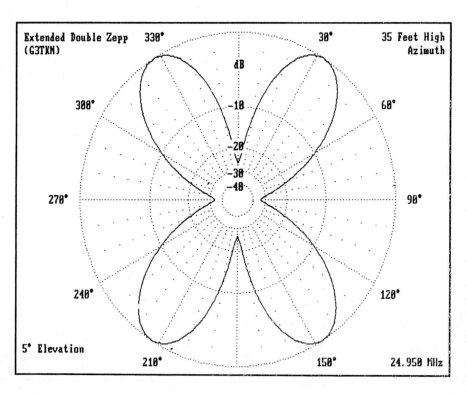

Figure 4-14. Pattern of the G3TKN antenna at 24 MHz.

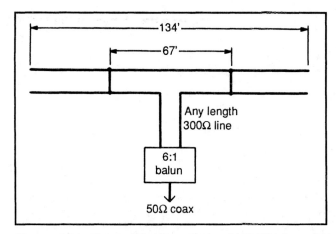

Figure 4-15. The 80/40-meter dipole of VK1PM is made with 300-ohm twin lead as the feeder. Jumpers between the two conductors are placed as shown. The end wires of the dipole are left open.

choke. Six turns, six inches in diameter will do the job. It's best not to jumble wind the coil. A neat trick is to wind the coil on a plastic soft-drink jug, cut off the ends of the jug, and tape the coil in place. That keeps the input and output ends of the coil apart.

The short loading wires provide a means of pruning the antenna for best compromise match on 18 and 24 MHz. A lot depends upon your particular installation. On the other hand, SWR may be so moderate that you won't have to do any pruning at all!

A Two-band Dipole Antenna

Much is written about two-band antenna designs using tuned traps in the radiating element. A different approach is shown (**Figure 4-15**) in a design by Ron May, VK1PM. This dipole covers the 80- and 40-meter bands. On 40 meters, the center section of the antenna acts as a folded dipole with a feedpoint impedance of about 300 ohms. The end sections, each a quarter wavelength long, are decoupled from the antenna and act as linear traps. On 80 meters, the full length of the antenna forms a half-wave element, fed with a T-match to the 300-ohm feedpoint. A 300-ohm TV-type feedline, with a 6:1 balun at the end, is used to match a nominal 50-ohm feedpoint (Palomar PB-6

Figure 4-16. Simplified elevation view of a two-story apartment building. Wood-frame construction is used, and the roof is composed of shingles on tar paper and wood backing. The experimental antenna was slung between points A-B-C, with the balun at high-point C. A small hole was drilled in the wall between the living room and the bedroom just below the roof so the antenna wire could pass from the front to the back of the house. Point C is about 28 feet above ground, and points A and B are about 18 feet above ground level.

balun). A coax line runs from the balun to the station. Overseas amateurs using 75-ohm coax can use a 4:1 balun. The idea can be applied to any two harmonically related bands, such as 40/20 or 20/10 meters.

Conversations with Pendergast: A Dipole for 20/40/80 Meters

"Aloha!" exclaimed Pendergast, sliding easily into my favorite chair. He placed his feet on the operating table, knocking a pile of unanswered QSL cards into the wastebasket. "How was your vacation in Hawaii?"

I carefully fished the cards out of the basket and replied, "It was *great*. I wish I was still over there! In addition to the sun and sand and those great *mai tais*, there was plenty of DX. What more could you wish?"

"I know all about the sun and sand and *mai tais*," replied Pendergast. "How about telling me about the DX? Did you take a rig over with you?"

"Yes," I replied, "I took a transceiver along. We were in a condominium apartment and I erected an antenna inside the building."

"Inside the building?" repeated my friend. "That sounds interesting. Tell old Pendergast all about it."

"Well, Old Pendergast, the apartment was a frame building with a heavy shingle roof. We were on the second floor, and the peak of the roof was about 28 feet above ground. I didn't want to risk any problems with the manager, so I put up the antenna inside the building. It ran from the front of the living room, up to the peak of the roof, then down to the rear of the bedroom. . . something like this (**Figure 4-16**). I had to drill a tiny hole in the wall at the top to get the wire through, but nobody will ever notice that!"

Pendergast looked at the sketch. "The ends of the antenna don't look very high," he objected.

"Only about 18 feet above ground," I replied. "But let me tell you about the antenna. I think I have a pret-

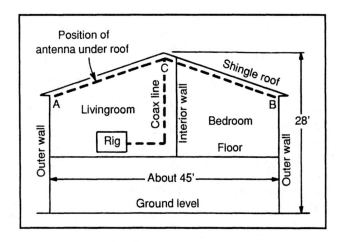

Figure 4-17. The 40/20-meter two-band dipole. A 1:1 balun is placed at the center of the dipole. Dimensions given are for resonance at 7.25 MHz and 14.1 MHz. If you want to change the resonant frequencies, the 20-meter section must be altered first, as adjustments to the center section affect the 40-meter resonance. Once the 20-meter section is adjusted properly, the tip sections are adjusted for resonance at 40 meters. A set of

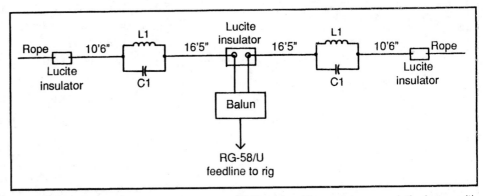

SWR curves, as shown in Figure 4-19, should be run using your exciter and an SWR meter. Dimensions are relatively noncritical, provided the traps are made as shown in Figure 4-18 and the antenna is erected reasonably clear of metallic objects. This antenna was built and tested in the backyard, in the clear, and moved to the interior location shown in Figure 4-16, with very little change in the SWR curves. A Bird no. 43 Reflectometer was used for tests.

ty good solution to a difficult problem that a lot of fellas may be up against."

"Very good," said Pendergast, as he took his notebook out of his jacket and prepared to take notes.

"The overall dimension I had to work with was just about 45 feet. I wanted to work 80, 40, and 20 meters. From experience at other portable locations, I felt that a balanced, center-fed antenna system was the best choice from the TVI standpoint, as an end-fed job can sometimes get you into trouble when the electrical wiring of the building is coupled into the ground return system of the antenna. A 20-meter dipole would easily fit into the 45-foot space, so that was chosen as the basic antenna element. I used a ferrite core balun with it and a random length of RG-58/U light-duty coaxial-cable feedline."

"What about 40 and 80 meters?" asked Pendergast.

"Well, let's take 40 meters first," I said. "I decided that I could add extension tips and tuned traps to make the antenna into a 40-meter radiator. This would provide me with operation on 40 and 20 meters. Before I left on vacation, I strung a test antenna up in

my backyard at about the same height I would have in the apartment and ran a set of SWR curves on it. The antenna is shown in **Figure 4-17**, trap construction is shown in **Figure 4-18**, and the resulting SWR curves are shown in **Figure 4-19**. As you can see, the SWR was below 2:1 for most of the 20-meter band and below 3:1 from 7.1 to 7.3 MHz."

"Can you shift the resonant points of the SWR curves back and forth?" asked Pendergast. "I can see you're a phone man, or an appliance operator. What would a *real* ham, let's say a CW operator, do about the antenna?"

"If you're so smart, why don't you design the antenna yourself?" I asked. When Pendergast did not reply, I continued. "You can shift the resonant points anywhere in the band you wish, provided you build the traps correctly. A trap acts as an insulator, or high-impedance circuit, on the higher band (20 meters), and as a form of loading coil on the lower band (40 meters). The traps should be self-resonant *lower* than the lowest operating frequency you wish to use on the higher band. Since I wanted to be able to work down to 14.0 MHz, the traps were self-resonant at about 13.9 MHz.

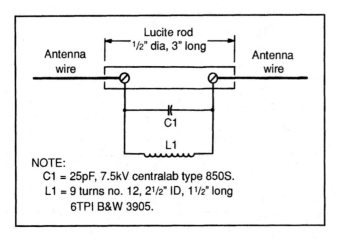

NOTE:
C1 = 25pF, 7.5kV centralab type 850S.
L1 = 9 turns no. 12, 2 1/2" ID, 1 1/2" long
6TPI B&W 3905.

Figure 4-18. The 20-meter trap. The coil and capacitor are suspended by their leads from a small insulator cut from a length of lucite rod. It is drilled for 6-32 bolts at each end. Antenna wires are wrapped around the bolts. The trap is assembled and dipped to 13.9 MHz. Adjustment is made by making the coil a little too big and then removing turns, a portion of a turn at a time, until the assembly is self-resonant at the desired frequency. Two traps are required. Once they are adjusted on the bench, they can be put in the antenna and no more adjustments are required to these units. Diameter and turns-per-inch of the coil are not critical as long as completed assembly tunes to the desired frequency. Manufactured prewound coil stock (B&W) is very suitable for trap assembly.

"The first thing you do is build the traps. Mine were made out of prewound, commercial coil stock and a high-voltage ceramic capacitor. Resonance was established with the aid of a dip meter and a calibrated receiver. A fraction of a turn at a time was removed from the coil until the trap resonated at the desired frequency. You start out with a few extra turns on the coil and remove them, a half-turn at a time, then a quarter-turn at a time, until you sneak up on the resonant frequency. Dip the trap by itself, in a clear space, with no metal around. I used a Millen dip meter and could adjust the traps to within about 20 kHz of where I wanted them. If you are a perfectionist, you can bend the last turn on the coil back and forth and hit the target frequency on the nose."

"The traps don't seem to affect 20-meter operation in any way," mused Pendergast.

"No, they don't," I replied. "The 20-meter doublet works the same whether traps or glass insulators are used at the end, *provided* the trap is tuned outside the low end of the band. If the trap is tuned to a frequency *inside* the band, it seems to affect the length of the antenna."

"Amazing," murmured Pendergast. "Now how about the 40-meter end sections?"

"Well," I replied, "they are determined by the *heuristic* method."

"The *what*?" asked my friend.

"Cut-and-try," I answered. "Luckily, information abounds in various handbooks and magazine articles on 20/40-meter trap dipoles. I chose a set of tip dimensions from my handbook, *Wire Antennas for Radio Amateurs*, and they worked right off—on the nose, 100 percent!

"As an added bonus, this antenna also works on 15 and 10 meters," I continued. "It works on the third harmonic of the 40-meter dipole for 15 meters and also exhibits a low value of SWR on 10 meters, although the actual operation of the antenna on 10 meters is a more complex matter. So there you have it— an antenna system for 40, 20, 15, and 10 meters that is only about 55 feet long!"

Pendergast scribbled furiously in his notebook. "Very good," he exclaimed. "Now how about operation on 80 meters?"

"That can be accomplished," I replied, "with certain reservations. You can work the antenna on 80 meters if you remove the traps and substitute loading coils in place of the traps. You now have a loaded dipole instead of a trap antenna. However, you must understand what's going on before you rush headlong and make the change."

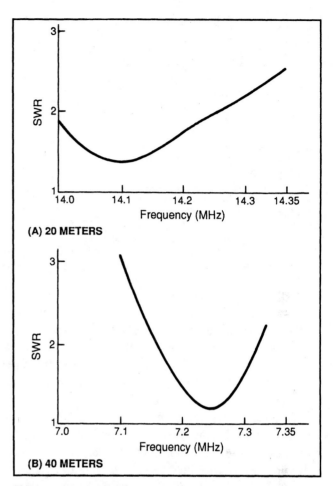

Figure 4-19. SWR curves for the antenna of Figure 4-17. The 20-meter section was cut for 14.1 MHz and the 40-meter section for 7.25 MHz. To lower the resonance of the 40-meter section, the tip sections of the antenna should be lengthened a few inches.

"How do you make the change?" asked Pendergast.

"Well, in this case, the antenna was indoors and wasn't very high above the floor of the two-story apartment. My traps were mounted in place with bolts and wing nuts. I merely removed the nuts, slipped the traps off, and substituted the loading coils in their place. I stood on a chair to do it, and it took about two minutes to do the job." I reached for Pendergast's notebook and drew a picture of the revised 80-meter dipole (**Figure 4-20**).

"What's the extra coil in the center?" asked Pendergast.

"One thing at a time," I replied. "This is an 80-meter dipole loaded with coils on each side. For highest efficiency, the coils are very high-Q. They're bolted in place of the traps, as you can see in the illustration. "The antenna is quite short for 80 meters and, as you know, short antennas have very low feedpoint resistance. Also, this antenna was going to be mounted very close to the ground. I estimated the feedpoint

Figure 4-20. The 40/20-meter two-band dipole of Figure 4-17 is reworked here for 80-meter operation. Traps L1-C1 are removed and loading-coil L2 consists of 38 to 43 turns, 3-inch diameter, 10 turns per inch. Approximate inductance is 50 microHenries. Using the above wire lengths, 43 turns produce resonance at 3.5 MHz, 40 turns at 3.68 MHz, and 39 turns for 3.73 MHz. An end turn of each coil can be trimmed to "zero-in" on a chosen design frequency. In order to raise the feedpoint impedance, a matching

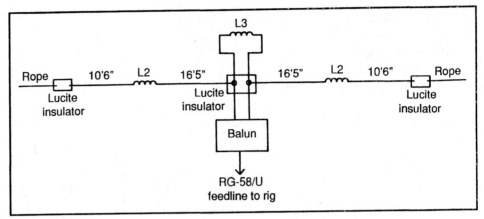

coil, L3, is placed across the feedpoint. The coil consists of 12 turns, 6 turns per inch, 1-1/4 inch diameter (about 2.0 microHenries). All coils are wound with no. 14 gauge wire. When 20-meter traps are substituted for the loading coils (to go back to 40/20-meter operation) the matching coil, L3, is left in the circuit, as it has little effect on the higher frequency bands.

resistance would be about 12 ohms, or even less. In addition, I measured the Q of the coils. It was about 350. The coils each have a reactance of around 1400 ohms at the design frequency of 3.8 MHz, so the loss resistance of each coil is 1400/350, or about 4 ohms per coil. Since there are two coils, the loss resistance is the sum, or 8 ohms. Then, there was going to be some more loss resistance introduced by nearby objects when I mounted the antenna inside the wood-frame building. The total input resistance, then, at the center terminals of the dipole was going to be 12 + 8, or 20 ohms, or maybe a little lower."

"Well, with a 50-ohm line, you're in trouble," said

Pendergast. "The SWR on the line will be no better than 2:1 at the resonant frequency, and will be worse off-frequency."

"You are so right," I replied. "And since the antenna is very short, the operating bandwidth is going to be small, so the SWR is going to go up rather rapidly when the antenna is operated off-frequency. What's needed is a matching network that will match the 50-ohm transmission line to the 20-ohm antenna. That's where the center coil comes in. It's placed right across the balun terminals."

"That doesn't look like an impedance matching network to me," objected Pendergast.

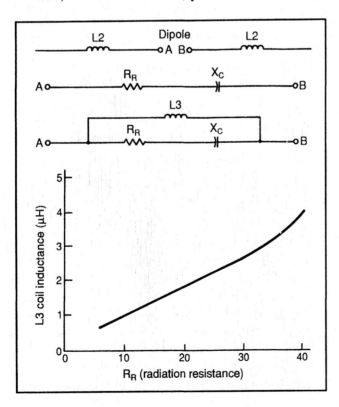

Figure 4-21. The dipole element can form a portion of a network the input impedance of which over a small range of frequencies is close to 50 ohms. The dipole, when loaded as shown in the top illustration, has a low value of radiation resistance and loss resistance, the sum of which is a function of the degree of loading (and the overall length of the antenna). This low impedance can be made a part of an equivalent parallel resonant circuit in which the total radiation resistance appears in series with the reactive branch of the circuit (center illustration). The input impedance of such a circuit varies nearly inversely with respect to the radiation resistance, R^R, of the dipole. Thus, the very low value of radiation resistance of a loaded dipole may be transformed to a larger value which will match the impedance of the transmission line (bottom illustration). The radiation resistance of the dipole can be made to appear as a capacitive reactance at the driving point by slightly shortening the element past its normal resonant length. The inductor (L3) consists of a small coil placed across the terminals of the dipole. The L/C ratio determines the transformation ratio of the network. Typical values for L3 are shown in the graph for 80-meter operation.

"Aha, it is," I replied. "Look at **Figure 4-21**. This is a simple, balanced L-network. The capacity, in this case, is provided by the antenna element, because *if* the antenna is shorter than resonance, it provides a capacitive reactance across the terminals."

"You mean you deliberately detune the loaded dipole a bit to provide a capacitive load?" asked Pendergast.

"That's right," I replied. "The whole idea is noncritical. For this antenna, the coil is about 2 microHenries. I didn't even attempt to detune the antenna, because all that happens is the resonant frequency of the antenna is shifted a bit from the normal value after the center coil is inserted, and the trimming action to shorten the antenna merely re-establishes resonance. Since the whole antenna is cut-and-try, I decided to just add the coil and see what the results were. The first try resulted in an SWR of about 1.5:1. I took one turn off the center to readjust the impedance match a bit and *voilà!* The SWR at resonance was about 1.2:1 (**Figure 4-22**). The bandwidth at the 2.5:1 SWR points was about 40 kHz."

"Pretty neat," admitted Pendergast. "How did you adjust the loading coils?"

"You can zero-in by lowering the antenna until you can reach the center coil with a dip meter," I said. "Then, with the feedline removed, adjust the loading coils until the antenna dips where you want it. This entails a bit of fiddling around. However, the ARRL *Antenna Book* has a very handy chart in the chapter about limited-space antennas. It is for loading coils which get you in the ballpark. I followed their information, made the coils about five turns too big, and

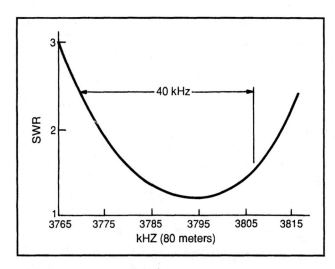

Figure 4-22. The SWR response of the loaded 80-meter dipole of Figure 4-20. Bandwidth between the 2.5 SWR points is about 40 kHz. SWR at resonance (3787 kHz) is 1.2:1. It was desired to move the resonant frequency up to 3805 kHz, and this was done by removing 3 inches of wire from each tip of the dipole.

then proceeded to trim the coils, dipping the antenna until it was just about where I wanted to be. Then I raised the antenna in the air, ran an SWR curve on it, and trimmed the coils a fraction of a turn. I found that removing a single turn from each coil changed the 80-meter resonant frequency about 50 kHz, and trimming an inch from each end of the antenna changed the resonant frequency about 10 kHz. But you're stuck with the narrow bandwidth no matter what you do. Even so, an operational range of 40 kHz is still enough to work plenty of stations. I centered my antenna at 3.8 MHz."

Figure 4-23. The 40/20-meter trapped, two-band dipole. A 1:1 balun is placed at the feedpoint. Dimensions are given for resonance at 7.25 MHz and 14.1 MHz. If the tuned traps (L1-C1) are removed and loading coil L3 substituted in each case, the antenna is sharply resonant in the 80-meter band. As the text explains, the 80-meter loaded dipole is also resonant on 20 meters. The 20/40-meter trap consists of a 9-turn coil, 2-1/2 inch diameter and 1-1/2 inch long wound of no. 12 wire (B&W 3905-1, or equivalent) in shunt with a 25 pF, 7.5 kV capacitor

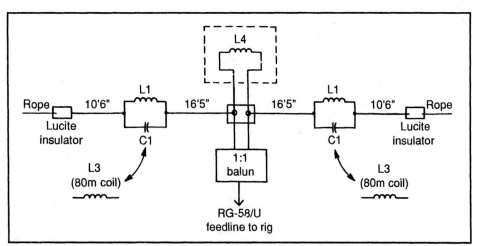

(Centralab type 850S). The trap is self-resonant at 13.9 MHz. The 80-meter loading coils (L3) are 38 turns, 3 inch diameter, 10 turns per inch of no. 14 wire. The coils are trimmed for resonance at the desired 80-meter operating frequency. Bandwidth is about 40 kHz. The matching coil (L4) consists of 12 turns, 6 turns per inch, 1-1/4 inch diameter of no. 14 gauge wire. L4 is trimmed, a turn at a time, for best SWR at resonance on the 80-meter band. The antenna will also work well on 20 meters, as described in the text.

"Well, since you precut your antenna at home, how did it work in Hawaii?" asked Pendergast.

"Plenty good," I replied. "I worked 6W8DY in Senegal on 80-meter SSB with the antenna mounted in the apartment, using my transceiver. I don't know who was more surprised, the 6W8 or me! And from KH6 to 6W8 is a long, long way on any band!"

"Congratulations," said Pendergast. "That proves the old saying, DX is 90 percent operator and 10 percent antenna."

"Thanks," I said. "I guess that's a compliment."

Another Visit with Pendergast: More on the Multiband Dipole

"You foxy fella," exclaimed Pendergast. "You didn't tell me everything about the multiband dipole. You're holding things back."

"Well, there is more to it," I admitted. "The design I described was a center-fed antenna having an overall length of about 55 feet, including the insulators (**Figure 4-23**). The antenna wire was broken at points equidistant from the center for the inclusion of matching networks. With a pair of tuned traps the antenna provided resonance on 40 and 20 meters, and with a pair of loading coils (L3) the antenna provided operation over a narrow segment of the 80-meter band.

"Since the antenna is quite small compared to an 80-meter dipole, the impedance at the feedpoint in the center is quite low and some form of matching network is required. A simple matching coil (L4) placed across the antenna feedpoint does the trick, boosting

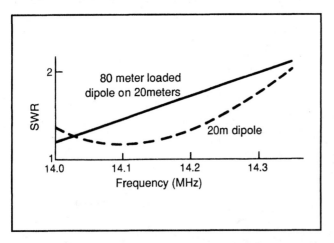

Figure 4-24. Operation of the 80-meter dipole on 20 meters compares favorably with operation of the 20-meter dipole. The harmonic of the 80-meter loaded dipole falls very close to 14.0 MHz, as shown by the SWR plot. This simple antenna, then, provides a choice of 80/20- or 40/20-meter operation by the use of either traps or loading coils. Not bad for a simple 55-foot long antenna!

the impedance so that the balun and transmission line 'look into' about 50 ohms.

"When the traps are used, the operational bandwidth—that is, the bandwidth between the 2:1 SWR points—covers the 20-meter band, about half of the 40-meter band. For 80-meter operation, the bandwidth, under the same conditions, is about 40 kHz."

"That's right," interrupted Pendergast, "but I understand that it's possible to achieve good 20-meter operation with the 80-meter loaded dipole. Is that correct? You didn't mention *that*."

"*No*, I didn't mention it, and *yes*, you are correct," I replied. "Interestingly enough, the 80-meter loading coils act somewhat as high-impedance RF chokes at 20 meters, providing an excellent degree of isolation between the outer tips of the antenna and the inner, 20-meter dipole portion. The coil is about 63 microHenries . . ."

"You said 50 microHenries before," said Pendergast stiffly.

"That was a first-order guess," I replied. "Sixty-three microHenries is more nearly correct. The number of turns in the loading coils determine actual antenna resonance, and the number varies by about six turns in each coil from one end of the band to the other. But, you distract me. Let's get back to 20-meter operation of the 80-meter antenna.

"The loading coils, as I have said, act as RF chokes on frequencies higher than antenna resonance, and at some higher frequency they permit a second resonance to occur. The point of second resonance is a function of coil inductance and the length of the inner sections of the dipole. In this case, the inner sections were intentionally cut for 20 meters. Now, *if* the loading coils really act as RF chokes at 20 meters, you have a 20-meter dipole. And the SWR measurements tend to prove just that (**Figure 4-24**). Here's an SWR plot of the 20-meter dipole with the end sections disconnected and a plot of operation of the 80-meter loaded dipole on 20 meters."

Pendergast looked closely at the sketch. "It looks to me as if the fourth-order resonant frequency of the loaded 80-meter antenna falls very close to 14.0 MHz," he stated.

"It certainly does," I replied. "By itself, the inner, 20-meter portion of the antenna has a self-resonant frequency of about 14.1 MHz, so it looks as if the loading coils disturb the resonant frequency by only about 100 kHz. That's not bad. You'll note that the slope of the two SWR curves is nearly identical, so the bandwidth of the two antenna types is just about the same."

"Was the 80-meter center impedance matching coil left in the circuit for 20-meter operation?" asked Pendergast.

"Yes," I replied. "I saw no reason to remove it. As you can see from the SWR curves, the antenna exhibits a good SWR curve on 20 meters. The little center matching coil doesn't affect 20-meter performance to any degree."

I reached up to the high bookshelf and took down a bound volume of *QST*s. "Here's an interesting article by W4JRW in the April 1961 issue of *QST*," I said. "It's entitled 'Multiband Antennas Using Loading Coils.' The author describes a loaded 80-meter antenna that also resonates on 40 meters. He claims the idea is an old one, described in the *Bureau of Standards Circular C74, Radio Instruments and Measurements*, published in 1924. The circular describes loaded antennas and states that the 'harmonic frequencies are no longer integral multiples of the fundamental, as in the case of the simple antenna.'

"W4JRW took that idea and used high-inductance loading coils—about 120 microHenries—to make up a two-band dipole for 80- and 40-meter operation. He hinted that by using 'various lengths of wire' and 'various values of coils' antennas could be built for 80 and 20 meters, 80 and 15 meters, and other such combinations."

"Did he show any designs of that type?" asked Pendergast.

"No," I replied, "and I must admit I had forgotten about the article. I only remembered it after I had tried the loaded 80-meter dipole on 20 meters. Then a bell rang, and I spent an hour or two looking through back issues of *QST* until I found the W4JRW article. So I guess I sort of reinvented the wheel."

"Well, that's interesting," said Pendergast, suppressing a yawn. "I guess W4JRW beat you to the punch."

"Yes," I admitted. "Great minds think along the same channel."

"In any event," said Pendergast, "between you and W4JRW, it has been proven that a loaded dipole can be made to work on two frequencies, and by proper placement and size of the loading coils, the two frequencies can be any two high-frequency amateur bands, such as 80 and 40 meters, 80 and 20 meters, or the like."

"That's right," I replied. "I suggest you obtain the April 1961 issue of *QST* and read the original article. It contains a lot of food for thought. It may be possible to make up a compact, 80-meter beam—or make a 20-meter beam work on 80 meters—using this princi-

ple. Perhaps some smart lad will carry these little experiments further."

"Any remarks you'd care to make about the center loading coil?" asked my friend, as he made quick pencil sketches in his notebook.

"Well," I replied, "this is a good matching scheme that isn't well known among amateurs, although the idea is used every day in commercial practice. Take the case of the usual 80-meter dipole, or inverted-V antenna. In most cases, the antenna is quite close to the ground in terms of wavelengths of height. A typical 80-meter dipole may be 30 feet in the air. That's equivalent to an electrical height of only 0.115 wavelength. At that low height the feedpoint impedance could be as low as 10 to 15 ohms, depending upon ground conductivity. The fella then erects an 80-meter dipole at a reasonable height, and finds out that the SWR curve on a 50-ohm transmission line is terrible. At resonance, the SWR could be as high as 3:1, and it becomes even worse off-resonance."

Pendergast sniffed. "I have an 80-meter dipole about 40 feet high and the SWR at resonance is about 1.5:1. I cut it for 3800 kHz." He paused a bit, then said, "I'll have to admit that loading it up is a tricky process, and when I operate off-frequency, the loading on my transceiver seems very odd to me."

"Could be," I admitted. "The feedpoint impedance figures given for a low dipole are either computed, or measured over a perfect ground. In a real-life situation with an imperfect ground and with nearby conducting objects, such as telephone and light lines, the input impedance could be something else again. A few years ago, I made careful measurements on my 80-meter dipole that was about 35 feet high and came to the conclusion that the input impedance at resonance was about 20 ohms."

"Well," replied Pendergast, "in any event, it seems much lower than 50 ohms, at least up to heights approaching 0.2 wavelength, and that's over 50 feet."

"That's right," I said. "And the simplest solution to this little problem is to place a matching coil at the center of the dipole, right across the feedpoint. All that needs to be done is to adjust the turns in the coil for the lowest value of SWR on the transmission line. This is a simple form of L-network. My discussion applied only to the compact, loaded dipole, but the impedance matching scheme applies equally well to the full-size dipole, as its input impedance is still quite low, because of its low height, in terms of wavelengths.

"The solution is very simple. Place an impedance-matching coil across the center of the dipole and

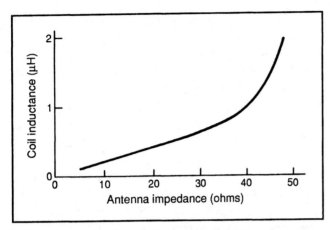

Figure 4-25. Inductance of the center impedance matching coil as a function of antenna input impedance. Start with maximum inductance in the coil and short out a turn at a time until the lowest value of SWR is achieved on the transmission line.

adjust the number of turns in the coil for the lowest SWR at the resonant frequency of the antenna. The impedance range you're interested in lies between approximately 30 and 10 ohms. Above 30 ohms, the coil really isn't necessary. To achieve a good match to a 50-ohm line, the coil inductance should be as shown in **Figure 4-25**. If you don't know the input impedance of the antenna, you can start with the full coil in the circuit and gradually reduce it a turn at a time until you get a good match. A 3-microHenry coil is about right. A coil composed of 17 turns of no. 14 wire, one inch in diameter and two inches long, will do the job. Wind it on a short length of plastic PVC pipe. The coil, in fact, can serve as the center insulator for the antenna. With a jumper, short out a turn at a time until you achieve a satisfactory value of SWR at the resonant frequency of the antenna. For most antennas, you'll end up with about 8 or 9 turns in the circuit."

"Simple enough," said Pendergast. "I suppose the idea works whether or not you use a balun at the center of the dipole?"

"Correct," I replied. "I usually use a balun, but many fellas don't. It's strictly a matter of preference, I think."

The W4JRW Loaded Dipole and a Few Words about Antenna Bandwidth

"You might be interested in a note I received from Bill, W4JRW. He has been playing with an experimental dipole antenna using loading coils that exhibits resonance on 10, 20, 40, and 80 meters (**Figure 4-26**). The dipole is only 51 feet long and is center-fed with a 50-ohm coaxial line. Three loading coils are used in each half of the antenna. The self-resonant frequencies are 3.9, 7.25, 14.2, and 28.6 MHz."

"Too bad it doesn't work on 15 meters," observed Pendergast. "It's a cut-and-try operation," I replied. "If you want to take additional time and you're an avid experimenter, no doubt the design could be altered to accept 15 meters."

"It sounds like just the thing for Field Day," admitted Pendergast.

"On another subject," I continued, "the greatest mystery to many amateurs seems to be in the area of standing wave ratio. That still confuses a great many amateurs. I thought when Walt Maxwell, W2DU, ran his fine series of articles in *QST* that the SWR problem had been put to rest for good. But that isn't the case at all."

"Well, why worry about SWR at all?" queried Pendergast. "If the antenna works, it works. I think the SWR meter is the invention of the devil. All it does is confuse the issue. My motto is: Don't bother me with the facts—my mind is made up."

"The SWR meter can certainly serve a useful purpose," I replied, "but some amateurs make a fetish out of their SWR reading."

"Look at this," said my friend, flinging an instruction manual across the table to me. "Here's an instruction book for a linear amplifier. The manufacturer states that the amplifier is to be run into a 50-ohm load with the SWR not to exceed 2:1. Why? What will happen at 2.1:1? Or at 5:1? Will the amplifier explode at a high SWR reading? Or will your report drop from S9 plus to S6 in Outer Baldovia?"

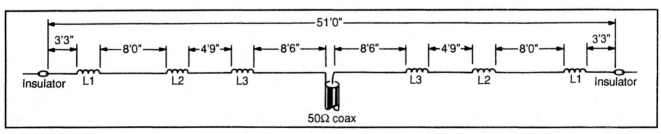

Figure 4-26. The multiband antenna of W4JRW. This "loaded" antenna exhibits resonance at 3.9 MHz, 7.25 MHz, 14.2 MHz, and 28.6 MHz. Coil pairs marked L1 are 81 microHenries each, coil pairs marked L2 are 25 microHenries each, and coil pairs marked L3 are 7 microHenries each. Each coil is approximately 3 inches long. Overall antenna length is 51 feet.

"It may seem obscure, but there are very good reasons why manufacturers state the maximum SWR limit for their equipment. One reason is that when the equipment is operated into a high value of SWR, it may not tune properly. It's possible to run right off the scale of the loading control of an amplifier if the antenna presents a high SWR at the equipment. Then, again, a high value of SWR may lead to flash-over in the amplifier. If the network voltage is too high at the antenna terminals, the output loading capacitor of the pi-network may flash. If the amplifier is underloaded, the peak plate voltage may flash-over the tuning capacitor. And if the amplifier employs a screen grid tube, the screen dissipation may be exceeded if the amplifier is improperly loaded."

"What about a grounded grid amplifier?" demanded Pendergast. "There are plenty of them using 3-500Zs. What happens to the tubes when the amplifier is operated into an antenna having a high standing wave ratio?"

"If the amplifier can be loaded properly into the antenna, nothing will happen," I replied. "Trouble can arise if the amplifier is loaded up into an antenna having a high SWR, and if the operator shifts frequency *without retuning* the amplifier. If this is done, the amplifier becomes improperly loaded. In addition, the plate circuit is out of resonance. This can lead to dangerously high levels of grid current for an underloaded condition or flat-topping in an overloaded condition.

"It's best to have a relatively low SWR on the antenna system. By that I mean 3:1 or less. But it's not imperative to beat your brains out for a 1:1 ratio. Even if you get it, the SWR will rise as the antenna is operated off the design frequency. Where you really run into trouble is on 80 meters, where the width of the band is large in comparison to the frequency. Very few 80-meter antennas will show a low value of SWR across the band. And since most of them are close to the ground in terms of wavelength, the radiation resistance is very low. Look at **Figure 4-27**. This is the SWR plot of an 80-meter dipole about 25 feet above the ground. That's a typical antenna. The best value of SWR is about 1.8:1. You can see the reason for this when the antenna is measured with a *General Radio RF Bridge* (**Figure 4-28**). Look at the plot on the Smith Chart."

"Smith Charts make me nervous," observed Pendergast in a mild voice.

"They tell you a lot more than an SWR meter," I replied. "In this instance, the dipole is seen to have a feedpoint resistance value of about 28 ohms at 3830 kHz. At 4.0 MHz, the feedpoint resistance is nearly

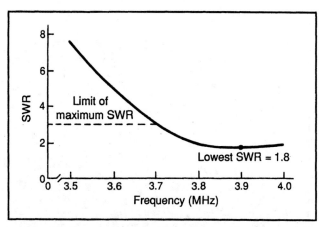

Figure 4-27. SWR plot of an 80-meter dipole cut for 3850 kHz and located 25 feet above the ground. If the maximum limit of SWR set by the equipment is 3:1, the antenna shouldn't be operated below 3.7 MHz. SWR rises rapidly below 3.7 MHz, reaching 7.5:1 at 3.5 MHz. The lowest value of SWR is 1.8:1 at 3.9 MHz. The dipole is fed with a 50-ohm coaxial line, and SWR measurements were taken at the station end of the line, which is about 75 feet long. Changing the line length won't change the value of SWR on the line.

40 ohms, but the antenna presents a high value of inductive reactance at the input end of the feedline. At 3.5 MHz, the feedpoint resistance is 25 ohms, and the antenna appears highly capacitive. Note that the 3:1 SWR circle is drawn on the graph. If you stay inside that, your range of antenna operation is limited to the 300-kHz span from 3.7:4.0 MHz."

"Well, how do you lower the SWR on this particular antenna? Can you get it to work across the whole band?" demanded my friend.

"Well, as a starter, I suggest you read the chapter "Smith Chart Calculations" in the *ARRL Antenna Book*. This provides a clear description of the chart, which looks confusing at first. The chapter covers matching in detail. *The Radio Handbook,* published by Howard W. Sams Co., also discusses the Smith Chart and shows it was derived from a simple X-Y plot. And, for your overseas friends, the handbook *HF Antennas For All Locations,* by L. A. Moxon, G6XN (published by the RSGB), covers the Smith Chart and provides additional information on its use. These are good handbooks for the ham who wants to know more about antenna matching and matching networks.

"Back issues of *QST* (Jan.-Feb. 1966) and *CQ* (Nov.-Dec. 1963) also contain data on the Smith Chart. Back issues are for sale in classified columns."

"Do you have to use a Smith Chart?" Pendergast asked suspiciously.

"Don't be afraid of the Smith Chart," I replied. "It

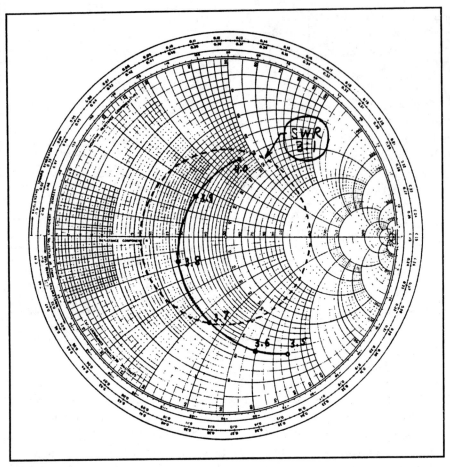

Figure 4-28. Smith Chart plot of the 80-meter dipole of Figure 4-27. The 3:1 SWR circle is drawn on the chart. The resonant frequency of the dipole is about 3830 kHz, the point the curve passes through the resistive axis (X axis) of the chart. Below this frequency, the antenna appears as a resistive-inductive reactance. At resonance, the antenna exhibits a load of about 28 ohms. At no point in the 80-meter band does the antenna present a 50-ohm load, and range of operation is limited to the frequency span of 3.7 to 4.0 MHz, within the 3:1 SWR circle.

might look confusing to those who haven't used it, but it's relatively simple. A variation of the Smith Chart concept was used by astronomers and navigators at the time of Columbus, so there's nothing new about it. Sometime, when you're in a more relaxed mood, I'll give you a quick rundown on this interesting and very useful device."

Pendergast, Dr. Liv, and I Discuss a Dipole for 7 and 21 MHz

"Excuse me. I didn't know you had company." I closed the door to Pendergast's shack, but not quickly enough so as not to hear him call, "No, No! Come on in! I have a friend here I want you to meet." I entered the room. Sitting beside Pendergast at the operating table was a young fella I didn't know. He had dark hair, a small beard, and a quick and humorous look about his eyes.

Pendergast rose and said, "I'd like you to meet a new radio amateur. Bill, this is Doctor Livingston I. Presume. He's a dentist and just received his Novice license."

"Pleased to meet you, Doctor," I said, shaking his hand.

Doctor Presume grasped my hand and remarked, "You have been in Afghanistan, I see."

"A good point, Doctor," I replied. "Congratulations on your Novice ticket. Are you on the air yet?"

"Call me *Doctor Liv*," said my new friend. "No, I'm not on the air yet, but I soon will be. I was just chatting with Pendergast and I hope to swindle him into helping me put up an antenna."

Pendergast blushed with pride. "I'm always ready to help the humble beginner," he remarked.

"Pendergast, I love your humility," I said. "What do you have in mind for the good Doctor Liv?"

"Well," Pendergast replied, "15 meters is jumping these days, and 40 meters is always good for a local ragchew, so I think he should put up an antenna that would work on both bands."

"Agreed," I replied. "What do you have in mind?"

Pendergast thought a bit. "Well, how about a 40-meter dipole? That's resonant at the third harmonic, which is 15 meters. If Doctor Liv put up a 40-meter dipole, he could work both bands."

I turned to the Doctor. "What kind of rig do you have?"

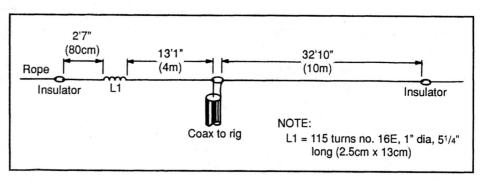

Figure 4-29. Short antenna tip beyond the loading coil may be adjusted to move antenna resonance on the 15-meter band. The antenna provides superior operation on both 15 and 40 meters. (Metric dimensions are in parentheses.)

"I just bought a *Kamikaze-200*. It's the new all-band, 100-watt rig," he replied.

"Very nice," I said. "However, there's one problem. Most of the solid-state jobs don't like to work into any antenna system that has a high value of SWR. In fact, they protect themselves against high SWR via a power-reduction circuit. Thus, the higher the SWR on the antenna, the less power output from the transmitter."

Dr. Liv frowned. "What's that got to do with using a dipole on its third harmonic?" he asked.

"Simply this. Third-harmonic resonance isn't quite three times the fundamental frequency. Let's say you have a dipole that's cut to resonance at 7.1 MHz. You might think the third-harmonic resonance would be three times 7.1, or 21.3 MHz. However, this isn't the case. The third-harmonic resonance actually turns out to be 21.8 MHz. This is far enough in frequency from the Novice band at 21 MHz to cause SWR problems with most types of solid-state equipment. Even some old rigs that have tubes in the final amplifier (supposedly immune to high values of SWR on the antenna system) might develop loading problems under such a condition."

"But I hear a lot of Novices on 15 meters who are using a 40-meter dipole," protested Pendergast.

"That may be so," I replied, "but there's a better way of doing the job which will provide operation on both 15 and 40 meters with very low SWR on the transmission line."

With a flourish Dr. Liv produced a large, lined notebook. "I'm taking your advice," he said with a smile. "Here's the start of my antenna notebook full of good ideas."

"Well, this idea came from JA3CZV," I said. "Look at **Figure 4-29**. This is a 40-meter dipole with one leg shortened and tuned to resonance with a loading coil. The coil resonates the short side of the dipole to 40 meters, but it upsets the current distribution on 15 meters to permit antenna resonance to occur at 21.2 instead of 21.8 MHz. On 40 meters, the SWR read-

ings for this antenna are below 1.6:1 across the CW band, rising to about 2:1 at 7.2 MHz. On 21 MHz, the SWR is quite flat, running less that 1.4:1 across the whole band."

"Very interesting," said Dr. Liv, as he copied the drawing into his notebook. "Is there any adjustment to be made to the antenna?"

"If you want to move the resonance about at 40 meters, you trim or lengthen the short-tip section after the coil," I replied. "Otherwise, leave it as it is."

"How do I plot an SWR curve for this or any other antenna?" asked the Doctor as he wrote busily in his notebook.

"All you need is an SWR meter," I replied. "The little imported jobs that sell for under $100 are just fine."

"I can see that you have been following the recent exchange rate between the dollar and the yen," observed Pendergast with a laugh.

I ignored the thrust. "The important thing to remember is that no adjustments to the transmitter, or changes in the length of the feedline, will affect the SWR reading. The *only* thing that will affect the SWR reading are changes made at the antenna feedpoint. If you find that transmitter tuning, or changes to the transmission line, affect the SWR reading, then it's possible that something is wrong with the SWR meter—or else you're measuring something in addition to antenna parameters."

Trimming the Coax

"I've heard from other Novices that you can change the SWR reading by changing the length of the coaxial transmission line," observed Dr. Liv.

"You can change your *transmitter loading* by changing line length," I replied. "In fact, some fellas do just that. They cut short extension pieces of transmission line of various lengths and splice them to the main transmission line, thus changing the overall length of line between the transmitter and the antenna. And sometimes, they find that a certain length of line

Figure 4-30. (A) Plot of SWR on 40 meters. (B) Plot of SWR on 15 meters.

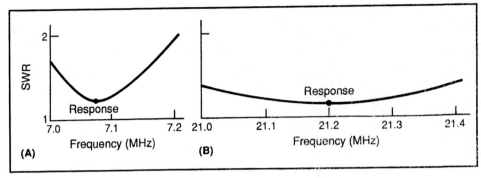

loads the transmitter better than other lengths. This is very true, and it's a good technique to keep in the back of your mind when you run into loading problems. It's a quick and dirty means to load a transmitter that's working into a line with a high value of SWR on it. But this sneaky trick doesn't change the *value* of SWR on the line; it merely changes the conditions of loading for the transmitter. If you're lucky and hit the right line length, the transmitter may load up properly, regardless of the SWR value. Now that's not to be taken as a blanket statement! I'm only talking about *reasonable* values of SWR—say, less than 2:1. If you have a really high value of SWR on the line, all bets are off and my statement is nonoperative."

"That stunt doesn't always work," said Pendergast. "It *usually* works with old tube-type equipment that has both tuning and loading controls for the amplifier stage. By juggling line length, it's possible to get most pi-network tuned stages to load into a line having a reasonably high value of SWR on it. It's helpful with solid-state output stages, too. But many times it won't work on a solid-state rig, or if it does permit proper loading, the SWR is still too high to prevent the transmitter from developing full output. You can spend a lot of time looking for the 'lucky' line length that may not exist!"

"Well, what can you do about it?" asked Dr. Liv. He reached in to his pocket and took out the instruction booklet for his new *Kamikaze-200*. He thumbed rapidly through it and said, "Yes, here it is. The manual states that with an SWR of 1.5:1 the output is 70 percent of normal, and with an SWR of 2.0:1 the output is 45 percent of normal. That's not so good. As I understand it, every antenna is resonant at only one point in the band, and the SWR is lowest at that point. This means the SWR is higher at other points in the band, right?"

"That's right," I replied, "and this brings us back to the question you asked about running an SWR curve for a given antenna. Let's take the antenna shown in

Figure 4-30. You run an SWR curve by measuring the SWR at various points across the band. The SWR-meter instruction manual tells you how to make an SWR measurement, so I won't insult your intelligence by repeating that. It's common practice to make an SWR measurement every 50 kHz, starting at one end of the band and going to the other. On 10 meters, which is a rather wide band, the measurements may be made every 100 kHz to save time.

"Write down the measuring frequency and also the SWR reading. Then when you've gone across the whole band, make up a graph. The SWR measurements fall along the Y-axis and the frequency falls along the X-axis. Look at **Figure 4-30.** This is a plot of the SWR measurements made for this Japanese antenna across the 40-meter band. Measurements were taken at 7.0, 7.05, 7.1, 7.15, and 7.2 MHz. Note that the curve is smooth and symmetrical. Also note that the lowest value of SWR falls between two of the measuring points."

Pendergast peered at the curve. "It looks to me as if the frequency of lowest SWR is about 7.075 MHz," he announced.

"That's right," I replied. "And if you went back and made another measurement at 7.075 MHz, that would verify this fact."

I produced a second curve. "Here's the SWR measurement of the same antenna on the 15-meter band. Note how broad the SWR curve is. This is normal for an antenna working on the third harmonic. And now, gentlemen, although this has been time well spent, I will take my leave, as I have work to do."

A Compact 7- and 21-MHz Antenna

This wire antenna, designed by G3TKN, fits into a 55-foot span and works on two bands. It is a 7-MHz dipole with the center section folded up to form a simple matching stub on 21 MHz, where the antenna operates as a two-element collinear array providing about 3 dBd power gain. Antenna dimensions are given in **Figure 4-31.**

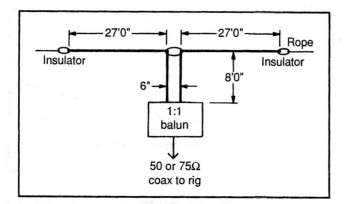

Figure 4-31. Seven- and 21-MHz broadside antenna.

The center stub is made of two no. 14 enamel-coated wires with a 6-inch separation. Three spreaders are required and can be made from plastic rod or 3/8-inch diameter wooden dowel. Give the wood a weatherproof coat of varnish. Pass the wire through holes drilled in the ends of the spreaders. Hold it in place by winding short lengths of no. 22 wire around the dowel and the stub wire passing through it. Feed the antenna with a 1:1 coax balun and a coax feedline. Optimize feedline SWR on 21 MHz by varying the length of the stub an inch or two at a time. The antenna performs well when elevated 30 feet, or higher. On 40 meters the pattern is that of the conventional dipole; on 15 meters it is also bidirectional but with sharper lobes.

The "Carolina" Windom Antenna

This antenna, popularized by W8GZ in the early twenties, is still with us in various forms. Edgar Lambert, WA4LVB, sent me an interesting suggestion for the antenna. It seems the idea was conceived by W4UB, WY4R, and WA4LVB. The antenna is shown in **Figure 4-32**. The flat-top is cut for 3550 kHz and is off-center fed with a 4:1 balun and a coax line. Since Edgar told me about it, I have heard several of these

antennas on 20 meters and they seem to poke out a good signal. Edgar says it's a good approximation of the mythical "all-band" antenna.

Another 7- to 21-MHz Antenna

It's well known among amateurs that a center-fed dipole will work (almost) on its third harmonic. Some hams have had good success using a 7-MHz dipole on the 21-MHz ham band. Unfortunately, because of end effects, the dipole isn't exactly resonant at the third harmonic, but at some frequency slightly above it. Thus, a dipole cut for 7.1 MHz will be resonant at a frequency higher that the 21-MHz band. For resonance on the third harmonic, the wire should be 68.46, not 66, feet long (**Figure 4-33**). The general formula for a harmonic antenna is:

$$\text{Length (feet)} = \frac{492(N - 0.05)}{f(MHz)}$$

where N is the number of half waves in the antenna.

This formula holds true when the antenna is a straight wire. But what happens when the wire is bent back upon itself? Or, what happens when the wire is artificially loaded for harmonic resonance?

Harmonic "Loading"

Let's take the case of the 7-MHz dipole (**Figure 4-34**). As is, its fundamental resonance is 7.1 MHz. Its third-harmonic resonance is 21.95 MHz. The problem is to load the antenna to a lower frequency in the 21-MHz region without disturbing its resonance in the 40-meter band. This can be done by attaching "butterfly loops" at the high-voltage points in the antenna corresponding to 21-MHz operation. The loops will have little, if any, effect on 7-MHz operation. The size of the loops must be determined experimentally, and

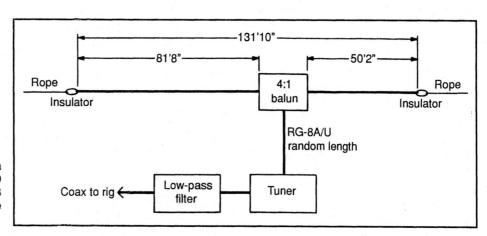

Figure 4-32. The "Carolina Windom" antenna works 80–10 meters with a tuner. WA4LVB recommends that the antenna be 35 feet or higher above ground.

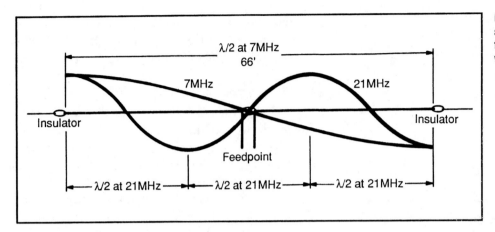

Figure 4-33. Forty-meter dipole showing voltage distribution for fundamental and third-harmonic waves (F–F = Feedpoint).

they should be equal in size. The loop need not be round—almost any shape seems to work—and resonance is adjusted by changing the shape and size of the loop. I made my loops out of no. 12 enamel wire, with a diameter of about 1 foot. The loops were attached to the flat-top temporarily by means of small copper battery clips. After loop placement was adjusted for resonance at 21.2 MHz, the loops were soldered permanently to the antenna wire. I varied the loop diameter several times before I finally hit resonance (as determined by an SWR meter) at my chosen frequency in the 15-meter band.

Another situation where this idea would work is the case of a 10-MHz dipole, the third-harmonic resonance of which is well above 30 MHz. It should be possible to place loading loops at the 10-meter high-voltage points in the flat-top to bring antenna resonance within the 10-meter band. Someday I'm going to try this interesting antenna. If you hear me, you'll know the scheme works!

Another Two-band Antenna

I had an experimental license (KM2XDW) for conducting tests on 18 MHz. Although most of the time I've used a dipole antenna, I've recently experimented with half-waves in phase, as shown in **Figure 4-35.** The old reliable "two half-waves in phase" design has been used for many years. Unfortunately, such an

antenna cut for 18 MHz just wouldn't fit into the restricted space in my backyard. The solution was to make the flat-top shorter and increase the length of the folded center section. This section acts somewhat in the manner of a matching transformer, allowing the antenna to be fed with a 1:1 balun and a coax line.

The antenna, cut to fit the space, and its dimensions are shown in the drawing. Interestingly, it was found that the antenna also exhibited resonance in the 10-meter band! By luck, the total wire length in the antenna was just about 1-1/2 wavelengths on 10 meters. The SWR curves for 18 and 28 MHz are given in **Figure 4-36.** Using the formulas given in **Figure 4-35,** the antenna may be cut for any two frequencies that have the ratio of 1.57:1. Thus, an antenna cut for 14 MHz will also present a second reso-

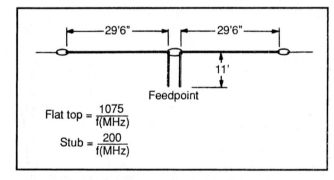

$$\text{Flat top} = \frac{1075}{f(\text{MHz})}$$

$$\text{Stub} = \frac{200}{f(\text{MHz})}$$

Figure 4-35. A two-band antenna for 18.1 and 28.5 MHz. The antenna is fed with a 1:1 balun and coax at F–F.

Figure 4-34. "Butterfly Loops" placed at high potential points along the harmonic antenna lower harmonic resonance with little effect on fundamental frequency resonance.

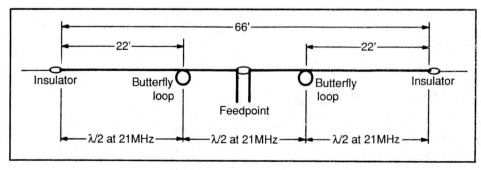

Figure 4-36. SWR curves for a two-band antenna.

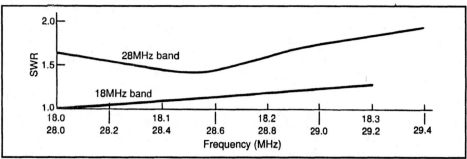

nance at $14 \times 1.57 = 21.98$ MHz. That's a little too high in frequency to be of practical use, but by adding butterfly loops at the high-voltage points on the wire for the harmonic frequency, that resonance can be lowered to the 21-MHz band with little, if any, effect on 14-MHz operation.

General Case

These antenna examples show that by changing the shape of a long wire, and by adding capacitance at the high-voltage points at a harmonic frequency, the higher-resonance point may be moved about. The idea that resonances in a long wire fall only at approximate multiples of the fundamental frequency applies only when the wire lies in a straight line. In addition, the harmonic resonant frequency determined by the configuration of the wire can further be manipulated by proper application of capacitance loops. If you want a simple multiband antenna center-fed with a coax line, you can run your own experiments along the lines of those shown here. Armed with an SWR meter and a notebook for keeping records of your experiments, the sky's the limit!

A Simple Multiband Antenna Array for 7, 10, 14, 18, and 21 MHz

It's difficult to put out a loud signal from a city lot. It's equally difficult to work more than one band from a city lot. Yes, I know all about trap dipole antennas, G5RV antennas, and off-center-fed antennas. They all have their problems. The G5RV and OCF are long wires and require plenty of space. The trap dipole may prove to be fragile, and it is difficult to make waterproof traps. However, there's another approach to the problem: the Lazy-V antenna.

The Lazy-V is a novel antenna that may fit your situation to a "T." It takes up little room, no traps are required, and only one pole is required to support the antenna. Interested?

Well, the antenna is based on the idea of using a 40-meter ground-plane vertical (about 33 feet 6 inches

high) as a support for higher-band dipoles. The dipoles, in fact, act as guy wires for the vertical antenna. Nothing new about this idea.

In diddling around with the dipoles, however, various experimenters have found that they seem to perform much better if they are folded back into a "V," with the ends adjacent to the vertical support, and the far ends held away from the tower with a rope (**Figure 4-37**). By "much better," some operators say that the dipoles seem to radiate more low-angle DX energy when folded back upon themselves than when they form an in-line configuration—or so the conventional wisdom goes.

There's a lot of literature about using the Lazy-V dipole idea in directive arrays for 160, 80, and 40

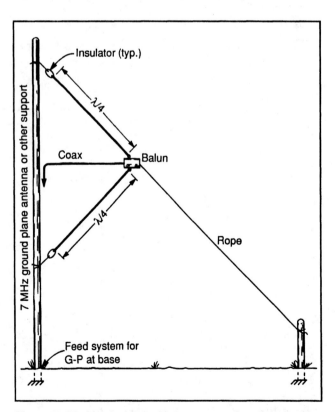

Figure 4-37. A typical Lazy-V antenna can be supported by a 7-MHz ground plane. Keep the coax several inches clear of the ground-plane antenna.

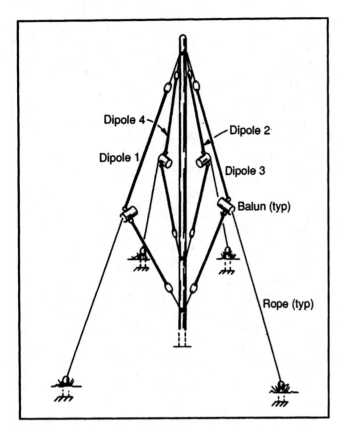

Figure 4-38. Four dipoles 90 degrees apart mounted on a mast form a four-band switchable antenna system.

meters (see the listing of further reading at the end of this section). In general, the scheme is to use four (or more) dipoles spaced around a supporting tower. One dipole is electrically loaded to present the proper reactance to act as a reflector for a second driven dipole. Four of these dipoles can be switched remotely from the shack, permitting the operator to quickly rotate the beam heading of this interesting array (**Figure 4-38**).

Judging from what the users of these two-element beam arrays achieve in DX contests, it's obvious that they pack a real wallop!

This is a one-band approach. However, how about using individual Lazy-V dipoles for different bands, supported from a 40-meter ground-plane antenna? That would provide multiband capability from a single supporting structure.

The Single Lazy-V Dipole Approach

Recently some operators have had luck with just a single Lazy-V dipole, extolling its low-angle gain and seeming DX improvement over a vertical or sloper antenna. If true, this would make this simple antenna a real winner.

It is instructive to look at a single dipole and see how it plays. A general determination of performance can be made with an antenna analysis program. I chose to do this task with the MN 4.5 program of K6STI. There are other programs that will do the job equally as well.

If the antenna does what some enthusiasts believe it does, the next step would be to try multiple dipoles, one each for a single band, and see how this layout functions as a multiband antenna. I will describe just

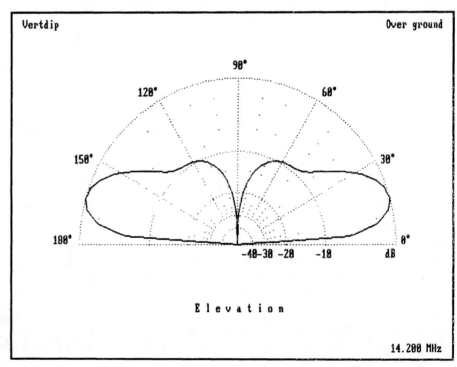

Figure 4-39. Pattern of a vertical dipole with the base 7 feet above ground. Maximum takeoff angle is about 17 degrees.

Figure 4-40. A dipole tilted at 45 degrees exhibits slight front-to-back ratio. The pattern is "away" from the support located at 180 degrees.

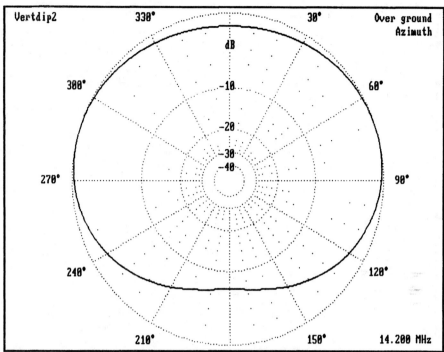

such a combination of antennas, suitable for 7-, 10-, 14-, 18-, and 21-MHz operation. Eighty-meter operation was not considered, as the resulting antenna would be too large, and 24 and 28 MHz were dropped because these bands are not worth very much at the bottom of the sunspot cycle. The five bands selected, however, are very much alive with plenty of DX, and this simple antenna may help you snag some of it!

Another investigation would be to analyze two dipoles in a beam configuration. This has been done by others (see "Further Reading" at the end of this section), and for me to do it again would be reinventing the wheel. Therefore, I dropped this idea.

A Vertical Test Dipole

I wanted to know the field pattern of the Lazy-V dipole and how it compares with a vertical dipole and a dipole inclined at a 45-degree angle. These three configurations can be compared quickly on the computer.

The first experiment was to evaluate the vertical dipole. My model was cut to a length of 33 feet 6 inches. I chose an element made of no. 18 wire, as I had plenty of that if I decided to build the antenna. The test frequency was 14.2 MHz, and the base of the antenna was placed 7 feet above ground, making the top of the antenna/mast reach the 40-foot level. These figures were inputted to the computer program, and the analysis showed that the feedpoint impedance at the center of the dipole was about 72 ohms and the

main lobe of the antenna fell at an elevation angle of about 16 degrees (**Figure 4-39**). High-angle radiation was nicely suppressed, being reduced by 10 dB or more at angles above 60 degrees. In comparison, a quarter-wave ground plane has a takeoff angle of about 25 degrees.

The Tilted Dipole at 14 MHz

The next step was to tilt the dipole at an angle of 45 degrees. Feedpoint resistance increased to about 78 ohms, and a slight front-to-back ratio of about 5 dB was apparent (**Figure 4-40**). The elevation pattern, alas, exhibited a lot of high-angle radiation (**Figure 4-41**). At 15 degrees the pattern was down 3 dB when compared with the vertical. Maximum radiation appeared at about 58 degrees. Great stuff if you want to talk to an amateur a few hundred miles away. Not so good for 20-meter DX! As far as I was concerned, this eliminated the tilted dipole as an effective 20-meter antenna.

The Lazy-V Dipole at 14 MHz

The next step was to configure the dipole in the Lazy-V design (**Figure 4-37**). A computer run showed that the azimuth pattern was practically omnidirectional; the null of the tilted-dipole pattern had disappeared. The elevation plot looked something like that of the vertical dipole (**Figure 4-42**). Low-angle radiation peaked at about 16 degrees, but a high-angle lobe, absent in the vertical configuration, was apparent. By

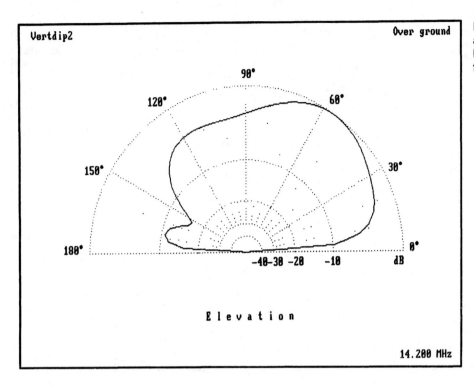

Figure 4-41. Pattern of a dipole tilted at 45 degrees exhibits unwanted high-angle lobe. Directivity is "away" from the supporting tower.

comparing the plots of the two antennas (**Figures 4-39** and **4-42**) it could be seen that the Lazy-V afforded no signal gain over the vertical, but instead produced some high-angle radiation that is relatively useless.

The next question to be considered was as follows: What is the effect of the supporting mast on the Lazy-V antenna? It was easy to eliminate or replace the vertical/mast support on the computer program. A 3-inch

diameter mast placed 2 feet away from the Lazy-V antenna had only a minor effect, with slight variations in the pattern, depending upon the distance of the mast from the Lazy-V antenna tips.

That's the summation of the 14-MHz runs. While the Lazy-V showed high-angle radiation, it still produced a low-angle lobe equivalent to that of the half-wave vertical antenna. Placing several Lazy-Vs around

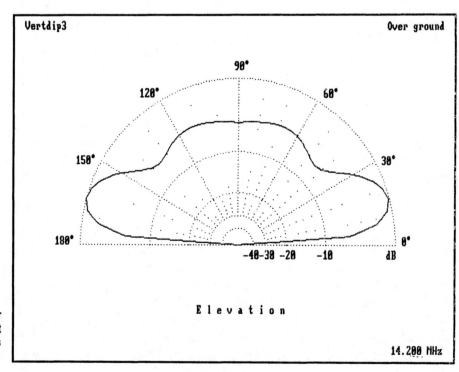

Figure 4-42. Pattern of the 20-meter Lazy-V dipole with the top at 40 foot height. Maximum radiation lobe is about 15 degrees.

Figure 4-43. Vertical plot of the 21 MHz Lazy-V with the top at about 40 feet. Lowest lobe is approximately 12 degrees.

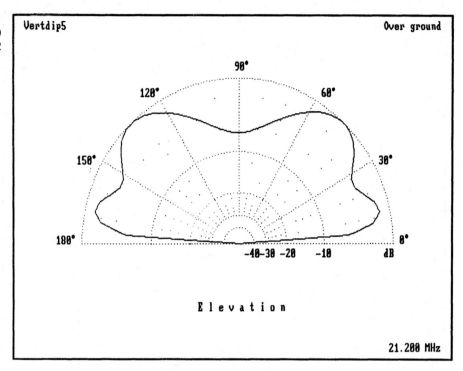

a ground-plane vertical would provide a multiband antenna that doesn't take up much space.

The 21-MHz Lazy-V

The next step was to reconfigure the computer program for a 21-MHz Lazy-V, with the top wire tied off at the same level as that of the 14-MHz design. Analysis showed the feedpoint impedance of the Lazy-V to be about 45 ohms. The elevation pattern had a split lobe, with maximum radiation at 13 and 47 degrees (**Figure 4-43**). The low-angle radiation was excellent, but the high-angle radiation would merely warm the ionosphere.

Radiation Patterns at 10 and 18 MHz

So far, so good. The Lazy-V looked promising

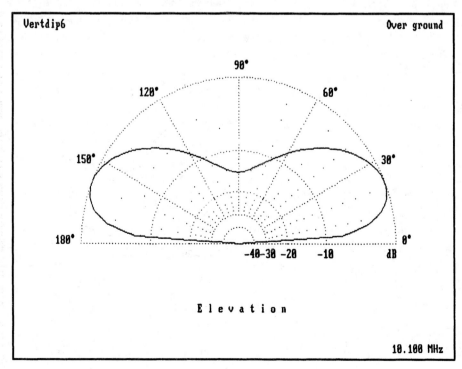

Figure 4-44. The Lazy-V pattern at 10.1 MHz. Lobe is at 23 degrees.

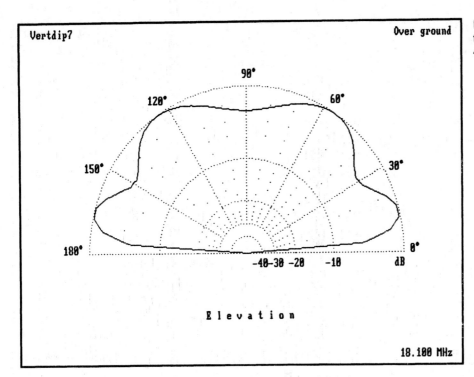

Figure 4-45. The 18-MHz pattern of the Lazy-V dipole with the top about 40 feet above ground.

enough to check it out on the two remaining bands: 10 and 18 MHz. At 10.1 MHz the feedpoint impedance of the Lazy-V was about 51 ohms. Good match! The azimuth pattern was omnidirectional, and the elevation pattern showed the main radiation lobe at an angle of about 23 degrees (**Figure 4-44**). Very good!

The bottom insulator of the antenna was only about 4.5 feet clear of the ground in this particular setup. Care should be taken to isolate this point from inquisitive fingers, as it is "hot" when you are transmitting!

The last step was to try a computer run at 18 MHz. Feedpoint impedance ran about 38 ohms, and the radiation pattern is shown in **Figure 4-45**. The lowest lobe fell at 13 degrees elevation, and there was considerable radiation at higher angles, peaking at about 58 degrees. This was a usable pattern, in spite of the amount of high-angle radiation.

Try the Lazy-V Yourself!

If you want to try the Lazy-V yourself, the backyard is a good place to start. And, I must admit the idea of placing four or more Lazy-V dipoles around a single mast is indeed tempting. Someday I must try this scheme in the backyard, but I don't expect the amazing results some of the backers of this antenna seem to be getting.

Building a Lazy-V Dipole Assembly

Here's the way I would go about building a multiband

Lazy-V antenna system. For simplicity I would limit the design to five bands, covered by the vertical antenna/support, plus four Lazy-Vs which make up the guy wires. The basic vertical antenna is made up of three sections of 10-foot TV mast (RadioShack 18-843) plus one 5-foot section (trimmed to length). A guy-ring and collar (15-835) are used as tie points at the top of the dipoles.

The vertical mast/antenna can be fed directly at the base, or the base can be grounded and the antenna shunt-fed with a gamma match. Five or six radials, about 20 to 30 feet long, are laid out across the grass in the yard. You can bend the radials to fit them within your property limitations.

The first step is to experiment with a single Lazy-V dipole. The apex of the dipole is pulled away from the tower by a rope and tied off at a convenient point. The bottom end of the dipole is led back and tied to the tower about 15 feet above ground. The aim is to make the included angle of the dipole at the apex about 90 degrees. A current balun is used at the feedpoint, and the coax line is brought back to the mast and runs down the side. I would keep the coax clear of the mast, as it might affect 7-MHz operation if it were taped to the mast. Just a suggestion.

At band center (14.2 MHz) the SWR on a 50-ohm line (RG-8X) should run about 1.8. Varying the distance of the dipole ends from the supporting vertical can change this figure for better or worse. As always, the dipole can be trimmed to place the point of lowest SWR at your favorite spot in the band.

Adding Extra Dipoles for Other Bands

Once you have gotten the "feel" of the 7/14-MHz combo, you are ready to add additional Lazy-V dipoles to your antenna farm. Add them one at a time, and review the SWR on the other antennas after a new dipole is added. Since each dipole is tuned to a different band, there should be little, if any, reaction between them. If, however, you notice a change in SWR when a dipole is added, it is possible to vary this figure by trimming the coax line of one of the antennas. They are closely coupled together, and an unused dipole, plus its coax line, may inadvertently detune or otherwise upset another dipole. It's not likely, but it could happen.

With the vertical, plus four Lazy-V dipoles, you can cover five bands. You'll need a multiposition coax switch at your operating position, plus an ATU unit. If your transceiver has a built-in ATU, that solves this little problem.

Contrary to some beliefs, this antenna system has unity gain, and like any vertical antenna it is sensitive to ground conductivity. Many handbooks have a table of ground conductivity in the United States. If you live in an area of good conductivity, you are in luck. Poor ground conductivity usually produces mediocre results with any vertical antenna.

For those interested in making two Lazy-Vs into a directive antenna, I refer you to the articles listed in the "Further Reading" section at the end of this section.

The Open-Sleeve Dipole

The "Open Sleeve Dipole" has been around for a long time, but it is not a household word in amateur radio. This simple antenna is composed of two or more adjacent dipoles—only one fed—and each is resonant at a different frequency (**Figure 4-46**). I first ran across this design about 1946 when it was incorporated in a television antenna for the lower VHF channels. The antenna was invented either at Stanford Research Institute (now SRI, Inc.) or at the U.S. Naval Post-graduate School (Monterey, California), or maybe somebody else invented it. A cursory search of the records revealed no less than six separate patents on the scheme, all issued between 1946 and 1950. The earliest patent covers three monopoles for use on a jet aircraft. Although not specified, the range covered was probably 100 to 156 MHz.

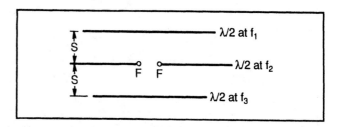

Figure 4-46. The three frequency system is composed of a fed dipole plus closely spaced conductors resonant at higher frequencies. Spacing S is small compared to element lengths. The feed point is F-F.

The bone of contention was the use of the sleeve dipole in broadband TV antennas for home use. The concept was modified and improved for harmonic operation, the goal being to preserve the bidirectional pattern over a 3:1 frequency range, suitable for low-band TV.

No doubt the lawyers grew rich as the squabble over patents dragged on. The matter was finally resolved about 1953. I am indebted to George Kearse, W5AWU, who was head of the Antenna Laboratory at Amphenol, Inc. for copies of the early patents and a summary of the litigation.

While useful in TV antennas and in certain log-periodic designs, as far as amateur radio is concerned, the primary use of the sleeve dipole is in multiple-band HF operation.

The 17th edition of *The ARRL Antenna Book* has a good write-up on this antenna (section 7-4) and provides insight into the design of various "multiband" open-sleeve dipoles. And finally, it should be noted that the open-sleeve design is used in the radiator portion of the Hy-Gain Explorer 14 triband Yagi beam.

A Practical Three-Band Sleeve Dipole

The November 1994 issue of *RF Design* magazine has an article by Gary Breed, K9AY, covering in detail the theory of the sleeve antenna, calling it a "Closely-coupled Resonator." Ah, well. A rose by any other name would smell as sweet.

Gary's article is of great interest to amateurs, as it provides the know-how to build a multiband dipole antenna, including the technique of controlling the feedpoint resistance and reactance on each band. In brief, Gary's multiple-resonant antenna consists of a driven dipole, resonant on the lowest band of choice, with additional conductors around it placed at appropriate distances. These are resonant on higher bands. When properly built, the antenna provides a near-unity match at the resonant frequency on each of the

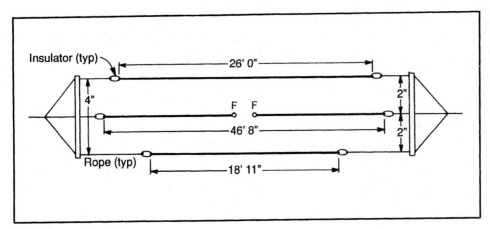

Figure 4-47. The open-sleeve dipole for the 10-, 18-, and 24.9-MHz bands. The antenna is made of no. 12 AWG. The design height used for computer analysis is 45 feet. Insulated spacers keep wire in alignment.

chosen bands. The result is a triband dipole having no traps, decoupling networks, or tuned stubs.

An Open-Sleeve Dipole for 10, 18, and 24 MHz

The K9AY dipole provides operation on the three WARC bands of 10.1, 18.1, and 24.9 MHz without traps, coils, or switching. The assembly is shown in **Figure 4-47**. The driven dipole is resonant on the lowest frequency band, and the additional wire resonators are tuned to 18.1 and 24.9 MHz. There is no direct connection between the driven dipole and parasitic resonators.

The antenna is made of no. 12 AWG enamel wire. Spacing between the wires is 2 inches. The overall antenna length is 49.5 feet. The antenna wires are held in position by insulated spacers placed every couple of feet along the antenna. The insulators can be made of 3/8-inch square material such as Lexan or polystyrene. Any good RF-insulating material will do the job.

The best way to build the antenna is to stretch the wires between two fixed points, about shoulder high. With the wires under tension, the insulators can be fixed in position and the end bridles aligned to place equal tension on all wires.

The feedpoint demands attention. Gary fed his antenna directly with coax. I prefer the use of a 1:1 current balun at this point. This helps to keep RF current off the outside shield of the transmission line. However, the weight of the balun causes the center dipole wire to sag, unless additional spacers are used at the center point to keep everything ship-shape and in Bristol fashion.

The radiation on all bands is the familiar figure-8 pattern. Gary recommends the antenna be placed about 45 feet above ground for best results.

The SWR response is a function of wire lengths, spacing, and wire diameter. The K9AY article provides equations for those who wish to experiment with this design.

Use the antenna as an inverted-V? That may be a little tricky unless you can arrange the mechanical layout to keep all wires taut. It might be worth a try.

References

1. Design and construction of the trap antenna is covered in detail in *Simple Low-cost Wire Antennas*, published by *Radio Amateur Callbook, Inc.*

2. O'Neil, "Trapping the Mysteries of Trapped Antennas," *Ham Radio*, August 1976, p. 46.

Further Reading

Here are some articles on using the Lazy-V dipole in antenna arrays.

Christman, Duffy, Breakall, "The 160 Sloper System at K3LR," *QST*, August 1994, pages 36–38.

Pietrazewski, "7 MHz Sloper System," *The ARRL Antenna Book*, 1991, pages 4–12 to 4–14.

Mitchell, "The K8UR Low-band Vertical Array," *CQ*, December 1989, pages 42–46.

Leo, "The Lazy-V Array—An Antenna To Consider," *QST*, February 1995, page 67.

Margelli, "Credit Where Credit is Due," *QST*, May 1995, page 86.

Moxon, "HF Antennas For All Locations," *RSGB*, 2nd edition, 1993, pages 227–230.

Chapter 5

Transmitting and Receiving Loops

Antenna experimentation is one of the few fields in which an amateur can participate armed only with enthusiasm, a tape measure, an SWR meter (or antenna analyzer), and inexpensive tools. A Ph.D. degree in higher mathematics or computer technology isn't required.

One of the best candidates for home experimentation is the quad antenna (**Figure 5-1**). The quad loop can be built in many configurations. The support structure may be as uncomplicated as a set of bamboo poles, and the whole arrangement can be built for only a few dollars. Add a single-loop parasitic element to the driven loop, and you have a two-element quad beam. In many areas of the world where aluminum tubing is hard to find, or prohibitively expensive, the quad antenna is the best answer to the amateur's need for a high-gain, high-frequency antenna.

The Single-Element Loop Antenna

While the loop antenna has been around since the early days of radio, use of a large loop for HF transmission wasn't seriously investigated until 1938 when Clarence Moore, ex-W9LZX, developed a two-element loop antenna for shortwave broadcasting. The Moore design was an instant success, and the so-called quad antenna has been popular with amateurs worldwide for the past five decades.

The simplest quad is a single loop that provides horizontal polarization when fed as shown in **Figure 5-1A**. The loop has a bidirectional pattern similar to that of the dipole. Loop gain and feedpoint impedance are a function of the shape of the loop. The circular loop has the highest gain and feedpoint resistance. This provides a power gain of about 1.13 dB over a dipole with a feedpoint impedance of 135 ohms. The square design has a gain of about 0.85 dB over a dipole and a

feedpoint impedance of 120 ohms. The triangular, or "delta," loop provides a gain of about 0.55 dB over a dipole and a feedpoint impedance of 105 ohms.

An intermediate-design loop, which provides a power gain of 1.5 dB over a dipole and a feedpoint impedance of 50 ohms, is shown in **Figure 5-2**. This quad loop (while a bit unwieldy for the lower frequencies) is an excellent antenna for the higher bands, as it provides bidirectional gain and can be fed directly with a 50-ohm coaxial line. A similar design, to match a 75-ohm line, is also shown.

The delta loop and the circular loops have a feedpoint impedance somewhat different from that of the square. All of these designs, however, can be matched

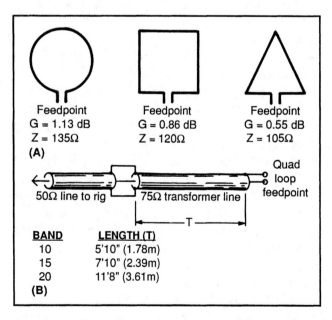

Feedpoint
G = 1.13 dB
Z = 135Ω
(A)

Feedpoint
G = 0.86 dB
Z = 120Ω

Feedpoint
G = 0.55 dB
Z = 105Ω

50Ω line to rig · 75Ω transformer line

Quad loop feedpoint

← T →

BAND	LENGTH (T)
10	5'10" (1.78m)
15	7'10" (2.39m)
20	11'8" (3.61m)

(B)

Figure 5-1. (A) The simple transmitting loop. Directivity is in and out of the page. The triangular loop may be inverted, with the apex at the bottom and the feedpoint at the apex. (B) Quarterwave transformer for use with quad loop antennas. Use of a balun at F–F is recommended.

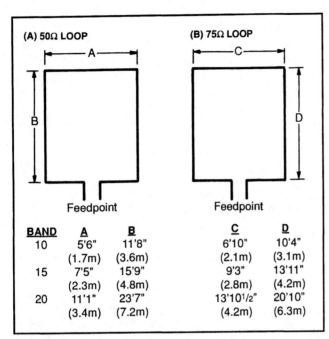

Figure 5-2. Single-element quad loops for 50- and 75-ohm feedlines. Use a balun at the feedpoint.

BAND	A	B	C	D
10	5'6"	11'8"	6'10"	10'4"
	(1.7m)	(3.6m)	(2.1m)	(3.1m)
15	7'5"	15'9"	9'3"	13'11"
	(2.3m)	(4.8m)	(2.8m)	(4.2m)
20	11'1"	23'7"	13'10½"	20'10"
	(3.4m)	(7.2m)	(4.2m)	(6.3m)

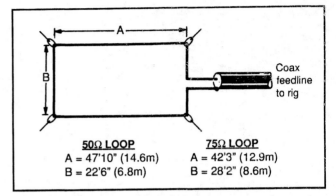

Figure 5-3. Vertically polarized 40-meter loop for 50- or 75-ohm feed. Mount the loop in the vertical plane as high above ground as possible. Bring the feedline off horizontally. Use of a balun at the feedpoint is recommended.

50Ω LOOP
A = 47'10" (14.6m)
B = 22'6" (6.8m)

75Ω LOOP
A = 42'3" (12.9m)
B = 28'2" (8.6m)

to a 50-ohm transmission line by the use of a quarter-wavelength, 75-ohm transformer between the line and loop. Data for such a transformer is given in **Figure 5-1B**. The loop antenna is balanced to ground at the feedpoint, and it's a good idea to isolate the outer shield of the coaxial feedline from antenna current. This can easily be done by winding the line into a four-turn coil about 8 inches in diameter directly below the loop. The plane of the coil should be at right angles to the plane of the loop.

One of the advantages of the loop antenna is that it can be supported at the midpoint by a single pole. Properly built, the loop isn't obtrusive and can be used in areas where more conspicuous ham antennas are frowned upon.

The 50-ohm or 75-ohm loop can be turned on a side to provide a vertically polarized array for low-frequency operation. For 40 meters, for example, loop height is only about 22 feet, and the extensive radial system that's required for a good groundplane antenna isn't as necessary (see **Figure 5-3**).

The Cubical Quad Beam Antenna

Adding a parasitic element to the driven loop produces the famous cubical quad antenna pioneered by ex-W9LZX. The quad is a unidirectional array providing a power gain of over 5 dBd with a good front-to-back ratio. Both gain and F/B ratio depend upon

element separation and tuning, as is the case with the traditional Yagi beam design.

It's difficult to surpass the advantages offered by the simple two-element quad. This antenna is light and has low wind resistance, and it provides high gain in a small package. The feed system is uncomplicated.

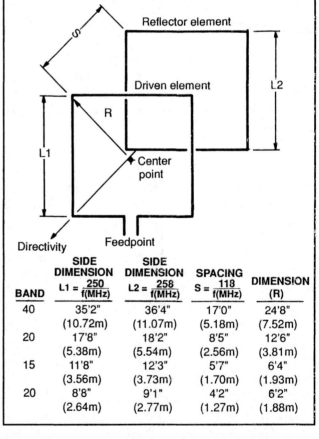

BAND	SIDE DIMENSION $L1 = \frac{250}{f(MHz)}$	SIDE DIMENSION $L2 = \frac{258}{f(MHz)}$	SPACING $S = \frac{118}{f(MHz)}$	DIMENSION (R)
40	35'2"	36'4"	17'0"	24'8"
	(10.72m)	(11.07m)	(5.18m)	(7.52m)
20	17'8"	18'2"	8'5"	12'6"
	(5.38m)	(5.54m)	(2.56m)	(3.81m)
15	11'8"	12'3"	5'7"	6'4"
	(3.56m)	(3.73m)	(1.70m)	(1.93m)
20	8'8"	9'1"	4'2"	6'2"
	(2.64m)	(2.77m)	(1.27m)	(1.88m)

Figure 5-4. Design data for a two-element quad. Dimension R is the approximate distance from the center point of the loop assembly to the point of attachment of the wire.

Also, because the elements are continuous and have no tips, rain static problems (often a headache with the Yagi beam) are nonexistent. The cubical quad beam is thus an ideal antenna for the DXer who wishes to obtain good results with a minimum cash outlay.

A Practical Two-Element Cubical Quad

Data for a practical two-element quad are given in **Figure 5-4**. Boom length is about 0.12 wavelength. This provides a compact design and a good match to the coaxial transmission line, because feedpoint impedance of the quad is a function of element separation as well as tuning. The reflector loop is pre-cut to the correct length and requires no adjustment after assembly. Important dimensions are shown in the illustration, length R being the distance from the center point of the assembly to the point of attachment of the wire to the support structure.

The quad crossarms should be constructed of insulating material. Many quad assemblers have run into problems when using metal arms for the array. It's possible to insert insulating sections in metal crossarms, but the builder is advised to stay away from this complicated technique. Fiberglass poles, bamboo, and PVC pipe have been used successfully for quad arms. Most homemade quads use a section of 2- or 3-inch diameter aluminum tubing for the boom. The two-element quad usually requires 2-inch tubing, but a quad for 6 or 10 meters can use a smaller diameter boom. Boom-to-crossarm clamps are available from several manufacturers, but many builders make their own out of a plywood sheet and galvanized-iron angle brackets. If you take this approach, make sure the edges of the plywood are sealed against moisture penetration. Two or three coats of outdoor house paint will do it.

A more exotic design uses a "spider" arrangement that employs multiple crossarms supported from a central point on the mast, at the middle of the array.

How High the Quad?

Experience has proven that the quad antenna performs well even when mounted close to the earth. For instance, the main lobe of a quad antenna mounted one-quarter wavelength above the ground is at an elevation angle of 40 degrees, whereas the angle of maximum radiation of a dipole at the same height is straight up.

At a height of three-eighths wavelength the angle of radiation of a quad is about 32 degrees, below that of a Yagi or dipole at the same height. Finally, at a height of a

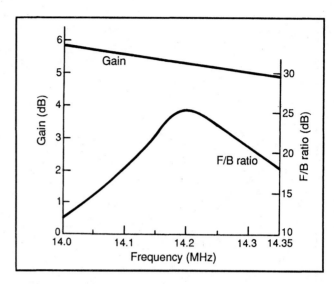

Figure 5-5. Gain and F/B response of the two-element quad.

one-half wavelength, the radiation angles of the quad and the dipole (or Yagi) are about equal. (The height of the quad is measured to the bottom of the lower element.)

The upshot of this is that the quad does better in terms of low elevation angles than does either the dipole or the Yagi beam. True, a height of one-quarter wavelength isn't a good one as far as low-angle, long-distance DX is concerned, but if you're stuck with it, it's better to use a quad than almost any other antenna because of the lower angle of radiation.

Those amateurs lucky enough to get the quad up in the air 40 to 60 feet will quickly understand why the quad achieved worldwide popularity in a very short time. Build a quad and enjoy!

Quad Characteristics

Gain and F/B ratio of a typical two-element quad are shown in **Figure 5-5**. Note that maximum gain and best F/B ratio do not occur at the same frequency. This is true of most small parasitic arrays.

Quad gain is fairly constant with regard to element spacings between 0.1 and 0.2 wavelength. Best F/B ratio seems to peak at an element spacing about 0.15 wavelength and can reach as high as 30 dB. The azimuth plot of a typical quad is shown in **Figure 5-6**.

The W2TBZ Quad-Loop Beam Antenna

I hadn't seen Sid, W2TBZ, for over 15 years, and our QSOs on the air were few and far between. "Keep in touch," I had said, and when I finally heard from him, Sid had a new antenna idea that he was using with great success on 15 and 20 meters.

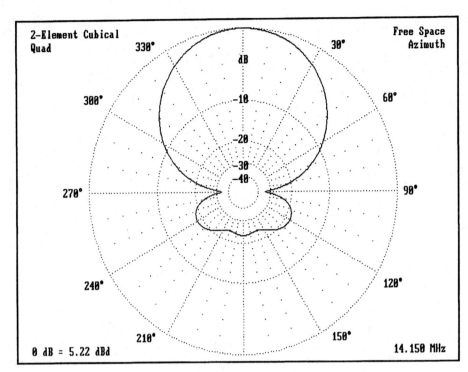

Figure 5-6. Azimuth plot of a two-element, 20-meter quad.

To stay in touch with his friends, Sid needed an inexpensive wire beam that could easily be erected and would provide a modest gain and a low angle of radiation. He tried various antennas. The final version, a 2-loop quad beam, is shown in **Figure 5-7**.

Estimated gain of this bidirectional array is about 4.5 dB over a dipole.

The AG9C Horizontal Loop Antenna

I think the loop antenna has more interesting varia-

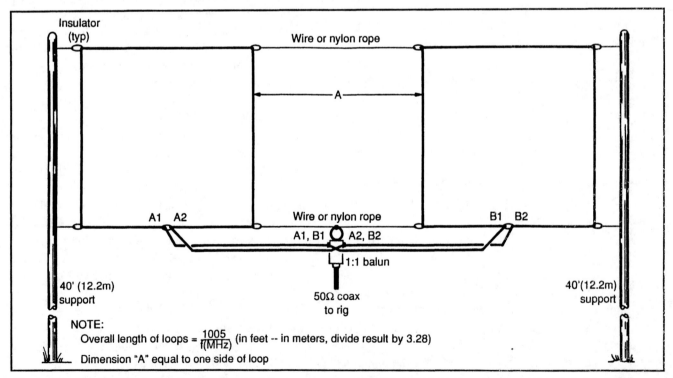

Figure 5-7. The W2TBZ loop beam. The phasing lines are made of 300-ohm TV line. Length of the phasing line = $468/f_{MHz}$ × velocity factor of 300-ohm line. Balun is supported at the center of the lower nylon rope.

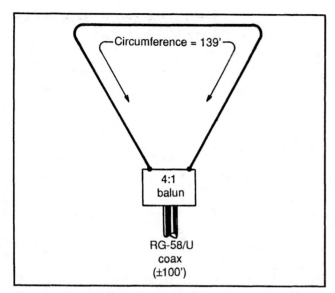

Figure 5-8. Top view of the AG9C horizontal delta loop. The antenna works without a tuner on 40, 20, and 15 meters. A tuner permits operation on 80, 30, and 10 meters.

tions than any other antenna! Bob Morrison, AG9C, has had excellent DX results with a full-wave horizontal delta loop he uses on 40, 20, and 15 meters "as is," and with a tuner on 80, 30, and 10 meters (**Figure 5-8**). The only materials you need are about 139 feet of no. 14 copper-weld wire, a 4:1 balun, a few insulators, and a length of 50-ohm coax line.

Bob examined the antenna radiation pattern at 7, 10, 14, 21, and 28 MHz using MININEC3 with the Sommerfield-Norton option. He assumed a 20-foot height and poor ground ($k = 5$, and $\Gamma = 0.002$ siemens/meter). In general, Bob found that gain patterns are comparable to a dipole cut for each of these frequencies. One exception, he noted, is that the loop patterns are more omnidirectional than those of similar dipoles.

"The design is very forgiving," Bob comments.

"Loop antenna patterns remain excellent when side lengths are unequal and/or the three corners have unequal heights."

Bob's observed SWR readings on the loop (taken through 100 feet of RG-58/U) are: 40 meters—1.55 at 7.0 MHz, 2.4 at 7.3 MHz; 20 meters—1.2 at 14.0 MHz, 1.7 at 14.35 MHz; 15 meters—1.38 at 21.0 MHz, 1.70 at 21.45 MHz; 10 meters—2.7 at 28.0 MHz, 3.7 at 28.5 MHz, 5.9 at 29.0 MHz, and 3.6 at 29.7 MHz.

You can move the minimum SWR point in the 10-meter band by changing the total length of the wire in the loop 6 inches at a time.

Bob says the loop can be used on 80 and 30 meters by adding an antenna tuner in the station. The input impedance of the loop on 80 meters is very high, as it is at a half-wave resonance. The mismatch at the balun causes high SWR and considerable power loss in the balun and coax line. Nevertheless, a tuner easily matches the feedline to the transmitter. Antenna radiated power is reduced, but adequate, over the CW portion of the 80-meter band.

A Rectangular Loop Antenna for 80–10 Meters

From Walt, AF3V, I heard of a second interesting multiband antenna (see **Figure 5-9**). A rectangular loop in the vertical plane, its overall length is about 58 feet with the bottom wire about 7 feet above ground. Its unique feature is the knife switch (S) placed across the insulator in the center of the bottom wire. Easily reached, the switch permits the operator to change from an open loop to a closed one quickly. The feedline is a homemade, open-wire line about 42 feet long. It drops down vertically to within 8 feet of the ground and then extends horizontally to the station, perpendicular to the plane of the antenna. The antenna is

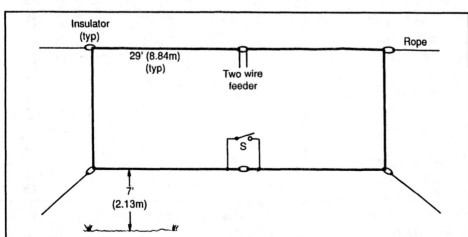

Figure 5-9. The multiband loop at AF3V. The switch permits the operator to change from open loop to closed loop. The loop operates on all bands between 3.5 and 29.7 MHz.

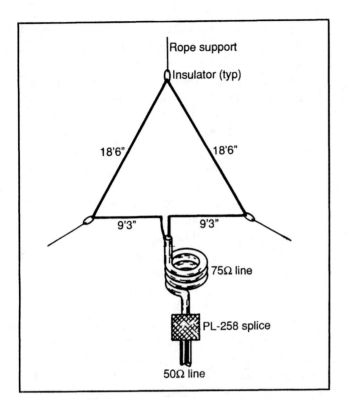

Figure 5-10. Delta loop for 18 MHz. The coax transformer is 9 feet long, plug tip to plug tip. It's wound into a coil about 6 inches in diameter.

adjusted to resonance by means of an old Johnson "Matchbox" tuner. The antenna switch is closed for operation on 7, 10, and 21 MHz and is open on the other bands. With a different length feedline, different switch settings may be necessary.

Walt supports the center of the top section to offset the weight of the feedline. He says the antenna outperforms the center-fed horizontal wire he had previously, and reports that the pattern appears reasonably omnidirectional on all bands.

The 18-MHz Delta Loop

The delta loop in **Figure 5-10** is a good "first" antenna for 18 MHz. It has a slight gain over a dipole and is very "user friendly." The feedpoint impedance of the loop is about 120 ohms. Use a 75-ohm quarter-wave transformer to provide a reasonable match to a 50-ohm coax line. The transformer is wound into a coil to choke off RF currents that might flow on the outside of the coax shield.

The loop's feedpoint terminates in an SO-239 coax connector mounted on a small insulator plate. The transformer has PL-259 plugs on both ends. Make the splice between the transformer and the 50-ohm line with a PL-258 splice adapter. After making the con-

nection, weatherproof the plugs and adapter with coax tape or heat-shrink tubing.

The loop is supported at the apex and the side insulators are tied off to objects nearby. The radiation pattern is similar to that of a dipole and is horizontally polarized.

A Multiband Version of the Delta Loop

You can operate the delta loop on the 18-, 21-, 24-, and 28-MHz bands if you feed it with two-wire balanced line as shown in **Figure 5-11**. Transmitting-type 300-ohm ribbon line is satisfactory. You can also use open-wire line. Match the line to a coax feed system via an antenna tuner (ATU or Transmatch) located at the station.

If you have difficulty loading the antenna on a band, change the length of the line between the antenna and the ATU. There is a standing wave on the line, and a particular line length may present an unacceptable load to the tuning unit. To solve this problem, add a few feet of line (a foot or so at a time) until you get a satisfactory match.

The Bi-square Array for 18 MHz

The diamond-shaped bi-square beam is much larger than the delta loop, but provides about 3 dBd gain.

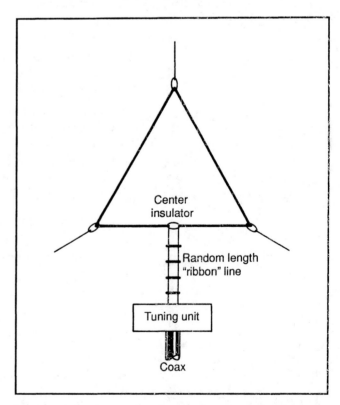

Figure 5-11. Balanced line feed with the antenna tuning unit at the station permits multiband operation of the delta loop shown in Figure 5-10.

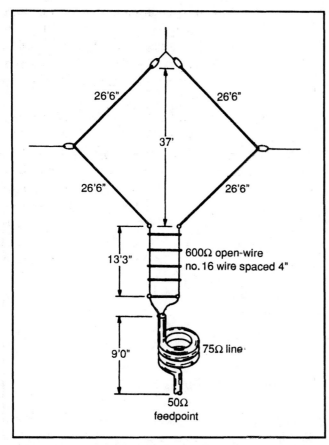

Figure 5-12. The "bi-square" beam provides a bidirectional pattern and about 3 dB gain over a dipole. Note that the top of the loop is open.

This is a great antenna to try if you have the space. It's shown in **Figure 5-12**.

The loop is a half wavelength on a side and open at the top. The feedpoint impedance at the bottom of the loop is about 2900 ohms. I use a two-wire, 600-ohm quarter-wave stub to provide a more reasonable impedance value of about 122 ohms. Match it to a 50-ohm coax line by adding a quarter-wave transformer made of 75-ohm coax. Wind the 75-ohm line into a coil about 6 inches in diameter to reduce RF currents flowing on the outside of the coax. Under these conditions, the SWR on the transmission line is less than 1.2:1 across the band once the antenna is adjusted for resonance.

Tuning the Antenna

Resonate the loop and stub to 18.1 MHz with a dip meter or antenna analyzer. Temporarily close the stub at the bottom using a movable short with a one-turn loop in the middle. I made mine with two copper alligator clips so I could move it up and down the stub a few inches. I adjusted the position of the short until I achieved antenna resonance quickly with the MFJ-

259 SWR Analyzer. As soon as you find resonance, remove the short and place an SO-239 coax receptacle across the bottom of the line.

You'll need to waterproof the coax receptacle and all plugs and splices in the system. It's imperative to use coax tape or other weatherproofing compounds to keep water out of the line.

The HB9ADQ Delta Loop for 7, 14, 21, and 28 MHz

The delta loop shown in **Figure 5-13** can operate on four bands. Maximum current is in the horizontal wire for best low-angle radiation. The loop can be slung between two trees for ease of installation. Maximum radiation is at right angles to the plane of the loop (into and out of the page).

The loop is fed with a two-wire transmission line. The original design called for a 600-ohm line, which could be made up easily by any old-timer with experience building a Zepp antenna. Modern substitutes are the Saxton Products Corp. 1562 insulated open-wire line (using a polyethylene web) or the Saxton 2500 open-air line. The length of the line is adjusted for minimum SWR on the coax feedline. When the 600-ohm line is used, a 20-pF capacitor is connected across the feedpoint.

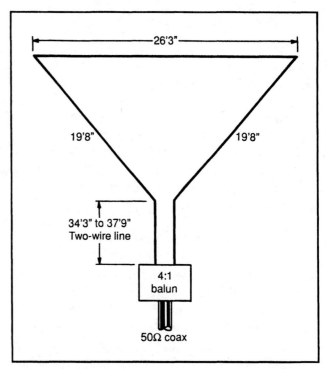

Figure 5-13. Four-band loop for 7, 14, 21, and 28 MHz. A balanced feedline and balun provide match to 50-ohm coax. Adjust the length of the two-wire line for lowest SWR on the coax.

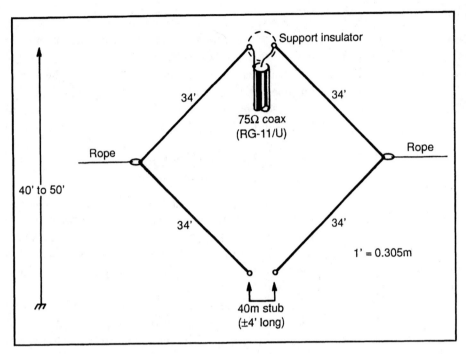

Figure 5-14. The two-band quad loop of W7CJB can be hung from a 40-foot high tower. On 80 meters, the antenna operates as a dipole folded back upon itself. On 40 meters, the antenna acts as a quad loop, horizontally polarized. The bottom end of the antenna is open for 80 meters and closed with an adjustable, shorted stub for 40 meters.

The open-wire line can be extended to reach the station where it's fed with an antenna tuner that provides balanced output in the range of 100 to 600 ohms.

The loop need not be in the vertical plane. It can be laid on its side or at a 45-degree angle and still do the job.

The 80/40-Meter Loop Antenna of W7CJB

Here's the simple two-band loop used at W7CJB. Old-timers will recognize this, but it may be a new idea to some of our recently licensed friends (see **Figure 5-14**). Basically, it's a loop dipole that's opened opposite the feedpoint for 80-meter operation. This point is jumpered for 40-meter operation. The antenna is 34 feet on a side and is fed at the apex with 75-ohm coaxial line (RG-11/U). A good (but not exact) impedance match is obtained on each band, and the antenna loads properly with most transmitters having a nominal 50-ohm antenna preference.

The loop can be hung vertically from a tower, or tilted outward from the tower if height is a problem. It has been used with towers as short as 40 feet.

With the bottom of the loop closed, the bottom legs are trimmed to provide resonance in the 40-meter band. The loop is then opened and resonance checked in the 80-meter band. You can temporarily fold back equal lengths of wire in the lower legs to find resonance at 3.9 MHz; you can then clip this off and use a 4-foot stub to short the antenna for 40-meter opera-

tion. The clip-on stub is a quick method of band changing and costs next to nothing.

The 4Z4RS Two-band Quad Loop

More and more amateurs are discovering that the single quad loop makes an excellent and inexpensive single-band antenna. It has the radiation pattern of a

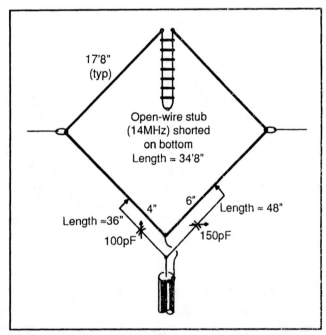

Figure 5-15. The 4Z4RS two-band quad loop antenna for 20 and 15 meters. The loop is cut for 20 meters and has a shorted stub that acts as an electrical switch for 15 meters. Parallel-connected gamma matches provide a good match to coaxial line. Approximate gamma dimensions are shown.

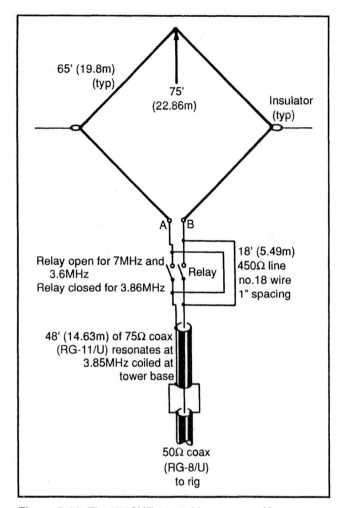

65' (19.8m)
(typ)

75'
(22.86m)

Insulator
(typ)

A   B

Relay open for 7MHz and
3.6MHz
Relay closed for 3.86MHz

Relay

18' (5.49m)
450Ω line
no.18 wire
1" spacing

48' (14.63m) of 75Ω coax
(RG-11/U) resonates at
3.85MHz coiled at
tower base

50Ω coax
(RG-8/U)
to rig

Figure 5-16. The W6CHE 40- to 80-meter quad loop.

dipole and provides a small amount of gain over a dipole mounted at the midpoint height of the loop.

Dave, 4Z4RS, has modified his quad loop to work on two bands without the need for an antenna tuner or balanced feed (**Figure 5-15**). His design is for 20 and 15 meters. The loop perimeter is one wavelength, 70 feet 9 inches, on 20 meters. The top of the loop is open and shorted one-half wave; 20-meter open-wire stub is attached at this point. The length of the stub is 34 feet 8 inches.

The loop is fed at the bottom by two gamma matches that are parallel-connected to a coaxial transmission line. The whole assembly, including the gammas, is made of wire, and the loop is maintained in position by nylon ropes attached to the side points.

General dimensions for the gammas are given in the drawing. The length of the gamma wires and the value of the capacitors determine the degree of match. For adjustment, the 20-meter gamma capacitor is set at minimum capacitance and adjustments are made to

the 15-meter gamma to reduce the SWR on the transmission line below 1.5:1. The connection between the gamma and the loop is made by a copper clip that can be moved about to find the proper tap point. Once the 15-meter gamma is set approximately, the 20-meter gamma is adjusted for lowest SWR on the transmission line on that band. The adjustments tend to interact. A second adjustment of each gamma will bring the SWR to near unity at the center frequency of each band. When properly adjusted, the loop provides a very low SWR across each band with typical readings of SWR at the band edges being 1.5:1, or less.

The higher the loop is suspended in the air, the lower will be the main lobe of radiation. DX operation will be improved if the apex of the loop is over 35 feet high. This puts the bottom of the loop about 10 feet above ground level.

The W6CHE Two-band Loop Antenna

It's not easy to get an effective DX antenna that will work on both 80 and 40 meters. By "80 meters," I mean both CW operation at the low end of the band and SSB operation near the DX slot at 3.8 MHz. However, it looks as if Jack McCullough, W6CHE, has found an answer—providing you have a modest tower and a small amount of real estate. Jack's solution to the 80/40-meter dilemma is shown in **Figure 5-16**. The basic antenna is a single 80-meter, diamond-shaped quad loop measuring 65 feet on a side and hung from the top of a 75-foot tower. Since the overall height of the diamond from base to apex is about 90 feet, the loop plane is tilted out at the base, away from the tower. The assembly thus is not in the vertical plane. If you have a higher tower, the loop can be mounted in the vertical plane.

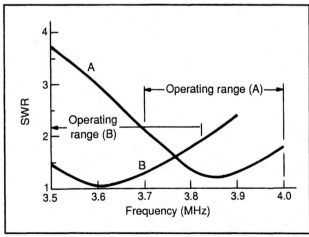

Figure 5-17. Operating range of the W6CHE loop with relay (A) closed or (B) open.

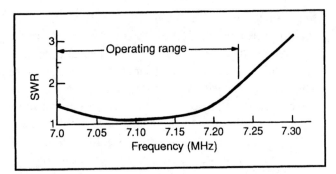

Figure 5-18. Operation of the W6CHE loop at the end of the 40-meter band (relay open).

The loop is fed with a 50-ohm coax line, plus a 48-foot section of RG-11/U (75 ohm) coax that serves as a matching transformer. The line is cut to 3850 kHz with the aid of an antenna analyzer or SWR meter.

80-meter operation—A double-pole relay is placed between the matching section and the feedpoints of the loop. When the relay is closed, the loop is resonant at 3.8 MHz. When the relay is open, the loop is lengthened by an 18-foot section of 450-ohm open-wire line. The loop is now resonant near 3.6 MHz (see **Figure 5-17**). Thus, with the flick of a switch, the antenna can be made resonant at either end of the 80-meter band, providing a low value of SWR to the transmitter.

40-meter operation—Operation across the lower portion of the 40-meter band is possible when the relay is either open or closed. The best situation is shown in **Figure 5-18**, with the relay in the open position. The operating range, as defined in the curves, is about 7.0 to 7.25 MHz.

The secret of moving the quad loop about in frequency is the length of the matching stub. Obviously, a different length stub is required for operation at the high end of the 40-meter band.

The final W6CHE loop control system is shown in **Figure 5-19**. Two relays and two stubs are used. One stub is 15 feet long and the other is 4 feet long. In series connection, they represent a stub about 19 feet long. The stubs are switched in and out of the circuit by means of a two-pole, three-position rotary switch at the operating position. Power is applied to the relays via a separate switch that energizes the DC supply. Switching sequences for the various frequency ranges are listed in **Table 5-1**.

A Nifty Bi-Square Beam for 10 or 12 Meters

If you're interested in DX operation on either 10 or 12 meters, you'll eventually need a beam antenna. You

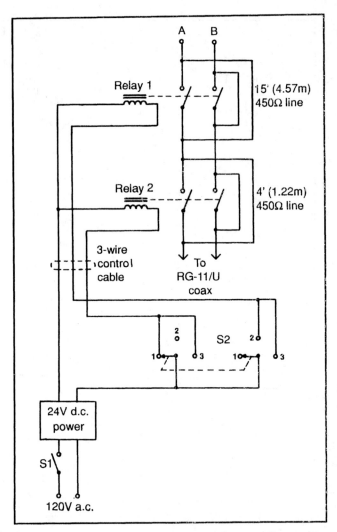

Figure 5-19. A dual-relay arrangement for operation on the different segments of the 40- and 80-meter bands (see Table 5-1).

can work a lot of "easy" DX with a dipole, but sooner or later you'll wish you had a beam for the more exotic DX stations. An easy solution is to buy a Yagi beam kit, but it's less expensive to build your own wire beam from scratch. Here's an inexpensive beam for your consideration.

The bi-square beam is a derivation of the so-called "Lazy-H" array (**Figure 5-20A**), a favorite of point-to-point stations in the maritime and fixed services. The Lazy-H consists of two half-wave dipoles in

Frequency Range	SW1	SW2	Total Stub Length
3500–3650 kHz	open	—	19 feet
3550–3750 kHz	closed	Position 1	15 feet
3700–3900 kHz	closed	Position 2	4 feet
3750–4000 kHz	closed	Position 3	—
7000–7125 kHz	open	—	19 feet
7125–7300 kHz	closed	Position 1	15 feet

Table 5-1. Switching sequences for W6CHE loop.

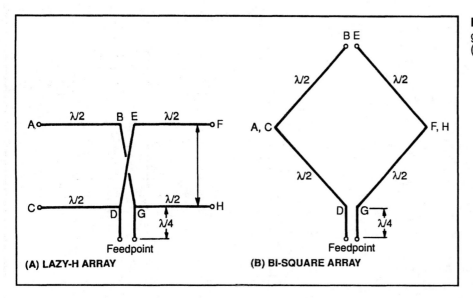

Figure 5-20. Simple bidirectional wire gain antennas: (A) Lazy-H array and (B) bi-square array.

phase over a similar pair of dipoles. Spacing between the top and bottom dipole pairs is a half wavelength. Proper phasing of the pairs is achieved with a transposed open-wire transmission line fed at the center of the lower pair of dipoles with a quarterwave, open-wire stub. The feedpoint impedance at the bottom of the stub is about 220 ohms.

A more practical version of the Lazy-H antenna is the bi-square beam shown in **Figure 5-20B**. This arrangement requires only a single center pole support. The Lazy-H dipole pairs are connected together at the outer tips, resulting in a diamond-shaped wire arrangement. You can eliminate the transposed line connecting the center of the pairs. The quarterwave stub is retained.

The feedpoint impedance at the bottom of the stub is close to 150 ohms. There's a reduction in feedpoint impedance because the top and bottom radiating elements of the bi-square configuration are closer to each other than they are in the Lazy-H antenna.

The bi-square radiation pattern is a figure-eight (bidirectional) at right angles to the plane of the array. The power gain over a dipole located at the center height of the array is about 3.5 dB.

Building the Bi-Square Beam. The bi-square is an easy, inexpensive beam to build. You'll need about 100 feet of no. 16 enamel or Formvar™ coated wire and four insulators. The quarterwave stub needs five spreaders cut from 1/2-inch diameter phenolic (or plastic) rod. One of the spreaders serves as the bottom insulator for the antenna wires. The diamond-shaped antenna is open at the top (two insulators required). Overall height is a little less than 30 feet. I hung mine from a yardarm at the 45-foot level of my crank-up

tower. The proximity of the metal tower to the plane of the loop didn't seem to cause any harm.

Dimensions for the 10- and 12-meter versions of the antenna are given in **Figure 5-21**. The sides are pulled out by ropes and tied off to convenient points on nearby trees. The bottom of the quarterwave stub is about 7 feet above the ground.

The yardarm holds the loop about 3 feet away from

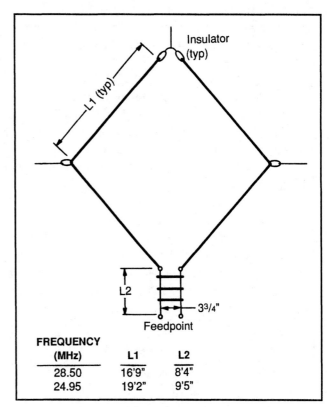

FREQUENCY (MHz)	L1	L2
28.50	16'9"	8'4"
24.95	19'2"	9'5"

Figure 5-21. The bi-square antenna dimensions for the 10- and 12-meter bands; feedpoint impedance is about 150 ohms.

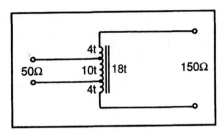

Figure 5-22. A 1:3 balanced transformer wound on a ferrite toroid (Amidon FT-240-67).

the tower. The loop isn't quite in the vertical plane because I pulled the bottom of it 6 feet away from the tower in order to reach the bottom of the stub easily from the garage roof.

The bi-square antenna's bandwidth is very broad; the antenna may be cut to the dimensions given without further ado. Purists may wish to trim the antenna to a specific frequency in the 10-meter band. Design frequencies for the antenna shown are 28.5 and 24.95 MHz. The 10-meter antenna covers the whole band with an SWR of less than 1.5:1—quite an achievement!

Adjusting the Antenna to Frequency. It's easy to set the resonant frequency of the antenna "on the nose." The bottom of the stub (F–F) is shorted by a jumper that has a one-turn loop in the center. The loop is just big enough to fit over the coil of a dip oscillator or analyzer. My shorting bar is made of two interconnected copper alligator clips, so I can move it up and down the stub for adjustment. Move the shorting bar up and down the stub, an inch or so at a time, until the resonant frequency falls where you want it. Finally, cut the stub to the determined length.

Matching the Antenna to the Feedline. As I stated earlier, the feedpoint impedance of the antenna is about 150 ohms. The antenna is symmetrical with respect to ground, and the feedpoint is balanced to ground. Two transformations are required to match the antenna to a 50-ohm unbalanced (coaxial) line. The 50-ohm point is first transformed from unbalanced to balanced by a 1:1 balun. The 50-ohm balanced condition is then transformed to 150 ohms.

The transformation from 50 to 150 ohms can be performed in a number of ways. One is to use a ferrite toroid transformer (**Figure 5-22**). Take a core 2.4 inches in outer diameter and 0.5 inch high (Amidon FT-

240-67, or equivalent) with a permeability of 40. Sand it to remove rough edges, and then wrap it with a layer of electrical vinyl tape. Wind 18 turns of no. 14 enamel wire around the core, tapped four turns from each end. Space the winding around the entire core. Fasten the completed transformer to the phenolic mounting plate with epoxy cement, and mount the assembly in a waterproof box for protection from the weather.

A Linear Matching Transformer. The second matching scheme uses a linear transformer (**Figure 5-23**). The design is based on a balanced L-network. The circuit in **Figure 5-23A** was built using a receiving-type variable capacitor for initial tests. The dimensions shown allow adjustment of the capacitor, which quickly drops the SWR on the transmission line to unity at the design frequency of the antenna. The last step is to replace the variable capacitor with a fixed one and substitute a section of transmission line for the network inductors (**Figure 5-23B**). This works like a charm. A 50-pF, 5-kV ceramic capacitor (Centralab 8505-50Z, or equivalent) is substituted for the variable unit. Place it in a plastic refrigerator container to keep moisture away. The short line section is made up in the same manner as the quarterwave stub.

Results. For a few days, the dipole was left in position as a comparison with the bi-square. In all tests, the bi-square outperformed the dipole. On receive, signals that were almost in the noise were perfectly readable on the bi-square antenna. No doubt about it. The bi-square delivers the goods!

A 15-meter Version? The bi-square should work well on 15 meters, if you have the space. Multiply all 10-meter linear dimensions by 1.34 to obtain the antenna size for this band.

The DL2FA Half-Loop Antenna

Every once in a while, an interesting antenna comes along that causes me to ask, "Why didn't I think of that idea?" A case in point is the groundplane loop antenna described by Hans Wuertz, DL2FA, in *cq-DL*, the monthly publication of the German Amateur Radio Club. An English translation of the pertinent

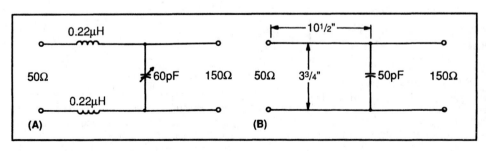

Figure 5-23. Linear matching transformers. (A) L-network uses lumped L and variable C (five turns, 1/2 inch I.D., no. 14 wire, eight turns per inch). (B) Linear network transformer made of no. 16 wire. Ends of the wire are bent inward 1 inch to connect to the balun. Dimensions for 24.95 MHz.

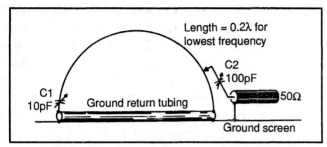

Figure 5-24. The DL2FA groundplane loop with gamma-match feed. The tap point is approximately 0.04 wavelength. Ground return tubing is soldered to the ground screen. Semicircle length is 27 feet 6 inches for 80–40 meter operation.

data on the loop was later published in *Radio Communication*, the journal of the Radio Society of Great Britain (RSGB).

The basic configuration of the DL2FA loop is shown in **Figure 5-24**. The design is half of a full-wave loop antenna with the other half formed by the ground image. With a 0.2-wavelength half-loop for the lowest operating frequency, DL2FA claims that the antenna can be tuned to cover a 2:1 frequency range (3.5 to 7 MHz, for example).

Even though the radiation resistance of the antenna is low, the efficiency of the antenna is excellent, and at 3.5 MHz the field strength is only 2 dB less than a full-size vertical.

To achieve low loss, the loop and ground return are constructed of 3/8-inch diameter copper tubing. The copper tubing that runs along the surface of the ground is soldered to a groundplane or mat made of chicken wire (size not specified).

Measured data for the groundplane loop are shown in **Table 5-2**.

Tuned Loops for 160-Meter Reception

Interest in 160-meter operation has risen and fallen since the exciting days of 1923. As a result of the expansion of the band by the FCC a few years ago, interest is reaching a new peak, with more and more stations coming on the band every day. Sad to say, a

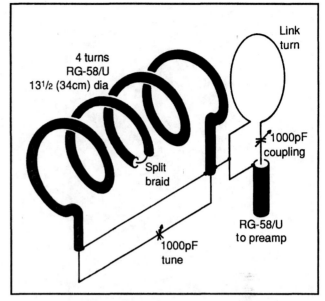

Figure 5-25. An oblique view of the W1FB loop as discussed in the July 1997 issue of *QST* magazine. The loop is made of 175-inch long section of RG-58/U coaxial line. The shield braid is split at the center of the length and a section about 1 inch long is removed. The line is then formed into a four-turn coil about 13-1/2 inches in diameter. The split in the shield is at the bottom of the coil, as are the connections. The outer braids are connected together as a common ground point, and the inner conductor is tuned to resonance with a compression-type variable mica capacitor. A three-gang broadcast capacitor with a dial will provide a more comfortable tuning mechanism. The coax is formed into a four-turn coil and held in position with electrical tape. The pickup loop is made of insulated hookup wire and centered inside the coaxial coil. It's a good idea to tape the split braid at the center of the coil so a short doesn't occur at this point. The *tune* capacitor is adjusted for maximum signal strength. The *coupling* capacitor is decreased in value until a drop-off in signal strength is noted. Minimum coupling provides greatest loop selectivity.

lot of newcomers give up in disgust at the racket they hear in their receivers: static, broadcast harmonics and intermodulation, TV sweep QRM, and lots more.

Hams have grumbled about difficult receiving conditions on 160 meters for years, and a few of them have done something about it. One area of interest centers around the compact receiving loop antenna

Band	Semicircle Length	C1	Bandwidth (–3 dB points)	Efficiency	Comparison with 1/4-wave vertical
3.5–7.0 MHz	27'6" (8.4 m)	332 pF	5.7 kHz	70% (3.5 MHz)	–1.91 dB
			to 67 kHz	96% (7.0 MHz)	–0.55 dB
7.0–14.0 MHz	13'9" (4.2 m)	184 pF	11 kHz	77% (7.0 MHz)	–1.52 dB
			to 147 kHz	97% (14.0 MHz)	–0.50 dB
14–28 MHz	6'10" (2.1 m)	102 pF	24 kHz	83% (14.0 MHz)	–1.22 dB
			to 323 kHz	98% (28.0 MHz)	–0.47 dB

Table 5-2. Groundplane loop dimensions and performance data. (Courtesy of *Radio Communication*, published by the Radio Society of Great Britain.

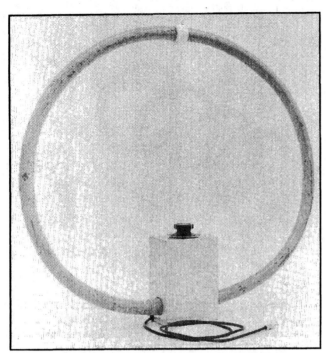

Photo 5-A. The W6PO tuned receiving loop. Bob broke the electrostatic shield at the top with a section of phenolic material for ease of construction. The loop itself is made up of five turns of colored hookup wire, each wire having insulation of a different color. A sixth turn provides the coupling loop for the preselector. The wires are passed through the loop halves before assembly. Plumbing fittings are soldered to the copper tubing at the bottom to affix the loop to the 3 × 4 × 5 inch aluminum box. The tuning capacitor (350 pF) is atop the box and the coaxial cable to the receiver comes out the side of the box. Connecting the individual loop wires in series is easy, as they are color coded. Depending upon the number of active turns, the loop can tune from 4 MHz down to about 1300 kHz. Three-quarter-inch diameter copper water pipe is used for construction.

(**Figure 5-25**). The small loop was very popular for general broadcast reception during the twenties, but faded into obscurity, except for direction-finding purposes, over the next few years.

The pattern of the small loop antenna resembles that of the dipole—a figure-eight in the plane of the loop. The input resistance of the loop antenna is very low if the loop is small in terms of wavelength. For typical receiving loops, it's on the order of a few hundredths of an ohm. Moreover, because the area of the loop is small compared with the wavelength, loop pickup compared with that of a full-size antenna is greatly reduced. Receiving loops generally need from 15 to 20 dB signal "boost" before they can compare with a typical half-wave dipole antenna.

Then why use a loop? Mainly because the loop has two excellent signal nulls that can be used to knock down local signals, interference, or line noise. On DX

signals, the loop appears to be relatively nondirectional due to the random polarization of the ionospheric-reflected signals. Also, because of the ability to virtually null out considerable local, manmade noise, the loop antenna can provide a superior signal-to-noise ratio in many circumstances.

In the case of natural static, if the null of the loop is aimed in the general direction of a storm, the static level can be reduced substantially. On the West Coast, summer static seems to come from the areas of central Canada, and placing a null of the loop in that general direction reduces bothersome static by several S-units.

Best of all, the tuned receiving loop can be rotated until it provides excellent rejection of those devilish signals from local TV receiver sweep oscillators that make reception miserable during the evening hours.

In order to be effective, the receiving loop must have an electrostatic shield around it to reduce coupling to the house wiring system. Unshielded loops may provide good reception nulls as the handbooks indicate, but when used indoors, as most loops are, they readily couple to the nearby electric wiring and pick up all kinds of unwanted noise directly from the power lines. The electrostatic shield helps prevent this from happening.

A few experimenters have used loops for amateur service on 160 meters. The two proven designs discussed here are worth their weight in DXCC QSL cards if serious 160-meter operation is desired. Remember, if you can't hear 'em, you can't work 'em!

The W6PO Loop. My good friend Bob, W6PO, erected a 160-meter loaded groundplane antenna and found to his dismay that while it was a "bear-cat" for transmission, it was nearly useless for reception. All he could hear was noise.

Bob built the shielded loop shown in **Photo 5-A**. To boost the gain of the loop, a small preamplifier was added between it and the receiver. Loop Q is quite high and the background noise peaks sharply as the loop is tuned through resonance. With the values given, the loop tunes from 1.4 to 3.2 MHz. The Q of the loop and the tuning selectivity are poor above about 2.8 MHz.

The loop works extremely well sitting atop the receiver. The passband to the –3 dB points is about 20 kHz, so the loop must be accurately tuned for best signal. Null rejection is excellent and a S9+40 dB racket from a local TV receiver sweep oscillator can be knocked down to the noise level of the system, which registers about S4 during the summer daylight hours. As expected, the "nose" of the loop is quite broad, and for most reception the loop plane is left in an east-west position.

I used the loop for many months until W6PO started to make noises that he might want it back, so I decided to build my own.

The W1FB Receiving Loop for 160 Meters. The idea of bending copper tubing into a circle didn't appeal to me at all. Surely there must be a simpler way of building a shielded loop! Somewhere in the back of my mind, I remembered a *QST* article about a 160-meter loop. A quick look through the yearly indexes of *QST* revealed nothing. Finally, I started checking through the magazines issue by issue. I found what I was looking for in my July 1977 issue of *QST*. The cutesy title, which was cryptic to me, was "Beat the Noise With a Scoop Loop." This excellent review of the Doug DeMaw, W1FB, loop experiments disclosed a simple, shielded loop made of coaxial cable. **Figure 5-25** shows the electrical circuit of the loop. A quick and dirty homemade replica of the loop is now in use at W6SAI (see **Photo 5-B**).

Thrown together in one afternoon, the W1FB loop performed nearly as well as the more complex W6PO loop. Loop gain of the coaxial-cable loop was somewhat lower than that of the bigger "copper tubing" loop. Bandwidth of operation was the same when the coupling capacitor was properly adjusted (approximately 350–450 pF. Rejection of signals at right angles to the plane of the loop was excellent. The only problem with this haywire loop was that it was self-supporting. After a few days the cable would droop, and the loop would resemble a squashed hula-hoop. It was necessary to knead the cable back into the semblance of a circle—at least for aesthetics value!

Earlier articles on receiving loops had stressed that the capacitance between the loop and the shield be held at a minimum for best results. The capacitance per foot of RG-62/U cable is quite high, so a second loop was built using low-capacitance RG-58/U cable. No appreciable difference in performance could be noted when the second loop was properly adjusted, so it would seem that the W1FB loop is satisfactory as is.

The Loop Preamplifier. Either loop design provides signals to the receiver that are about 15 to 20 dB below those provided by a good outdoor antenna. Accordingly, a good low-noise preamplifier with a gain of about 20 dB is required. A representative preamplifier is shown in the W1FB article. Several are also available on the market. The unit I used, an AMECO PLF-2 which I picked up at a local flea market, is now obsolete. Other suitable units are made by MFJ and Palomar.

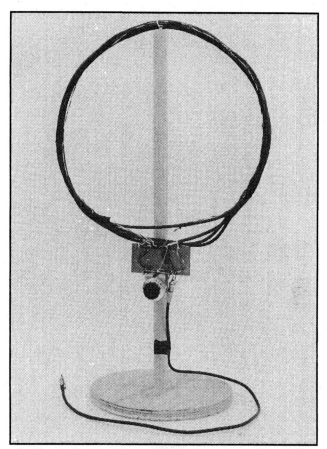

Photo 5-B. The "quick and dirty" version of the W1FB 160-meter receiving loop. The loop consists of four turns of RG-58/U coax with a one-turn pickup loop made of hookup wire. The shield of the coax line is broken at the center of the loop for 1 inch. The loop is resonated by a 500-pF capacitor (350-pF variable in parallel with 150-pF fixed). The series capacitor was replaced with a fixed capacitor when the correct degree of coupling to the preselector was determined. The loop stand is made of wood down rod and circular plate cut from plywood. Assembly time is about an hour. The compact loop sits atop the receiver.

Using the Receiving Loop. It's easy. Tune the loop and preamplifier for maximum background noise. Adjust the position of the loop for maximum rejection of line noise, or TV sweep oscillator noise. Or, if noise isn't a problem, adjust the loop for strongest received signal. As I said before, the loop pattern is extremely broad and the rejection null is very sharp. It won't take long to adjust yourself to the operation of this valuable 160-meter accessory.

Don't overcouple the loop to the preselector or you'll find it difficult to achieve loop resonance, and loop tuning will interlock with preselector tuning.

My friend Brian, K6STI, told me in a phone call that I should try the loop in a horizontal position for best noise rejection. He was right! Now I'll have to rebuild my masterpiece of precision construction.

Chapter 6

160-Meter Antennas—Simple "Top-Band" Antennas You Can Build

Any antenna design capable of working on the other high-frequency bands will operate on 160 meters. Size is the problem. A half-wavelength at 1850 kHz is 253 feet and at 1950 kHz it's 240 feet. That rules out a coax-fed dipole for most amateurs. Those lucky enough to have the room would be well advised to erect their dipole for 160 meters as high as possible.

The next best bet is an end-fed quarter-wave Marconi antenna (**Figure 6-1**). The antenna shown will operate at any frequency in the band when properly adjusted for the lowest SWR reading. The antenna uses ground as the return circuit, and one of the chief problems of achieving good performance is that of obtaining a good ground connection.

If the residential water system is made of copper pipe, it may be used for a radio ground. Connection should be made via a short, heavy lead to a nearby cold-water pipe. Flexible braid removed from a defunct length of RG-8/U coaxial cable makes a good ground lead.

Not all piping systems make a good ground, and it may be necessary to drive several rods into the earth and connect them to the water pipes. This will require some experimentation.

Another idea popular on 160 meters is the radial ground. This is an insulated wire a quarter-wavelength long (about 126 feet for operation at the low end of the band). One end of the wire is attached to the common ground point of the transmitter or ATU, and the wire is run along near (but not touching) the ground. I use a radial ground wire in conjunction with a water-pipe ground for 160-meter work, and it seems to be a good combination.

The radial ground wire can run through the bushes or along a fence. The far end of the wire should be covered with tape because it can be "hot" with RF during transmission.

Once you get on the band and make contact with a few stations, you'll find out a lot more about 160-meter antenna systems. Some of the better stations

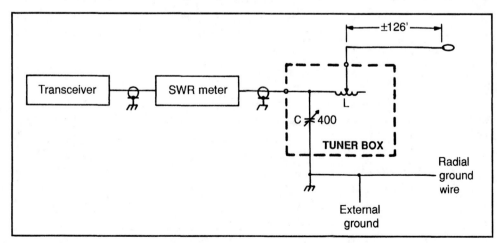

Figure 6-1. A simple Marconi antenna for 160 meters. Variable capacitor (C) is 400 pF. Inductor (L) is an airwound coil, 2 inches in diameter, 8 turns per inch, 4 inches long (32 turns). The inductor is adjusted for lowest SWR when the capacitor is adjusted to provide a 50-ohm load. Both controls may simply be adjusted for lowest SWR on the meter. The antenna wire should be as high as possible. See text for information on ground connection. Note that the antenna may be made shorter, but more inductance is required in the coil.

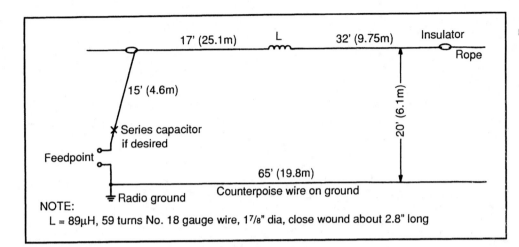

Figure 6-2. The compact 160-meter antenna at AF3V.

NOTE:
L = 89µH, 59 turns No. 18 gauge wire, 1⁷/₈" dia, close wound about 2.8" long

have quite exotic antennas. The vertical antenna is much prized; a station with a good vertical and a fine ground system can really place a big signal on the band. For everyday operation and a lot of fun, however, a simpler antenna will do the job.

When operating the 160-meter band, it's interesting to remember that the frequencies are the oldest operating range for amateur radio, and that you're following in the footsteps of a lot of famous amateurs and experimenters. No doubt, a lot of interesting experimental work is going on in this band right now. Some amateurs are experimenting with loop antennas for low-noise reception as well as with large Beverage antennas. And there are experimental beam antennas on 160 meters, too! Why not get on this exciting amateur band yourself and take part in the interesting work going on today!

A Mini-Antenna for 160 Meters

It's unfortunate that a halfwave antenna for 160 meters has to be so big. Walt Bollinger, AF3V, must have thought about this as he tried to put out a reasonable signal on the band from a small lot. His solution to this problem is shown in **Figure 6-2**. This configuration is a loaded Marconi antenna the overall length of which is about 50 feet. It's mounted about 20 feet above the ground. A 6-foot ground rod is used in conjunction with a 65-foot long counterpoise wire running beneath the antenna, just below the surface of the soil. As illustrated, the antenna operates over the range of 1.8 to 1.825 kHz with an SWR figure of 1.5:1, or less. If a variable capacitor is connected in series at the feedpoint (X), the antenna will operate over the rest of the band with low SWR. The approximate capacity necessary to achieve this without exceeding the 1.5:1 SWR is as follows: 1.85 to 1.92

MHz, 700 pF; 1.92 to 1.97 MHz, 450 pF; 1.97 to 2.00 MHz, 350 pF.

Walt uses a three-gang variable capacitor removed from an old tuned-RF broadcast receiver (QRP only). It has three 365-pF capacitors on a common shaft. "For its size," Walt says, "I think this antenna will surprise almost everyone. It seems reasonably omnidirectional and provides me with a lot of fun on the 'top band.'"

A Wire Antenna for 160, 80, 40, and 20 Meters

A friend of mine moved to a temporary location and wanted to get on the high-frequency bands with an unobtrusive antenna. He and I thought about it for a while, and finally decided on an end-fed wire working against a radial ground system (**Figure 6-3**). On 160 meters, the antenna is about 3/16 wavelength long; on 80 meters, about 3/8 wavelength; on 40 meters, 3/4 wavelength; and on 20 meters, about 3/2 wavelengths. On all bands except 160 meters, the feedpoint impedance runs between 65 and 180 ohms. On 160 meters, it's less than 10 ohms plus ground losses. Ten radials, each 50 to 60 feet long, laid upon the surface of the ground will do the job. The more radials the better.

In this particular installation, the vertical portion of the antenna is about 35 feet, or approximately a half-wavelength on 20 meters.

Since the antenna terminates just outside the radio room, the network is placed in a waterproof box that can be reached in seconds when a band change is desired.

The antenna is adjusted first on 80 meters. The terminals at A-A are shorted together with a one-turn loop and the antenna is cut for resonance at 3.5 MHz, with the aid of a dip meter. The flat-top is pruned to achieve the proper electrical length. This makes the antenna slightly short for operation on 40 and 20

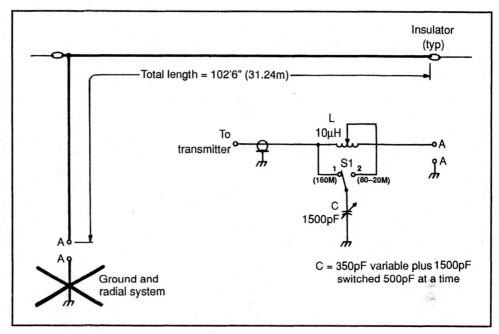

Figure 6-3. A multiband, end-fed wire antenna for 160 to 20 meters.

meters, but the L-network takes care of the situation. It also permits antenna operation at the high-frequency end of the 80-meter band with a low value of SWR at the transmitter. The L-network capacitor is reversed by S1 for 160-meter operation. The frequency response without retuning on this band is only about 25 kHz.

While its performance on 20 meters isn't equal to that of a Yagi on a 60-foot tower, this antenna does permit plenty of enjoyable QSOs in a location where a more robust and permanent antenna would be impossible to erect.

The W1BB Antenna for 160

One of the top-notch operators on 160 meters, as all "low-band" enthusiasts know, was Stew Perry, W1BB. He was working 160 DX when most of us were running around in three-cornered pants. Stew had this suggestion for a good beginner's DX antenna for 160 meters (**Figure 6-4**). It's an easy antenna to

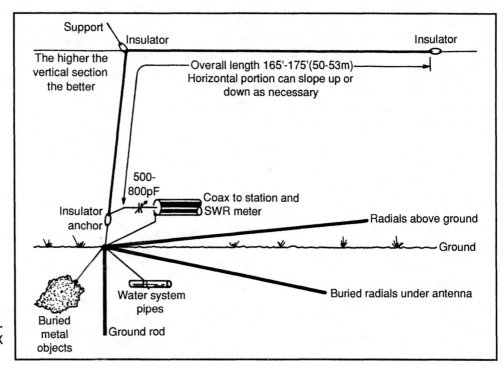

Figure 6-4. W1BB's suggestion for a good beginner's DX antenna for 160 meters.

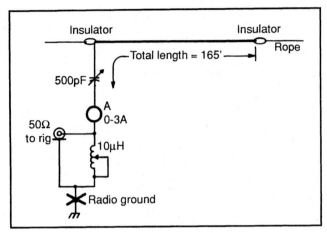

Figure 6-5. The series-tuned Marconi for 160 meters depends on a good radio ground to function properly. Don't let the power distribution ground get mixed up with the radio ground.

erect, tune-up, and load. Basically, it's about 5/8-wavelength long and works against a ground connection. The length is chosen to provide as high an input impedance as possible, consistent with a simple matching system. Nothing could be simpler than this match—a single series-connected capacitor.

The antenna consists of a 40- to 50-foot vertical wire top-loaded by a horizontal wire about 120 feet long. Overall wire length should run from 165 to 175 feet. The higher the vertical portion, the better the antenna will work.

As with the old Marconi antenna, ground-system efficiency is important. W1BB used several 8-foot ground rods and a nearby buried water-pipe system, and had several buried ground radial wires. For good luck, he added several above-ground radials. Stew said, "The better the ground system, the better the results!"

A low-voltage variable capacitor of about 700 pF is placed in a waterproof box at the base of the antenna. Simply tune the capacitor for lowest SWR at your favorite operating frequency in the 160-meter band. The far end of the wire may then be pruned for lowest SWR, if desired.

Stew said that with a good ground system, this antenna is almost as good as a quarter-wave vertical with an elaborate ground system. Best of all, it's not as noisy on reception as a straight vertical. Stew tested the antenna in many DX openings, and many 160-meter operators remember his outstanding signal.

The "Radio Ground" on 160 Meters

My good friend W1BB was an avid 160-meter operator. He once told me that a fine "top-band" compro-

mise antenna for hams with little space was an extended Marconi working against a good ground system. Taking his advice, I put up a 165-foot, series-tuned long wire (resonant at 1500 kHz) working against ground (**Figure 6-5**). The ground consisted of the cold-water copper pipes in the house, plus two ground rods—one at each end of the house—and a single quarter-wave radial wire running through the bushes about two feet above ground.

This antenna worked quite well. However, when I went on 160, the ceiling light in the family room lit up! Obviously, the RF was getting into the house wiring somehow.

Using an MFJ-206 Antenna Current Probe tuned to 160 meters, I started "sniffing" the house wiring for RF energy. Aha! I could put the transmitter on low power, lock the key, walk through the house with the probe, and actually trace the electric wires hidden in the walls. The house's whole electrical system was "hot" with RF.

My first thought was that the wiring was picking up induced RF energy merely by being in the near field of the antenna. But the amount of RF measured seemed too high, considering the physical separation of the Marconi antenna from the house. If this wasn't the pick-up path, what was?

The probe indicated that the power cable to the transceiver was full of RF energy. Most confusing. The rig actually had two grounds on it, didn't it? They were the radio ground system I installed, plus the neutral and ground conductors of the power line. A little thought revealed the problem.

Separating the Radio and Electrical Grounds. **Figure 6-6** shows that two ground points exist: the intentional radio ground at the equipment, and the elec-

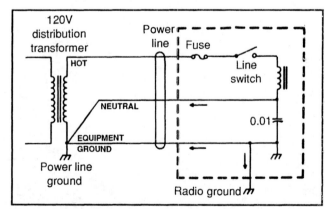

Figure 6-6. RF ground currents reach the earth via the equipment power line as well as by the radio ground (arrows). RF and radio grounds should be decoupled by placing an RF choke in the power line.

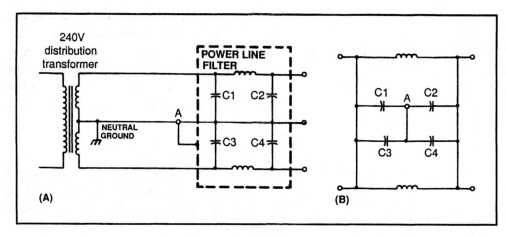

Figure 6-7. (A) A typical power-line filter. If a metal box is used, it is grounded to the neutral wire. (B) If RF impedance of the power line is high at the operating frequency, the ground return point *A* is not at ground potential and the line capacitors act as bypasses around the line chokes.

trical ground at the power distribution transformer. The latter also serves as a radio ground, as RF ground currents in the antenna circuit return via both paths. The unwanted path through the power cable is closely coupled to the other power conductors and feeds RF energy into them. And, if the power wiring has appreciable impedance at 160 meters, any RF fed into the power line can wander into some very unlikely places.

My solution was to wind the line cord of the transceiver around a ferrite rod (Amidon R-33-050-750) 7-1/2 inches long and 1/2 inch in diameter. This was held in place by two plastic cable wraps. The RF antenna current immediately increased 30 percent (!) after the line choke was installed. Encouraged by this success, I took an 8-foot extension cord, wrapped it around a second ferrite rod, and placed it in series with the first line choke. This increased the antenna current an additional 5 percent and the family room light did not go on when I hit the key.

I sniffed the house wiring with the probe again. There was still a little RF present, but it was greatly reduced. It looked as if the problem had been solved.

Problems with a Linear Amplifier. Now that everything had cooled off, I decided to put my 160-meter homemade linear amplifier on the air. It used a single 3-500Z and ran about 1-kW PEP input.

As I fired it up, a loud cry came from the other end of the house. The family-room lights magically turned themselves on, along with the light in the entry hall!

Since I had used up all my ferrite rods, I looked in the junk box and found a fine industrial RF filter for the 240-volt line. It was a well-known brand built in a nice plastic box with heavy conductors on each end (**Figure 6-7A**). Unfortunately, placing it in the power line to the amplifier made no difference in the amount of RF in that line. It seemed that the impedance of the power-line neutral wire was sufficiently high at 160

meters to allow the neutral to rise above RF ground at the filter. If this guess was correct, the capacitors in the filter served merely to bypass the RF around the line chokes (**Figure 6-7B**).

Grounding the common point of the capacitors to the radio ground at the amplifier helped but did not solve the problem. Now the amplifier had a radio ground point, plus two power-line ground points— one at the distribution transformer and a second at the transmitter radio ground. This complex grounding situation left me uneasy, so I tossed out the 240-volt line filter and wrapped the power cord to the amplifier around two ferrite rods held together with plastic tape. (I used two rods because the amplifier power cable was heavy and difficult to wrap around a single rod.)

I was happy to note that the lights no longer came on as I keyed the amplifier. All was as it should be. Thus, I learned that when a Marconi antenna is used, the ground system may be more complex than it looks. It's important to decouple the power line from the RF ground system, and the easiest way to do this is to wrap the power cable around a ferrite rod. The old-style line filter made up of inductors and capacitors just doesn't do the job if the neutral line is used as the filter return ground point.

Another Inexpensive 160-Meter Antenna That Works

No room for a quarter-wave vertical with 120 radials for 160-meter DX work? Too bad. Join me in crying the blues! About the best I can do is a random-length wire running from the house to my nearby antenna tower. I work it against the house's plumbing system as a ground. Recently, I added two 8-foot ground rods, one at each end of the house, and tied them to the copper water-pipe system. So far, so good.

After I'd been working with various end-fed antenna

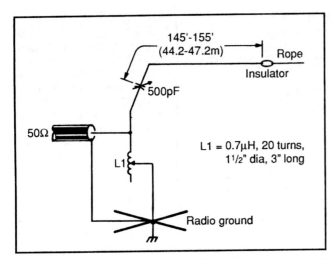

Figure 6-8. A simple end-fed 160-meter antenna and matching system.

systems for over six months, the backyard was littered with bits of copper wire. I finally ended up with a wire antenna that worked well, although not quite as well as the antennas the "big guns" were using. But if you share my problem of limited space and don't want to grow an antenna farm, this antenna is ideal for you.

Basically, it's a wire about 155 feet long. This makes it longer than a quarter-wavelength at 1.8 MHz. The feedpoint impedance of the longer wire is inductive and slightly higher than that of the quarter-wave wire. The inductive reactance is tuned out by a series-connected capacitor, and the feedpoint resistance of the antenna (about 23 ohms) is transformed by a shunt inductor to 50 ohms (**Figure 6-8**).

This design provides an inexpensive matching system to provide a 50-ohm feedpoint, required by today's modern transceivers. Solid-state amplifiers aren't very forgiving with respect to oddball antenna feedpoint impedances, and operation of the 160-meter band stretches the capability of these amplifiers—even under the best conditions.

My wire antenna solves that problem. You can change the antenna length and compensate for it with the variable capacitor. As the antenna is shortened toward the quarter-wavelength point, the capacitor value increases. As the antenna approaches three-quarter-wave resonance, the value of the capacitor diminishes. A happy medium is reached when the antenna is about 0.275 wavelength long. If the inductor and capacitor are variable, the operator can scoot from one end of the band to the other in just a few seconds.

Operational bandwidth of the antenna is quite good; an SWR of better than 1.5:1 can be maintained over 50 kHz without touching the network controls. I tune

up at 1825 kHz and am able to QSY up and down 25 kHz at the touch of the transceiver dial.

How well does it work? Well, I'll let you know after the next 160-meter DX contest! So far, it seems to be the best wire I've ever had on the "top band."

Building the Tuner

You can build the tuner on a metal chassis and panel, but it's not necessary (**Photo 6-A**). My tuner is built on a plywood base with a masonite panel. The unit is 8 × 8 inches. I recommend using a vernier drive on the capacitor because the setting for lowest SWR is quite sharp. The setting of the shunt inductor, on the other hand, is less critical and the counter dial is a luxury. The 3-ampere RF thermocouple meter is very handy for tuneup, so if you can find one at a flea market, buy it and use it. I short out mine with a clip lead after tuneup to keep the meter from jumping around when I'm transmitting.

A Compact 160-Meter Marconi Antenna

When you haven't room for a big antenna, small is best. You may not be Number One on the frequency with a small antenna, but you're on the air and can enjoy yourself.

Here's a design for a coil-loaded Marconi antenna for the "top band" (**Figure 6-9**). The antenna is self-resonant at 2 MHz with the center loading coil L1.

Photo 6-A. The W6SAI tuner is built on a plywood base with a Masonite panel.

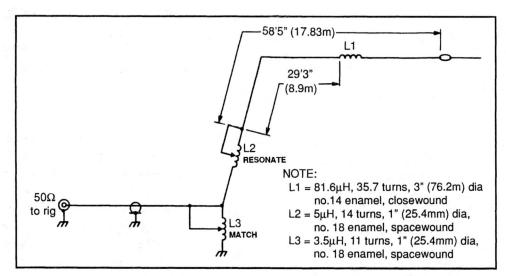

Figure 6-9. A compact Marconi-type antenna for the 160-meter band. Best results will be obtained with maximum amount of antenna wire in the vertical plane. The height of the horizontal portion should be at least 25 feet.

NOTE:
L1 = 81.6µH, 35.7 turns, 3" (76.2m) dia
    no.14 enamel, closewound
L2 = 5µH, 14 turns, 1" (25.4mm) dia,
    no. 18 enamel, spacewound
L3 = 3.5µH, 11 turns, 1" (25.4mm) dia,
    no. 18 enamel, spacewound

Series coil L2 at the feedpoint drops the resonant frequency as low as 1.8 MHz, and shunt coil L3 provides a match to a 50-ohm feedpoint.

An antenna can't be much simpler than this one. Its overall length is only 58.5 feet. The antenna is bent into an "L" shape, with the horizontal portion 25 to 30 feet above ground. It has been used with success with the continuous copper plumbing system of the house acting as ground.

Adjustment is simple. Coil L2 tunes the antenna to resonance and coil L3 provides the correct impedance transformation to a 50-ohm feedpoint. The adjustments are slightly interdependent, but can quickly be accomplished with the aid of an SWR meter. Antenna operating bandwidth between the 2:1 SWR points on the feedline is about 50 kHz.

The K4EF Antenna and Tuner

The "all-band" wire antenna and tuner designed by Ev Brown, K4EF, performs well on bands between 160 and 10 meters (**Figure 6-10**). The antenna consists of a 200-foot wire, with 50 feet in the vertical plane and the remainder run horizontally to a nearby tiepoint. The antenna works against ground in Marconi fashion. Ev originally used a single ground rod, but later laid out a ground screen beneath the antenna consisting of 1000 feet of no. 14 wire forming a mat about 20 feet wide and parallel to the horizontal portion of the overhead wire. After all this effort, he could detect no change in performance!

One reason efficiency is high is that the feedpoint resistance of the antenna is about 100 ohms at 3.5 MHz and nearly 4000 ohms at 1.8 MHz. The feedpoint is very "hot" on the 160- and 80-meter bands, and a high-voltage, transmitting-type capacitor is required to prevent flashover. Toroidal coils, wound on several stacked Amidon T-200 forms, were tried but proved unsatisfactory because of heating and inductance drift. The solution was the use of air-wound inductors.

Generally speaking, the tuner will tune any length of wire over 40 feet long at 7 MHz or higher, provided the wire is not a quarter-wavelength long. The antenna feedpoint resistance must be higher than 50 ohms in order to allow the tuner to do its job.

If the antenna is used exclusively on 160 meters, the antenna length can be chosen to match available com-

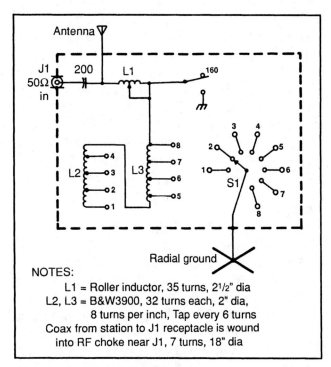

NOTES:
    L1 = Roller inductor, 35 turns, 2¹/₂" dia
L2, L3 = B&W3900, 32 turns each, 2" dia,
        8 turns per inch, Tap every 6 turns
Coax from station to J1 receptacle is wound
    into RF choke near J1, 7 turns, 18" dia

Figure 6-10. The K4EF wire tuner.

ponents. For example, if the tuner capacitor is only 200 pF, antenna length should be increased to about 210 feet. The coil inductance must by increased to about 80 turns (40 µH). Conversely, if a 1000-pF capacitor is available and you want to reduce the length of the antenna, a length of 175 feet is appropriate.

Ev says this antenna is outstanding on 160, 80, and 40 meters because the current loop is quite high in the air. On the higher bands, he's often able to compete with the "big boys" and frequently raises DX stations on the first or second call.

Ev likes the antenna so well he never got around to erecting his "Christmas tree" stack of Yagi beams on his 50-foot tower!

K1LPS on Radials ("On the Other Hand . . .")

One of the top DXers on 160 meters is K1LPS. Larry advises against being fooled by claims stating that a good ground (radial) system isn't required on 160 meters. "While a station using a vertical without radials will work stuff," he says, "a station using the same vertical with a good radial system will consistently outperform the equivalent antenna without radials on a given path."

K1LPS started out with an "L" antenna about 45 feet high with the end 90 feet running horizontally—quite a typical 160-meter antenna for the lean purse. He began with a single ground rod, plus four radials, none of which were more than 60 feet long. However, he found that results improved markedly as he improved his ground system. "The antenna was certainly not a pileup-beater by any means, but I eventually got there," he comments.

Encouraged by these results, Larry put up a better antenna. It was an L-shape, with 66 feet vertical and the remainder horizontal. He made careful measurements as he laid in a ground system, bit by bit. Starting out with a ground rod and four quarter-wave radials, he measured his feedpoint resistance as 45 ohms. Bandwidth between the 1.5:1 SWR points was about 70 kHz.

He next added 18 additional quarter-wave radials. The feedpoint resistance dropped to 38 ohms and the 1.5:1 passband disappeared, because the minimum value of SWR at antenna resonance was 1.6:1! Before he built a matching network, he added ten more radials, bringing the feedpoint resistance down to about 22 ohms. Using a fixed matching network, K1LPS achieved a match of unity at 1820 kHz, but the antenna bandwidth between the 1.5:1 SWR points had dropped to 40 kHz.

These various changes took place over an extended period of time. Signal reports were solicited from many stations at various distances each night after additions to the ground system. A good many hams kept track of Larry's progress, and there was a noticeable improvement as radials were added. After much work, it was

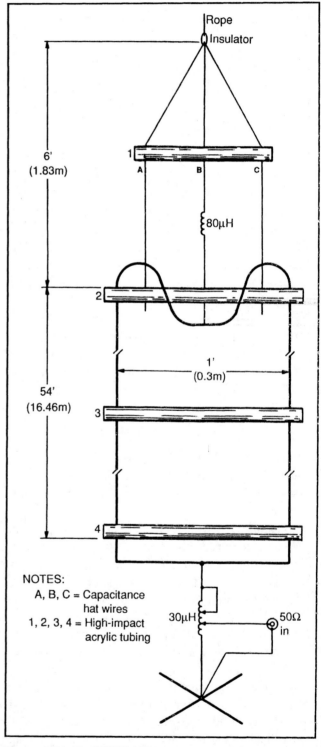

Figure 6-11. The W1FB 160-meter monopole antenna.

concluded that more than 44 radials didn't seem to make much difference. Finally, thanks to all his work, K1LPS made that elusive Japanese contact!

K1LPS says, "Yes, you can get by without radials. But if you want to work long-haul DX, find a way to get a good ground system installed. That's the difference between a passable signal and a pile-up breaker!"

In closing, Larry remarks, "A poor ground system has one thing going for it—a nice broad SWR curve across a relatively wide frequency range. But, then, so does a dummy load!"

The W1FB 160-Meter Monopole

Because it's difficult to be loud on 160 meters when you live on a city lot, I've long envied those lucky hams who live on country estates, with acres of land at their disposal. My good friend Doug, W1FB, pondered the problem and finally came up with a compact monopole antenna design that solves this problem for amateurs who can find 60 feet of space either straight up, horizontal, or at an angle (**Figure 6-11**).

Basically, the antenna is a "fat" monopole, top-loaded with an inductor and a capacitance hat. An arrangement such as this could end up being a rat's nest, but Doug has engineered the design through several models and arrived at a clean, compact, rugged package that's easy to install and adjust. Eighteen radials, each 130 feet long, are laid out beneath the antenna. The spacers are made of high-impact acrylic tubing and the array is made of no. 14 wire. Slung up in the clear, the measured SWR of the antenna between the 2:1 SWR points is 165 kHz. That's not too shabby for such a compact antenna!

More on the 160-Meter End-fed Antenna

Previously, I mentioned my long, 160-meter end-fed antenna, series-tuned with a capacitor and matched to 50 ohms with a shunt coil. I've had it on the air for some weeks now and find it the best antenna I've been able to put up on this particular piece of property, considering the zoning restrictions. The best DX to date has been Japan and Siberia, zone 19.

For those who have less space, the quarter-wave Marconi is still a good antenna. It can easily be matched to a 50-ohm feed system using the technique shown in **Figure 6-12**. The antenna is cut to your favorite operating frequency in the band by the formula length = 234/f(MHz). For 1825 kHz, the antenna is about 128 feet long. If the antenna is entirely vertical (an unlikely assumption), the feedpoint resistance

(R) at resonance will be about 36 ohms. As more and more of the antenna lies in the horizontal plane, the feedpoint resistance decreases. In my tests, with most of the antenna wire running horizontally about 40 feet above ground, the feedpoint resistance runs close to 15 ohms.

You see that a simple L-network (A), made up of a series-connected coil and a shunt capacitor, can be used. The coil is quite small, but the capacitor value is rather large. The coil can be a small B & W "Mini-ductor" about 2 inches in diameter, with a tapping clip for adjustment. Only 2.5 µH is required to do the job under all circumstances (see the chart in **Figure 6-12**). Note that maximum inductance is required when the feedpoint resistance is one-half the value of the input resistance of the network.

The tapped coil presents no problem, but obtaining the shunt capacitor can be vexing. Most end-fed 160-meter Marconi antennas fall into a feedpoint resistance range of 10 to 25 ohms. This calls for a shunt-capacitor value of approximately 3500 to 1500 pF. The total capacitance can be made up of several "postage stamp" silver mica capacitors placed in parallel with a large variable capacitor. In my case, I had a 900-pF variable capacitor picked up at a flea market and a rotary switch that adds fixed capacitance at 500 pF per switch position.

This combination allows excellent antenna matching to be obtained all across the 160-meter band. I use

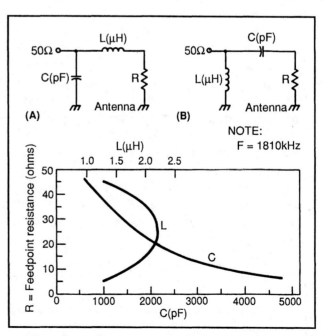

Figure 6-12. L-network components for 160 meters and a chart to determine component values for networks A and B.

an SWR meter to determine antenna match (the meter being placed between the network and the short coax line to the transmitter). A practice run, tuning up every 25 kHz across the band, provides logging points for the coil and capacitor settings, so no time is lost when I want to QSY from 1810 kHz to work a UAØ calling CQ on 1915 kHz.

The chart also shows why it's sometimes difficult to get a good match to a low-frequency mobile antenna. The matching coil becomes quite small for low values of feedpoint resistance and the shunt capacitor becomes quite large!

The 160-Meter Compact Dipole

Have you heard the DX coming through on the 160-meter band? Would you like to work some of it? A great idea, but a lot of would-be "top-band" DXers pause when they consider that a 1/2-wave dipole antenna is about 246 feet long when cut for the midpoint of the band. And while a vertical antenna would be appropriate, it requires a good ground connection and a system of buried radials.

An effective alternative is a short, coil-loaded dipole antenna. By reducing the dipole to half size, about 130 feet, the antenna becomes more feasible for the ham who lives on a medium-sized lot. A loaded antenna can be just about any length, however, if a compromise among length, efficiency, and bandwidth can be accepted. Bandwidth and efficiency drop sharply when the loaded dipole is much less than 1/4-wavelength long.

The bandwidth of a full-size 160-meter dipole mounted close to the ground (40 to 60 feet high) is quite narrow—only about 150 kHz between the 2:1 SWR points on the passband. Shortening the dipole and loading it to resonance sharpens the passband. The antenna design shown in **Figure 6-13** has a passband of about 50 kHz between the 2:1 SWR points. That's the penalty you pay to get a compact antenna on 160 meters! You can make the dipole shorter with larger loading coils, but your operating passband will shrink until it becomes impractically narrow.

Simplifying the Design. Table 6-1 reveals a num-

Design Frequency	Overall length (S)	Length center-to-coil (D)
1.80 MHz	130.0 ft.	32.5 ft.
1.85 MHz	126.5 ft.	31.6 ft.
1.90 MHz	123.2 ft.	30.8 ft.
1.95 MHz	120.0 ft.	30.0 ft.
2.00 MHz	117.0 ft.	29.3 ft.

Loading Coil (L1)	Turns (L1)	Matching coil (L2)	Turns (L2)
91.9 µH	38.9	3.9 µH	11.6
89.2 µH	38.0	3.8 µH	11.3
86.5 µH	37.2	3.7 µH	11.1
84.0 µH	36.4	3.6 µH	11.0
81.6 µH	35.7	3.5 µH	10.8

Notes:
Dimensions rounded to nearest tenth.
Coil L1 diameter = 3 inches. Use no. 14 wire, close-spaced.
Coil L1 length = approximately 2.5 inches.
Coil L2 diameter = 1 inch. Use no. 18 wire, close-spaced.
Operating bandwidth = 50 kHz between 2:1 SWR points.
Adjust tip sections for antenna resonance.
Adjust coil L2 for best match at resonant frequency.

Table 6-1. Coverage of the entire 160-meter band requires changing dimensions and component values.

ber of interesting points. Overall antenna length varies from 130 feet at the low end of the band to 117 feet at the top end. That's a difference of 13 feet. The center-to-coil distance also changes appreciably (from 32.5 to 29.3 feet). The loading coil (L1) inductance changes only slightly as the number of turns changes from 38.9 to 35.7. And, the matching coil at the center of the antenna changes hardly at all.

It seems to me that things could be simplified by using the center-band design (1.90 MHz) and then varying the resonant frequency of the antenna merely by changing the length of the tip sections. Leave all the other dimensions alone. Fold-back tip sections can be wrapped around the antenna wire and then unwrapped and left to hang down when operation is desired over a lower frequency range.

Adjusting the Antenna. Accepting the 1.90 MHz dimensions as par, then, what's to be done? The antenna is built, erected in place, and lowered so that a

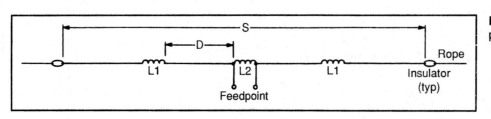

Figure 6-13. The 160-meter compact dipole (see Table 6-1).

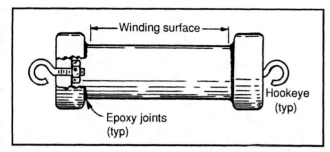

Figure 6-14. The loading coil is made up of PVC-type plastic pipe and end caps. Hookeyes permit connection to the antenna wire.

dip-meter can be coupled to the matching coil, L2. The end sections of the antenna are trimmed equally until resonance is established at 1.90 MHz, or at any other point you decide is your favorite operating frequency. (The feedline is removed for this test.)

Once the antenna resonance is determined, matching coil L2 is adjusted, a quarter-turn at a time, for the lowest SWR indication on the feedline at the frequency of antenna resonance. The antenna must be in the final operating position when this is done.

Building the Antenna. The loading and matching coils can be made up easily using PVC tubing, as shown in **Figure 6-14**. If the coils are given a good coat of acrylic spray, they'll be weatherproof. Some detuning may be noticed in damp or wet weather, or if snow clings to the coils.

The Low-Frequency DX Antenna at VE7BS

Bob, VE7BS, uses an inverted-V antenna with the apex at 105 feet and the ends at about 60 feet (**Figure**

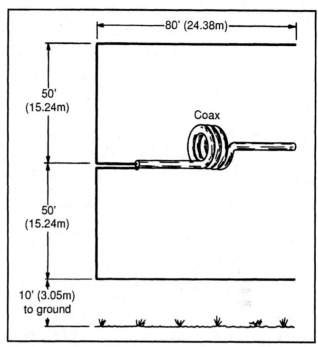

Figure 6-16. The VE7BS "Lazy-U" antenna for 160 meters.

6-15). This is his "comparison antenna" for the others he has experimented with from time to time. Bob says it's broadside to Australia and Europe, but works reasonably well in all directions. Three parallel wires are used in each leg, and the coax feedline is wound into an RF choke just below the feedpoint of the antenna.

Another 160-meter antenna VE7BS has used with success is the so-called "Lazy-U," shown in **Figure 6-16**. The vertical portion can be from 50 to 100 feet long, with the horizontal portions bringing the system

Figure 6-15. The inverted-V antenna for 160 meters at VE7BS. The wires all lie in the same plane. The apex is at 105 feet.

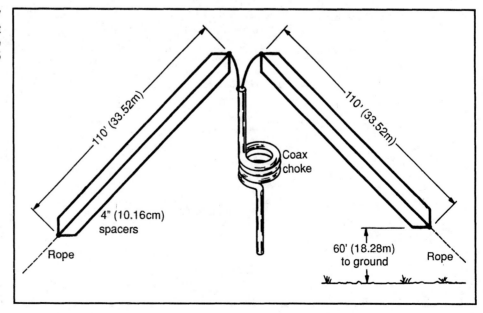

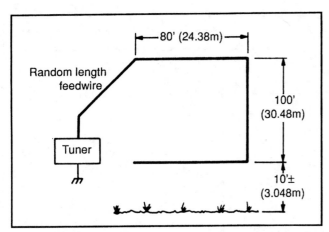

Figure 6-17. The G8ON vertically polarized antenna. The vertical section can be as short as 33 feet.

to resonance without contributing much horizontally polarized radiation. The VE7BS "Lazy-U" worked better than the inverted-V in some direction, and this was the antenna he used to land 5N8ARY (Nigeria).

An interesting adaptation of this vertical antenna that some 160-meter DXers use is the so-called "G8ON" antenna, named after the amateur who popularized it on the band (**Figure 6-17**). The antenna is a half-wavelength long, with the high-current portion in the vertical plane. The wire is end-fed from the top end.

VE7BS has some interesting remarks about radial systems as applied to 160-meter antennas. He advises the 160-meter operator not to worry too much about extensive radial systems. He says: "I managed WAC on 160 meters with a vertical without any radials, and K7VIC has one of the most potent signals on the band using a vertical top-loaded monopole without radials, so I wouldn't get depressed if I had no room for radials. For transmitting, I see nothing wrong with a 45-foot tower, top-loaded with a Yagi, working against a few properly disposed 8-foot ground rods near the base

and a cluster of short radials or chicken-wire mesh under the tower. As far as I can see, the main disadvantage of a relatively short, loaded vertical is the narrow bandwidth achieved without retuning." (Obviously, there are a lot of different opinions on the use of radials! If you have the ground space, I recommend you use as many as you can.)

The P29BR Antenna

Here's a simple 160-meter DX antenna (sketched in **Figure 6-18**) used by Bob Parkes, P29BR. Basically, it's a short, vertical antenna top-loaded by a single wire and inductively coupled by a toroid transformer to a coax line.

Bob recommends using from 25 to 40 radials. In his particular location, taking ground resistance into account, he estimates the antenna's efficiency to be about 40 percent.

With regard to the radials, few amateurs can lay out 135-foot, quarter-wavelength, 160-meter radials. The solution is just to do the best you can. Several ground rods at the antenna feedpoint are useful, as is a square of 1-inch mesh chicken wire laid on the ground. Dennis Peterson, N7CKD, uses a 30-foot square of chicken wire for a 160-meter ground screen, plus other random ground connections to a metal fence.

A Very Compact Dipole Antenna for 160 Meters

You can't get a full-size dipole up on 160 meters? You have a poor ground? You can't make a low-resistance ground connection? Join the club! Most amateurs have one or more of these problems. Unless you live in the middle of a large salt marsh, you're going to have to make compromises in your "top band" antenna system.

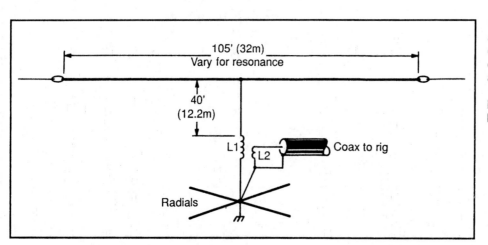

Figure 6-18. The 160-meter antenna at P29BR. L1 is 28 turns of no. 14 enamel; L2 is 20 turns of no. 14 enamel. Both L1 and L2 are wound on a 2-inch toroid, μ = 10 (Amidon T-200-2, or equivalent). Vary the turns of L2 for the best match.

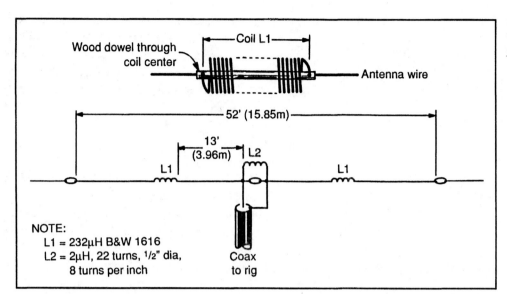

Figure 6-19. Assembly data for the 160-meter "mini-dipole."

Some lucky amateurs have enough space to squeeze in a large vertical antenna and lay out a number of radials. Others can erect loaded dipoles, or some form of Marconi antenna with a good ground system. What about the rest of us?

A friend of mine wanted to get on 160 meters. He had about 55 × 25 feet in his backyard to work with, and his ground was terrible—rocky, sandy soil.

The only simple solution I saw was to erect a highly loaded dipole antenna about 50 feet long. That would fit in the available space, and the dipole doesn't rely upon a ground connection to function properly. Such an antenna is shown in **Figure 6-19**.

The design is based upon a high-efficiency loading coil. This coil is air-wound, 2 inches in diameter and 10 inches long. It has 16 turns per inch of tinned copper wire. Two of these coils are used in this antenna, one in the middle of each leg. Because the coils are somewhat fragile, they're supported on an insulator made of a wooden dowel rod cut to the same length as the coil. The ends of the antenna wires are passed through small holes drilled in the dowel, removing tension from the concentric coil.

The radiation resistance of the antenna is about 3 ohms, but the feedpoint resistance is close to 20 ohms, due to the loss of the coils. This results in an antenna efficiency of about 13 percent. This may make purists who have experienced little loss in their high-frequency antennas shudder, but the 160-meter band is a different matter, and most of the small antennas used by amateurs on this band exhibit a comparable degree of efficiency. The radiated signal, then, is about 8 dB down from that of a 100-percent efficient antenna (a dipole, for example).

A simple matching coil is placed at the center of the antenna to match it to a 50-ohm coax line. When properly adjusted, the antenna has a bandwidth of about 25 kHz between the 2:1 SWR points on the feedline.

Antenna Adjustment. The first step after building the antenna is to sling it up between two temporary points, allowing it to sag down until the center feedpoint can be reached safely from the top of a step ladder. The halves of the antenna then are shunted with a two- or three-turn link coupled to a dip oscillator. The resonant frequency of the antenna is carefully measured (with the aid of a calibrated receiver) and the antenna tip sections trimmed equally, a few inches at a time, until the antenna is resonant at your design frequency. (This one was cut for 1820 kHz.)

The pickup coil is removed and another coil is installed for matching the antenna to the coax feedline. The antenna is erected in its final operating position. The number of turns in the matching coil is then adjusted until unity SWR is obtained at some frequency near the design frequency. You'll find that the presence of the coil tends to detune the antenna a bit, and by the time you've achieved a good match, the resonant frequency of the antenna will have moved. The final step is to readjust the tip sections equally until the resonant frequency is back where you want it.

The whole process sounds tedious, but it's really not. The experimental antenna was built at an easy pace over one weekend and all adjustments were made during one morning of the following weekend. And the antenna works fine! Granted, bandwidth of operation is restricted and antenna efficiency is low. However, running 150 watts input, contacts across the continent have been made on the band, and unless

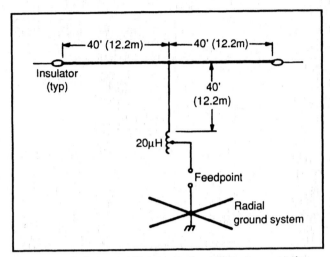

Figure 6-20. Compact T-antenna for 160-meter operation.

attention is drawn to the unusual antenna, most operators "on the other end" will assume you have a full-sized dipole, judging from the reports my friend has received with his little antenna.

Using an Antenna Tuner. Smart 160-meter operators know that a narrowband antenna such as this compact dipole can be "pulled" in frequency by using an antenna tuner at the station end of the coax feedline. The very high off-resonance SWR exhibited by the antenna can be reduced to an acceptable value by the tuner. Experiments have shown that the antenna, with a simple tuner, permits operation over 100 kHz of the 160-meter band—not bad for such a midget!

Keep TVI to a Minimum! Words of caution on this familiar topic: try *not* to run the antenna parallel to the house wiring system. It's easy to couple power from any 160-meter antenna into the house electrical wiring, but doing this can cause TVI, RFI, and other undesired reactions. In addition, because the coil loss of the antenna is high, don't try to run a lot of power into it. A good limiting figure for this antenna is 150 watts, so it will work okay with your exciter, but you'll burn up your antenna coils if you run your linear amplifier into it.

A T-Antenna for 160

Figure 6-20 shows a top-loaded vertical antenna used by some operators who are trying to be loud even though they live on small lots. In most cases, it's made of wire and slung between two trees. The 40-foot vertical wire is attached to the midpoint of an 80-foot wire that serves as the top-loading structure. The antenna is worked against ground, and resonated to

the operating frequency by means of the series-connected rotary inductor. The feedpoint resistance depends upon the ground resistance, as is the case with any Marconi-type antenna. With a ground system consisting of a ground rod, or connection to the cold-water-pipe system of the dwelling, plus two or three quarter-wave radials, the feedpoint resistance will run about 20 ohms. A simple L-network may be required between the coax feedline and transmitter to drop the SWR to a low enough value to permit an easy match to today's modern solid-state equipment.

With regard to the ground system for a 160-meter Marconi-type antenna, Mitch, KB6FPW, has some interesting experiences to relate. He erected an inverted-L antenna (imagine the antenna of **Figure 6-20** with half the top wire removed). The wire was cut to a total length of 3/8 wavelength at 1.9 MHz. Most of the wire was in the horizontal plane.

Mitch's first RF measurements, using water-pipe grounds, showed a feedpoint resistance of 100 ohms. Addition of a 4-foot ground rod and a quarter-wave radial wire, wrapped around the perimeter of a fence and terminated in another 4-foot ground rod, brought the feedpoint resistance down to about 50 ohms. Mitch next added several extra radials of various lengths and a third ground rod. The feedpoint resistance dropped to 40 ohms. A second quarter-wave radial wrapped around the house didn't seem to make an appreciable difference. Mitch figured he had reached the point of diminishing returns, and there the experiment ended.

Mitch says, "There is a common misconception about ground radials. It's often said that a quarter-wave radial looks like a low impedance at the input. If a short circuit (to ground) was applied to the far end of the radial, a high impedance would be reflected back to the input end. In free space this may be true, but when the radial is brought in close proximity to the ground, significant coupling exists—enough to change the character of the radial. Terminating a quarter-wave radial, laid close to the earth, with a ground rod at the outer end does not reflect a high impedance back to the input end. Instead, it improves the efficiency of the radial and actually lowers its impedance.

"Electrically short radials depend upon proximity to the earth. I have performed experiments on 1750 meters with a 100-foot radial. When the wire was held clear of the ground (at about 4 or 5 feet elevation), the radial current was unmeasurable with a 100-mA RF ammeter. As the radial was lowered to the earth, the radial current climbed to a maximum figure of 8.5 mA."

A "Rubber Duckie" for 160 Meters

The ham who lives on a small, treeless lot faces a real problem when contemplating 160-meter operation. One solution to this problem is a vertical antenna, but a quarter-wave vertical antenna on "top band" is over 130 feet high. Joe Moraski, KY3F, has a solution to the problem. He recommends a helix antenna operating in the normal mode—that is, a coil with small diameter compared to the operating wavelength. Maximum radiation is *normal* to the axis, hence the name. This is the same mode of operation as that of the 2-meter "rubber duckie" antennas used on handhelds.

There are no hard and fast rules about the length or diameter of this antenna. The rule of thumb is about a half-wavelength of wire is used to make the helix.

Antenna size is a matter of tradeoffs. The shorter and thinner the helix, the narrower the bandwidth. The longer and thicker it is, the harder it is to build and keep up in the air! A shorter helix is less efficient—consequently, the longer the better.

Since the helix bandwidth is narrow, a top hat is added to reduce antenna Q and add capacitance at the high-voltage point. The resulting reduction in circuit Q causes the feedpoint impedance at the antenna base to vary less rapidly with frequency change than the unloaded antenna. This means that the antenna can be used over a larger portion of the band than would otherwise be possible.

By experimentation, Joe found that a 20-foot antenna was a good operating compromise. Accordingly, he used two 12-foot sections of 4-inch diameter PVC water pipe cemented together with a coupler to make a 24-foot mast. He wound no. 18 insulated hookup wire on it at ten turns per inch spacing (**Photo 6-B**). This helix, in combination with a screen-wire capacitance hat on top, resonated in the 160-meter band when operated against a ground rod and quarter-wave counterpoise wire run around the backyard. Four 30-foot radials were added. A sketch of the antenna is shown in **Figure 6-21**.

Construction is simple if done in the proper sequence. The first step is to drill holes for the end tie bolts that terminate the winding. The holes are 10 feet apart. Galvanized bolts are used, with washers on each side of the PVC pipe. With a tape measure and felt-tip pen, make small marks at 1-inch intervals between the bolts. Next, fasten an eye lug to one end of a 140-foot length of no. 18 insulated wire. Fasten the lug to one bolt and wind the coil on the PVC pipe, using the pen marks as a guide—one turn per mark.

Photo 6-B. Base assembly of the KY3F vertical antenna for 160 meters. Final frequency adjustment is made by varying the number of turns at the bottom of the helix.

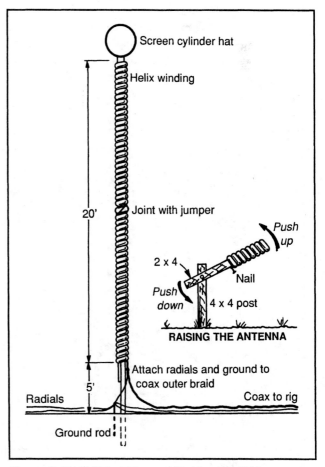

Figure 6-21. KY3F's 160-meter "Rubber Duckie."

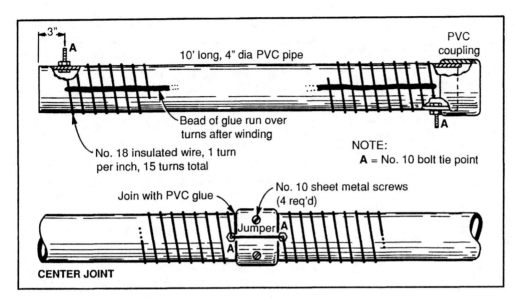

Figure 6-22. Mechanical details of the coil sections.

Use tape to hold the coil in place as you progress along the form. Wind the wire as tightly as you can, and when you reach the second terminating bolt, cut the wire and place an eye lug on the end that will fit over the bolt. With the winding properly spaced, run a bead of RTV along the length of pipe over the coil turns to lock them in place.

You have now completed half the antenna. Continue by winding a second similar coil on the second section of PVC pipe, making sure that both coils are wound in the same direction (left- or right-hand turns, but make sure they're both the same).

Now join the two pipe sections with the plastic splice section and PVC cement. Align them quickly and let the joint dry (**Figure 6-22**). Some PVC pipes have a built-in coupling joint—nice if you can locate one. For added strength, run four no. 10 self-tapping sheet-metal screws through the joints where the PVC pipes and splice section overlap. Finally, connect a wire jumper between the two coils to form one 20-foot coil.

The next step is to make the "top hat" (**Figure 6-23**). A section of 1/2-inch mesh chicken wire or drywall screen can be used. Wrap it into a cylinder about 1 foot in diameter and 4 feet long. Solder the overlapping wires. Drill the cap piece of the antenna for a no. 10 bolt, which is passed through the overlap portion

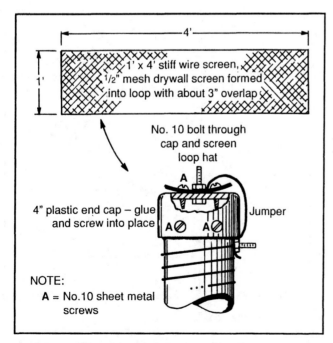

Figure 6-23. Top-hat assembly.

Photo 6-C. View of winding and capacitance hat on KY3F helix antenna.

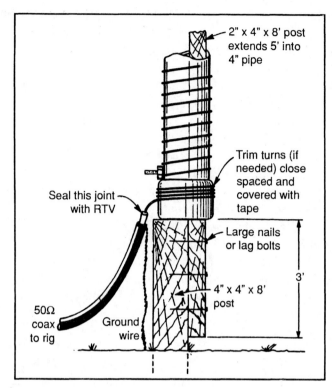

Figure 6-24. Mounting arrangement of the antenna to the post.

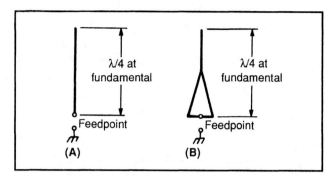

Figure 6-25. Antenna A shows classic response on the fundamental and third harmonic. Antenna B exhibits lower than normal resonance on the third harmonic, while the fundamental resonant frequency remains virtually unchanged.

25A. The vertical antenna element *A* exhibits a quarter-wave resonance at 3.6 MHz. By formula, the antenna is 65 feet high. The third-harmonic resonance, by formula, falls at 11.6 MHz. The actual third-harmonic of 3.6 MHz, however, is 10.8 MHz. Thus, there's a difference of 800 kHz between the actual third-harmonic of the fundamental frequency and the third-harmonic resonance of the vertical.

of the top hat. Use large washers on each side of the screen to enhance stability. Then run four no. 18 sheet-metal screws through the screen and cap to keep the screen from turning or buffeting in the wind (see **Figure 6-23**).

The final step is to attach the top hat to the top of the helix with a jumper wire. Glue the top hat in place and pass four sheet-metal screws through the hat to hold it securely to the PVC pipe (**Photo 6-C**).

The recommended mounting arrangement for the antenna is shown in **Figure 6-24**.

The 160-80 Meter Antenna at K6KBE

Independent experimenters have discovered that altering the shape of a driven element can change the harmonic resonance without appreciably altering the fundamental resonant frequency of the antenna. This is a good technique to use for a two-band antenna. Unfortunately, a typical linear element of uniform diameter does not exhibit resonance on the exact harmonic frequencies because of end effects. A 7-MHz dipole, for example, is *not* resonant in the 21-MHz band.

By changing the shape of the element, however, the third-harmonic resonant frequency can be lowered without changing the fundamental frequency to any great extent. The principle is illustrated in **Figure 6-**

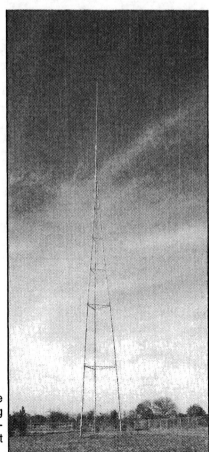

Photo 6-D. The self-supporting 160/80-meter vertical antenna at K6KBE.

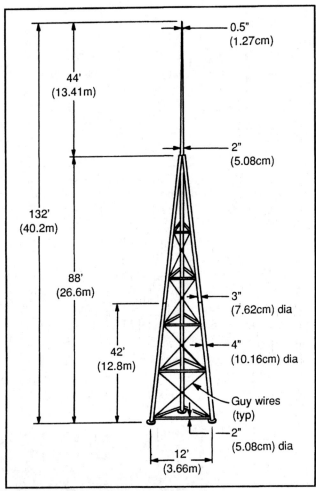

Figure 6-26. Details of the 160/80 meter vertical antenna at K6KBE. The three-legged tower is 88 feet high with a 44-foot whip on top.

this goal. The antenna element is made "fatter" near the area of maximum third-harmonic voltage. This provides additional capacitance to ground at this frequency. On the fundamental frequency, the voltage is lower at this point in the antenna element and the capacitive effect to ground is much less. In this manner, the third-harmonic resonance frequency is lowered without too much effect on the fundamental frequency.

Shown in **Figure 6-26** is an antenna developed by K6KBE for two-band operation. A three-legged tower having a very thin upper portion and a tapered lower section, this antenna shows resonance on both the 80- and 160-meter bands (**Photo 6-D**).

The tower is 132 feet high with a base 12 feet on a side. The design frequencies are 1.85 and 3.7 MHz. The SWR across the 160-meter band is less than 1.8:1 at the band edges and below 1.5:1 from 3.5:3.9 MHz, rising to 2.3:1 at 4 MHz.

The top 44 feet of the antenna consist of a flexible aluminum whip, 2 inches in diameter at the butt, tapering to 0.5 inch. The whip is actually 2 feet longer than this, with the extra length forming the joint to the main tower, which is 88 feet high.

The bottom 42 feet on the tower is made of aluminum tubing 4 inches in diameter, with a 0.093-inch wall thickness. The top portion (to the 88 foot level) is made of 3-inch diameter tubing having a 0.063-inch wall. The cross-guys are made of 0.25-inch aircraft cable. Turnbuckles permit the assembly to be tightened by the assembler until a very rigid structure is achieved.

Anyone who has heard K6KBE's signal on 80 or 160 meters knows this antenna works!

Broadcast Filters for 160 or 80 Meters

If you live in a residential or urban area, you can experience severe crosstalk and overload problems from local broadcast stations if you attempt to operate on

If the vertical resonance at the third-harmonic region could be "pulled" down to 10.1 MHz, then the antenna could operate in the 30-meter ham band (10.1 to 10.15 MHz). Can this be done without disturbing the resonance in the 80-meter band?

Figure 6-25B shows the technique to accomplish

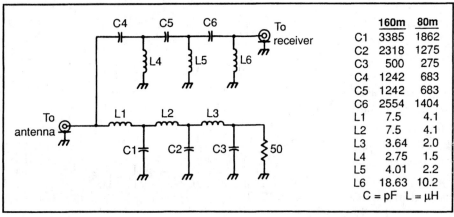

	160m	**80m**
C1	3385	1862
C2	2318	1275
C3	500	275
C4	1242	683
C5	1242	683
C6	2554	1404
L1	7.5	4.1
L2	7.5	4.1
L3	3.64	2.0
L4	2.75	1.5
L5	4.01	2.2
L6	18.63	10.2
	C = pF	L = μH

Figure 6-27. The broadcast filter for 160 or 80 meters.

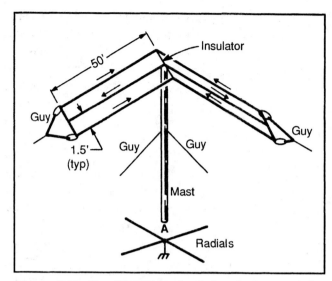

Figure 6-28. The K2GNC top-loaded vertical antenna for 160 meters. Flat-top currents essentially cancel, and the majority of radiation comes from the 88-foot vertical element. The antenna is base-fed at point *A* via coaxial line and a simple L-network. Spacing between the wires is about a foot.

160 or 80 meters. (A friend of mine, located a few miles from a local broadcast station, measured over 4 volts of RF pickup on his 80-meter vertical antenna. It completely locked up his receiver.)

Designed by K6KBE, the filter shown in **Figure 6-27** is an adaptation of an absorption filter used where suppression of harmonic energy is desired. In its original configuration, there are two complementary filters consisting of a high-pass section terminated in a resistor and a low-pass section to pass the desired signal. In this case, the reverse idea is used so that all energy *below* cutoff is routed to a dummy load while all energy above is allowed to pass.

The cutoff frequency for the 160-meter filter is 1.65 MHz; for the 80-meter filter it's 3 MHz.

The K2GNC 160-Meter Top-Loaded Vertical

K2GNC has an interesting antenna concept—a 160-meter antenna that uses the top-loading system popularized by the British Marconi Company (**Figure 6-28**). The vertical antenna consists of three sections of aluminum irrigation pipe, 4, 3, and 2 inches in diameter. Its overall height is 88 feet.

Bill uses 130 radials, with an average length of 100 feet, and a simple matching network to feed the antenna. The antenna works, as Bill's record of WAC and 115 countries to date on the "top band" proves!

The HGW Beam for 80 or 160 Meters

A beam antenna for 80 or 160 meters is a serious undertaking. I know of at least three 80-meter Yagis (there may be more), but I haven't heard of a 160-meter Yagi! Have you?

One practical approach to a beam for these bands is to use phased vertical antennas—a bad scene, as the verticals and companion ground screen take up a lot of real estate. Another idea is to use a tower guy wire, or a sloper, to simulate a beam antenna. That seems a more practical approach, as the cost is low and the ground area required for radial wires is much smaller. There's plenty of data around on the phased vertical scheme, but specific information on the use of a tower guy wire as a parasitic element for a vertical radiator is hard to come by.

The July 1994 issue of *BE Radio*, a supplement to *Broadcast Engineering*, featured a "Hot Guy Wire" (HGW) beam used by broadcast station XEWB in Vera Cruz, Mexico. The old two-tower directional array on 900 kHz, designed to provide maximum coverage around Vera Cruz and to protect XEW in Mexico City, was at the end of its useful life and was replaced by a single quarter-wave tower using a hot guy wire as a parasitic element (**Figure 6-29**). The northwest guy wire serves as an insulated reflector element, tuned by a capacitor at ground level to adjust the electrical length of the guy wire. Twenty ground radials, each about 165 feet long, were placed at the bottom of the guy wire.

Radio XEWB runs 50 kW, so it was decided to split the guy current between two adjacent guy wires connected together at the bottom ends. The radiation pattern of the antenna is shown in **Figure 6-30**. A power gain of 3.5 dBd is achieved, with a front-to-back ratio of 4 to 5 dB. Not bad for a simple beam antenna!

Hot-guy-wire technology has been proven outside the United States, but the FCC has yet to accept it for broadcast service. The FCC at present accepts only traditional formulas used to compute radiation fields, and the method-of-moments technology (in use by amateurs and others for over a decade) is still under consideration. In the interim, amateurs can make use of the several fine antenna design programs available for home computers to design HGW antennas for their own stations!

The dimensions shown in **Figure 6-29** can easily be scaled for either 160- or 80-meter operation. Some amateurs already have towers of sufficient height (about a quarter-wavelength) to put this technique to

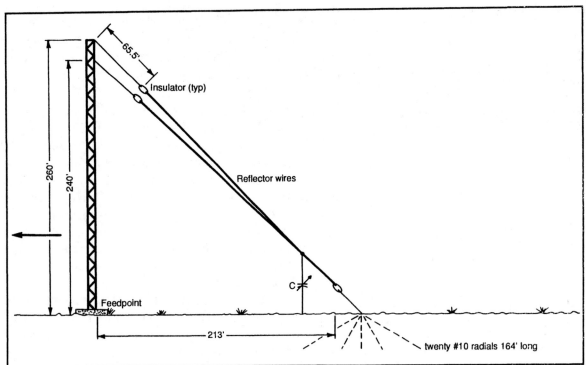

use. While the XEWB antenna was adjusted for maximum signal rejection to the rear, there's no reason why the HGW antenna can't be adjusted for maximum forward gain. Computer analysis shows that a reflector configuration, rather than a director arrangement, is preferable, based on current/voltage stresses and bandwidth. For amateur service, however, it may be worthwhile to investigate the director case. After all, gain is the name of the game, and problems in broadcast service are somewhat different than in amateur service. Surely the director case should be examined closely. This is easy to do with a computer program, or it can be done in the field by adjustment of the guy-wire length or tuning of the series capacitor.

The HGW principle could possibly be expanded to include more than one guy wire. A computer run should disclose if two guys, spaced radially 180 degrees apart, serving as reflector and director, could stimulate the response of a three-element Yagi.

Computer buffs, man your machines! I would appreciate input from you concerning this interesting antenna concept! Send me your program (either 5.25 or 3.5 inch disk is okay), and as your reward I will send you a genuine, prized W6SAI QSL card, which you can frame and hang on the wall of your station!

A Simple 160-Meter Ferrite-Rod Loop for Low-Noise Reception

For me, 160 meters has always been a problem band. Living in an urban area on a small lot, surrounded by other homes, the 160-meter QRN level at my QTH is very discouraging. With no effort at all, I can hear exotic DX such as light dimmers, TV sweep oscillators, line noise, and other unpleasant sounds. Using my transmitting antenna for reception is a waste of

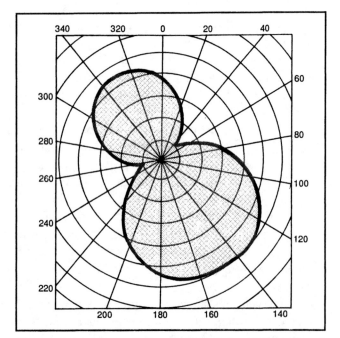

Figure 6-30. The radiation pattern of the HGW beam at XEWB.

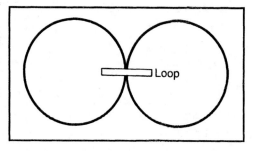

Figure 6-31. Pattern of the small loop antenna showing sharp nulls off the face of the loop. The large loop (quad) has nulls off the ends. When using a ferrite rod, nulls are off the ends of the rod.

time, as the noise level is many dBs over S9 much of the time.

On the other hand, I am fortunate that my transceiver has an auxiliary input for a separate receiving antenna. That opens up interesting possibilities when it comes to using an antenna for reception different than that for transmission.

My first experiment was with a loop antenna about 3 feet in diameter, feeding an "Ameco" preamplifier. Signal output of the loop was low, so the amplifier's additional gain was required in order to have readable signals. This setup worked well. Results were interesting. The loop had a broad figure-8 signal pattern (**Figure 6-31**) with deep nulls off the face of the loop. The nulls were quite sharp. In operation I would peak up the noise with the preamplifier and then rotate the loop for minimum noise.

What's Wrong with Bozeman, Montana? Over a period of time, I found that most loud static crashes came from the northeast, almost in a line from San Francisco to Bozeman, Montana. Aiming the loop null at Bozeman dropped the summer static noise up to 20 to 30 dB.

I still had to contend with local noise. Because I was surrounded by noise makers, I had no clue as to where to aim the loop. Experiments showed that I could achieve an impressive noise reduction when the loop was properly oriented. The direction of maximum noise rejection was easy to determine, and it probably had something to do with the electric wiring inside the house.

In any event, during the winter DX months Bozeman didn't cause any problem. Static was low, so I could adjust the loop for maximum local noise rejection.

Finally—Results! I played SWL for several weeks, listening to the big boys working 160-meter DX around sunrise. With my big antenna, I could not hear the juicy stations they were working. Nulling out the QRN and other racket with the receiving loop, I could hear down to a basic noise level, which was about S3

on the meter. Switching back and forth between the loop and the big antenna made a believer out of me! I could clearly hear SSB signals in a roundtable in Australia, many JA signals on CW, plus an occasional UAØ in Siberia. In most cases, when a DXer worked an exotic station I could hear it. (Working it was another matter!)

How About a Ferrite-Rod Loop?

Yes, how about it? The conventional loop I was using was too big. It sat on a little platform beside my operating desk, and I could rotate it by hand. But it was a nuisance, and top-heavy to boot. Many times it fell over when I was fiddling with it.

I've read descriptions of ferrite rod loops in various publications, but never had the urge to try one until I had to face the decision: If I wanted a noise-rejecting antenna, it had to be a loop, and that loop had to be small enough to fit on the operating table.

I was moved off dead-center by a simplified ferrite-rod loop design described in the November 1994 issue of *Radio Communication* (a monthly publication of the RSGB). This is a construction article by Richard Marris, G2BZQ, covering the assembly of a small ferrite-rod loop antenna for the top band. This simple

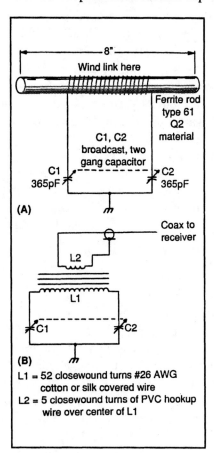

L1 = 52 closewound turns #26 AWG cotton or silk covered wire
L2 = 5 closewound turns of PVC hookup wire over center of L1

Figure 6-32. The layout and schematic of the ferrite rod loop.

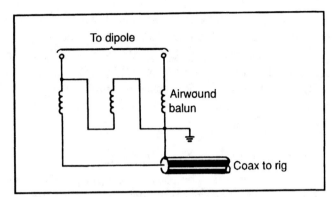

Figure 6-33. The airwound, trifilar balun covering the 1.8 MHz to 12 MHz range. Ten closely spaced trifilar turns of no. 14 enamel wire are wound on a 3-1/2 inch diameter form. (See text for details.)

gadget consists of a tuned circuit and coupling link on a ferrite rod. It covers the 160-meter band. The tuned circuit is balanced to ground and resonated by a two-gang variable capacitor. What could be simpler? (See **Figure 6-32.**)

G2BZQ reports that a long, thin ferrite rod with a center winding produces sharp, deep nulls required for noise reduction. His rod consists of two short nickel-zinc ferrites, epoxied end to end to form an 8-inch rod. The rod is Q2 material having a permeability of 125. The rods are 0.25 inch in diameter.

Richard uses a simple wood "V" jig to align the rods while the glue sets. The rods are then pushed inside a length of 5/16-inch outside diameter polycarbonate plastic tubing, available from aquarist shops. Aquarist shops? An English-American dictionary told me this is the equivalent of a pet store, or an aquarium shop for exotic fish, fish tanks, heaters, etc.

G2BZQ then places a short layer of masking tape over the tubing and winds the coil over the center of the tube-covered rod. Double cotton-covered or plastic-covered wire is used to slightly space the coil turns. Total coil length is about 1.5 inches. The pickup coil is 5 turns of hook-up wire, with the leads twisted together for connection to the feedline.

Loop Assembly and Testing

A copper-clad circuit board is used for assembly. The two-gang broadcast-type tuning capacitor is mounted to the board, with a short extension shaft for the dial to reduce hand capacity. The rod is mounted above the capacitor. Two surplus ceramic insulators plus nylon cable clamps hold the ferrite rod firmly in position, and an extra cable clamp affixes the end of the RG-58

coupling cable to the baseboard.

You can test the antenna on local noise, or use a nearby signal generator with a short antenna on it as a signal source. When you hit resonance, you'll observe a sharp increase in signal level.

Loop directivity is very broad, but the signal nulls are deep and sharp. Swinging the loop about will locate a position where the signal is at a maximum and the noise a minimum. I placed the little antenna on a "lazy Susan" from the kitchen.

You'll notice that signal output from the loop is very low. Many transceivers don't have enough RF gain to provide a comfortable signal level. Then a pre-amplifier (sometimes called a preselector) between the loop and the transceiver is necessary. There are several units on the market that will do the job.

A final note: A preselector should be protected during transmission periods. You may need a relay that will break the coax between loop and preselector to prevent overload damage to the input circuitry of the preselector.

A Balun Transformer for 80 and 160 Meters

The balun design shown in **Figure 6-33** is useful for both 80 and 160 meters. Because it has an air core, it will not saturate at a high power level as a ferrite core design might do, and because the windings have more turns (inductance) than the more common design, this balun performs better at the lower frequencies.

The balun is wound on a plastic (PVC) form 3-1/2 inches in diameter. The design consists of 10 trifilar turns on no. 14 Formvar™ (or enamel) insulated wire. The ends are held in place by 4-40 hardware. The windings are interconnected by short lengths of wire run between the appropriate terminals. The common connection of two of the windings is used as the ground point at one end of the balun and is attached to the coaxial shield. When completed, a plastic bottle is cut to fit over the balun as a rain shield. The balun is attached directly to the center insulator of the dipole and the coaxial line is dropped down directly beneath it.

Take care that the top end of the coaxial line is sealed from moisture. Water can seep into the line by capillary action of the shield, but a good coat of sealant (RTV, for example) will waterproof the end of the line. (Make sure your sealant doesn't contain acetic acid, or it will corrode the copper wires of the coax. Read the label before you buy.)

Chapter 7

Antenna Tuners, Baluns, and Matching Devices

A good definition of an antenna tuner (ATU) is a device that converts the electrical characteristics of the antenna system into values compatible with your transceiver. The general requirement of modern transceivers is that the load be single-ended (coaxial) and have a nominal 50-ohm value, with little or no reactance.

Most of today's antennas are designed for coaxial feed, but for various reasons, including multiband operation, they cannot present an acceptable feedpoint impedance to match the transceiver on some or all of the bands to be used. In addition, some antennas require a balanced line, as opposed to coax, for proper operation. The solution to the first problem is to place an ATU between the transceiver and the coax leading to the antenna.

The Single-ended ATU

This form of tuner has coaxial input and output ports. There are two general types. Look at the photos of the ATUs in advertisements in the ham magazines. Notice they have three main tuning controls. Some of the units have one rotary switch and two variable capacitors, while others have two rotary switches and one variable capacitor. This variation in design is due to

the fact that two types of networks are available to do the job (**Figure 7-1**). The first circuit uses a coil-capacitor-coil (L-C-L); the second circuit uses a capacitor-coil-capacitor (C-L-C). I like the L-C-L design better than the C-L-C type, as the former provides a degree of harmonic attenuation that the latter doesn't possess.

The L-C-L design theoretically provides better harmonic attenuation because the shunt capacitor provides a low-impedance path to ground for harmonics. The C-L-C circuit, on the other hand, impedes the harmonic path to ground because the inductor acts as an RF choke at the harmonic frequencies. However, in practice the tuner isn't designed for maximum harmonic rejection, but for a good impedance match. Leads are relatively long at harmonic frequencies and attention isn't paid to the small details that make a good harmonic filter. After all, that's not what the designer had in mind. In addition, maximum harmonic rejection doesn't occur at the same control settings that provide an impedance match.

Harmonic Rejection

A representative L-C-L tuner, properly adjusted for a 50-ohm load, provides about 25 dB second harmonic rejection when tuned to the 80-meter band. Third-har-

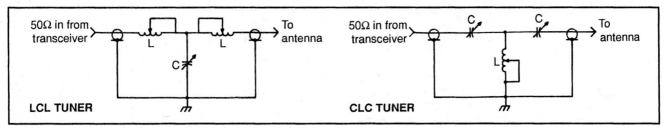

Figure 7-1. Two popular types of antenna tuners. The choice is largely a matter of preference.

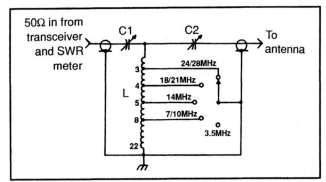

Figure 7-2. C-L-C ATU for 7 to 28 MHz. C1 and C2 = 200 pF. The receiving type is satisfactory for output power up to 100 watts PEP. L = 22 turns no. 18 AWG close wound on 1-3/4 inch O.D. form. Taps, counting from top end of coil: 7 MHz, 8t; 14 MHz, 5t; 18/21 MHz, 4t; 24–28 MHz, 3t; 3.5 MHz, 22t. (Data courtesy RSGB *Radio Communication*.)

monic attenuation is about 24 dB. In the low TV channels, harmonic rejection runs about 15 dB.

On 10 meters, a typical L-C-L tuner provides about 19 dB second-harmonic suppression. This would afford some protection to TV channel 2, depending on the exact frequency of your transmitter in the 10-meter band, and your ATU adjustment.

The ATU isn't a substitute for a low-pass antenna filter, particularly in rural areas where TV signals are weak and cable or satellite-TV isn't available. The tuner backs up a good TV filter, but is not a substitute for it.

Most store-bought ATUs use the C-L-C circuit. It's less expensive to manufacture than the L-C-L design, as it requires only one adjustable inductor, which in some units is a rotary unit with a counter dial. In any case, either type of ATU will do the job. The more expensive units have a built-in SWR bridge with a meter readout on the front. That's nice. Just twist the knobs for the lowest reverse SWR reading. Most built-in SWR bridges are fairly accurate at low SWR values, but under a condition of high SWR, only the best SWR bridge will tell the truth!

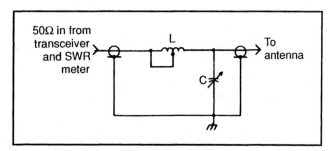

Figure 7.3. L-network for 1.8 and 3.5 MHz. C = 200 pF. Receiving type is satisfactory for output power up to 100 watts PEP. L = 20 turns no. 18 AWG spaced wire diameter. Tap with copper clip. Adjust along with C for lowest SWR. (Data courtesy RSGB *Radio Communication*.)

A practical and inexpensive C-L-C ATU suitable for use from 3.5 to 29.7 MHz is shown in **Figure 7-2**. Receiving-type capacitors are suitable for power levels up to 100 watts PEP output. A single-pole, six-position ceramic wafer switch (Electroswitch PA-6001, or equivalent) is used. The shafts of the variable capacitors are at RF potential, so an insulated shaft coupling should be used.

The L-Network ATU

The L-network (**Figure 7-3**) is another type of ATU. This network is half of the C-L-C circuit. It can be used to match a 50-ohm source to a higher value of impedance, like that presented by an end-fed antenna. As shown, it matches lower to higher impedance, but it can be reversed to match a high impedance to a low one. The C-L-C circuit is more flexible than the L-network, as it can match high or low in either direction. Circuit values shown are suitable for 160 and 80 meters.

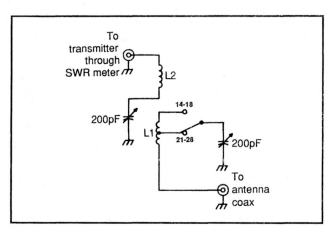

Figure 7-4. The five-band antenna tuner. (See text for coil data.)

An Antenna Tuner for a Triband Beam

Figure 7-4 shows a tuner designed by E. R. Cook, ZS6BT. It covers 14 to 30 MHz and consists of two tightly coupled, series-tuned circuits. An SWR meter is required for tuner adjustment.

For power levels up to several hundred watts, receiving-type variable capacitors can be used. The inductors are made from a single section of coil stock, 1-3/4 inch diameter, 16 turns per inch of no. 18 wire (Barker & Williamson 3023). It's cut to provide two closely coupled coils of 3-1/2 and 7-1/2 turns. Only enough wire is snipped out between the coils to make connection to the capacitors.

The tuner is simple enough to be built in breadboard fashion. A piece of 1/2-inch plywood serves as the base, and a sheet of 1/8-inch Masonite makes up the panel. The capacitors are mounted to the panel, and the band switch is affixed to the plywood base. Don't forget to connect all ground terminals together and to the shells of the coax receptacles, which are mounted on a small piece of angle aluminum stock. (Note that the rotor is the grounded terminal on the capacitor.)

Coil L1 (the antenna coil) is tapped for the higher bands. The tap point is determined by experimentation, but is approximately 3-1/2 turns from the capacitor end of the coil. A Barker & Williamson Inductance Clip 3943 can be used as a tap, or the adjacent turns of the coil can be depressed inward and a soldered joint made at the proper point with a small iron.

The switch is half of a double-pole knife-type. Try RadioShack's 275-1537. If you're lucky, you might find an old ceramic type, like those sold years ago in the "5- and 10-cent" stores.

Using the Tuner

It's helpful to connect a dummy load to the tuner for initial tune-up. The controls are adjusted for maximum transmitter loading consistent with minimum SWR. The capacitor settings should be logged for future reference.

In the unlikely instance that low SWR can't be obtained at a point in some band, changing the length of the line between the tuner and the antenna will help bring the antenna impedance in agreement with the matching range of the tuner.

It must be remembered that a multiband antenna can radiate harmonics of the transmitter. Thus, when on 14 MHz, for example, the antenna can radiate transmitter harmonics or spurious signals on 21 and 28 MHz. ZS6BT claims up to 30 dB harmonic rejection is provided by this little tuner.

A Mini-ATU for 14 to 30 MHz

Doctor Livingston I. Presume poked his head in the door and asked, "May I come in?"

"Certainly," I replied, "but I have a better idea. It's such a beautiful spring day, let's sit outside and absorb some sunshine."

I opened the door to the shack and sat down beside Doctor Liv on a wooden bench. The warm spring sunshine felt good and it seemed as if the long, cold winter was at last over.

"Where's Pendergast?" I asked. "I haven't seen him for some days."

Doctor Liv smiled. "Pendergast has nearly forgotten

Photo 7-A. The K6VQ mini-antenna tuner and SWR meter. Using an inexpensive CB-type SWR meter and a homemade tuner, this compact device is used with a compact transceiver for all-band operation. The SWR meter, removed from its case, is mounted in a hole cut in the lid of an aluminum utility box. The tuner is at the left. At the top of the panel is the miniature coaxial jack for the antenna line and below it are the controls for the tuner. From top to bottom: output capacitor switch, output capacitor C2, inductor switch S2, input capacitor C1, and input capacitor switch. The whole unit is almost small enough to fit in your pocket!

about ham radio. He's been romancing Rosie Radiator."

"Rosie Radiator? Isn't that the CB YL I saw him with a few times?"

"That's right," replied Doctor Liv. "Rosie and Pendergast have a thing going."

"Another good DXer falls by the wayside. Where's he going for his honeymoon?"

"You're a little premature," replied Doc. "Not until he gets his 2-meter gear installed in the car. I'm sure of that."

I looked up at the spring sunshine. "I'd like to be taking a trip myself," I said. "Sometimes I envy my friend Bill, K6VQ. He travels and sees the world. And he takes his transceiver along with him."

"What does he do for an antenna when he hits some out-of-the-way place?" inquired the good doctor as he shifted about on the hard bench.

I reached into my jacket pocket and brought out some photographs and a schematic drawing. "Well, Bill has built up a mini-SWR meter and antenna tuner. It had to be very small, since he travels light. Look at this (Photo 7-A). This box, which measures only 6 × 3-1/2 × 2 inches, has all the works in it. Take a look at the schematic (Figure 7-5). Note that he makes use of a CB-type SWR meter. He got his at a flea market for

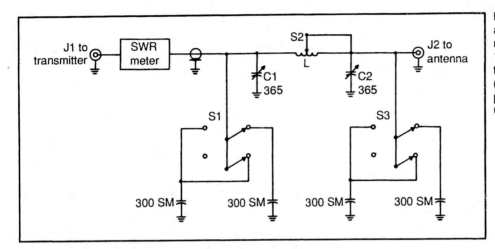

Figure 7-5. Schematic of K6VQ antenna tuner. C1, C2—365-pF mica compression, Philmore 1951. S1,S2—DPDT miniature toggle switch, C-H SF2BX191 (on-off-on). S2—Single-pole, 12-position, miniature silicone switch, Oak 3992117A.

a dollar because the diodes in it were burned out. To the left of the SWR meter are the controls for the pi-network matching circuit.

"This network is composed of a tapped coil and variable input and output matching capacitors. Bill was intrigued by the pee-wee, imported mica-leaf variable capacitors used in miniature transistor radios, so he bought two of them and checked them out. As you see, they are only a little bigger than a postage stamp."

"Will they stand the gaff with a 100-watt transceiver?" asked Doctor Liv.

"Bill put over 500 volts AC across the capacitors with no ill effects, so he thought he'd try them out in actual service. They worked just fine! He used two miniature switches to add extra circuit capacitance if he needed it. A mini-coil and small rotary switch

completed the network. He used inexpensive stereo fittings that match coaxial line. An inside view of the unit is shown in **Photo 7-B**."

"Beautiful," said Doctor Liv. He examined the device as if it were a fine jewel. "What kind of an antenna does K6VQ use with this match-box?"

"He uses a trapped, triband dipole for 10, 15, and 20 meters, and a random length for 40 and 80 meters. The transceiver likes to work into a very low SWR antenna load. The triband dipole, while an excellent performer on three bands, has a rather sharp SWR response. This reduces the transceiver output because of the built-in protection circuit that reduces transmitter output as the antenna SWR rises. You really need an antenna that's very flat if you want to operate a solid-state transceiver over more than a very narrow frequency range. This little matching unit does the job very nicely."

I handed the photos to Doctor Livingston. "Observe that K6VQ placed an aluminum shield plate running between the SWR meter and the components of the tuning unit. Other than that, wiring is very straightforward."

Photo 7-B. Interior view of the K6VQ mini-tuner and SWR meter. At the left is the SWR meter removed from its case. A homemade aluminum shield runs from top to bottom of the box and shields the SWR meter from the tuner (at right). Placement of the coil and the two miniature tuning capacitors is visible at the center of the assembly, with switches S1 and S3 above and below the tuning capacitors.

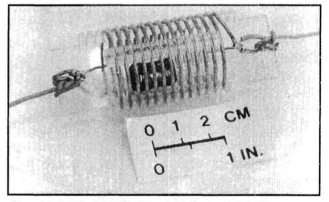

Photo 7-C. The K6VQ mini-trap for 15 meters. The capacitor is a 1.5 kV silver mica unit. Overall trap length is about 2 inches. Trap is dipped to 21.0 MHz on the bench before placing in antenna.

Figure 7-6. Schematic of a triband dipole for 20, 15, 10 meters. L1, C1—15 meter trap; 24 pF silver mica capacitor plus 2.3 µH coil; 14 turns, 1-inch diameter, 8 turns per inch. Adjust number of turns for resonance at 21.0 MHz. L2, C2—10 meter trap; 24 pF

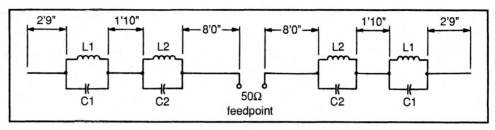

silver mica capacitor plus 1.3 µH coil; 8 turns, 1-inch diameter, 8 turns per inch. Adjust number of turns for resonance at 28.0 MHz.

"Tell me about the triband dipole," said Doctor Liv. "It would have to be small and light to go along with this unit."

"Right," I replied. "K6VQ decided to make up a very light and compact trap-style antenna for 20, 15, and 10 meters. The dimensions are conventional (**Figure 7-6**). His trap assembly technique is interesting. The antenna is made up of insulated hookup wire, which is very flexible. Each trap is made of a small air-wound inductor slid onto a short length of plexiglass that serves as a support for the coil and as tie-points for the antenna wires and capacitor (**Photo 7-C**).

"Bill wanted to use the smallest capacitor available, but little information could be found about the current and voltage impressed upon the capacitor in such a complex trap circuit. While the trap is a very simple device, its function changes with the band in use. As far as I know, no mathematical treatment has been made of the actual trap operation, so Bill tried the heuristic approach . . ."

"Heuristic?" queried Doctor Liv.

"Cut-and-try," I replied. "He used a 1500-working-volt, dipped mica capacitor for the 15-meter trap. For the 10-meter trap (not being able to find enough proper values of capacitance), he used three 500-volt capacitors connected in series. After assembly, the traps were trimmed to proper resonant frequency with a dip meter.

"It's OK to use RG-58/U for the coax. For an even lighter assembly, you can use RG-174/U; it is more lossy. But if the line is short it doesn't make much difference."

"Sounds very nice," said Doctor Liv as he returned the photographs to me. "I must build this SWR meter and antenna tuner combo soon!"

The Z-Match Antenna Tuning Unit

In 1990, a modified impedance matching network was described in *Amateur Radio*, an Australian publication. It was followed up by a simplified version shown in *Break-In* (in 1992), a New Zealand amateur

magazine. Finally, a how-to-build-it article on the network, now called a Z-match, appeared in *Amateur Radio* in February 1993.

The description of the Z-match activated my memory bank, and I rummaged around in old copies of *QST* magazine until I came up with two source articles describing the scheme.

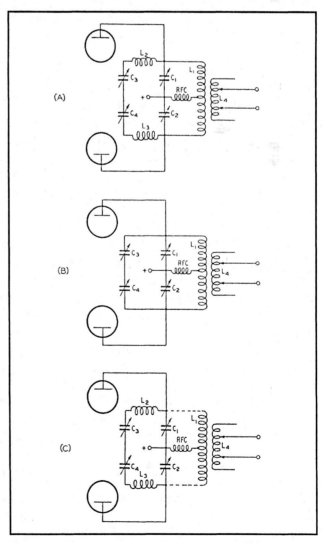

Figure 7-7. The circuit of the multiple-tuned tank (A) and equivalent circuits for low (B) and high (C) frequencies. (Drawing courtesy *QST*.)

Figure 7-8. Positions of the bands on the dial. To avoid confusion, the two ranges are shown separately.

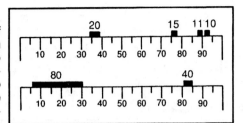

In actual tuning, starting from the high-capacitance end of the scale, the tank goes through the following bands in succession: 3.5, 14, 21, 7, 27, 28 MHz.

The first article was by Allen King, Jr., W1CJL. The idea was to design a push-pull tank circuit for a tube-style transmitter that would cover 3.5 to 30 MHz without bandswitching. A single tuned circuit was impractical because of the change in L/C ratio at the extremes of the frequency range. The solution to the problem was a multiple-tuned circuit—one that tuned to two different frequencies at the same time, preserving a reasonably constant L/C ratio across the range (**Figure 7-7**).

W1CJL explained circuit operation: "If L1 is a coil of relatively large inductance while L2 and L3 are small, the inductances of L2 and L3 can be considered negligible at low frequencies. In that case, condensers (sic) C3 and C4 for all practical purposes are connected in parallel with C1 and C2. Hence, the low-frequency limit of the circuit is determined by a rather large coil and a large value of capacitance, as indicated in **Figure 7-7B**.

"On the other hand, the four condensers in series with L and L3, also in series, form a circuit resonant to some high frequency. For this frequency, L1 is large enough to be looked upon almost as a choke and hence doesn't have a pronounced effect on the resonant frequency of the circuit. This is indicated in **Figure 7-7C**.

"At intermediate frequencies all three coils take part in the operation of the circuit, the effect being to provide a greater frequency ratio than would be possible with a single coil-condenser circuit. For any given setting of the tuning condenser (all four of them should be ganged for convenient operation) the circuit is res-

onant at two frequencies—for example, a low frequency of 3.5 MHz and a high frequency of 12 MHz.

"Power output can be coupled out of such a circuit by means of a tapped coil, L4, coupled to the low-frequency coil L1, the taps being adjusted for the impedance into which the tank is to work. It has been found that the coupling to the load remains substantially constant over the entire tuning range."

In the design described by King, the tuning ranges of the network were 3.45 to 8.5 MHz and 12 to 30 MHz. There was a tuning gap from 8.5 to 12 MHz. The positions of the amateur bands are shown in **Figure 7-8**. The sequence of tuning across a typical 0 to 100 degree dial is 3.5, 14, 21, 7, 27, and 28 MHz. (That's back in the days when the 11-meter band was an amateur assignment.)

This unique tuning device was commercially available as the National Company type MB-40 and MB-150 assemblies, which were rated at 40 and 150 watts, respectively. The clever idea really never got off the ground, as push-pull amplifier circuits were going out of vogue, and the multiple tuner had unwanted resonances that often enhanced TVI problems!

Figure 7-10. Multiband-tuner circuit using a center-tapped coil.

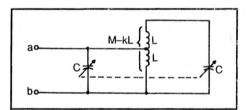

Multiband Tuning Circuits

The basic multiband circuit, however, had merits, even though the theory behind it was vague and little design information was available. Finally, in *QST* (July 1954) Ralph Johnson, W6MUR, provided the mathematical analysis of multiband tuning circuits. For simplicity, he analyzed a single-ended circuit instead of the push-pull arrangement (**Figure 7-9**). The capacitors are ganged and the coils have no mutual inductance.

W6MUR went through the mathematics and provided information covering the general case; he then went on to discuss a special case (**Figure 7-10**). This circuit uses a center-tapped coil with a split-stator tuning capacitor. He provided data to build an experimental circuit tunable from 3.45 to 11.4 MHz and 10.4 to 35.9 MHz.

Figure 7-9. Basic circuit of a single-ended multiband tuner.

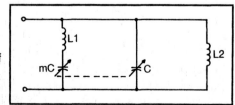

Ralph predicted the circuit would have wide application in amateur equipment and that "further experimental work will undoubtedly bring forth improvements and further modifications of the circuit."

Such was not the case, though. The multiband tank circuit sank without a trace until it was resurrected by some heads-up amateurs in Australia and New Zealand. They decided to employ the circuit as a wideband antenna tuner.

General Design Information

Before describing the Z-match tuner, some basic design data is needed for those experimenters who wish to play with this interesting circuit. W6MUR provides the following suggestions:

1. The tuning-capacitor range should be about 9:1 for best coverage. Taking stray capacitance into account, this calls for a minimum value of about 200 pF per section.

2. The coil is selected so one-half of the coil has a length-to-diameter ratio of 0.525.

3. For maximum capacitor setting, the number of coil turns of the half-coil should resonate near 6.19 MHz.

4. The final coil has twice the number of turns of the half-coil and twice the length.

5. The circuit can be tested using a dip meter. Adjusting the coil tap will vary the high-frequency tuning range.

A Practical Z-Match Tuner

The single-coil impedance matching network described by New Zealand amateur T. J. Seed, ZL3QQ, in *Break-in*, March 1992, is shown in **Figure 7-11**. The similarity between this and the Johnson circuit (**Figure 7-10**) is apparent. The final design—by Ron Cook, VK3AFW, and Ron Fisher, VK3OM (shown in *Amateur Radio*, April 1993)—modified the input circuit using an extra tap on the coil (**Figure 7-12**). This is the circuit of the Z-match at the present date.

Two tuning controls are required. One of the capacitors is a split-stator affair. For low power (up to 100 watts, or so), either a two-gang broadcast tuning capac-

Photo 7-D. The Z-match tuner. On the left is the loading capacitor with the double-section tuning capacitor at the right. Common ground lead connects input and output receptacles, bottom of main coil, and rotor of "TUNE" capacitor, C2.

itor (usually 350 pF per section) or ganged capacitors can be used. The output of the tuner is via a link coil. The terminals may be either balanced (for ladder line) or unbalanced (for coax). The original Australian design had a loose-fitting link that could be moved up and down the main coil a bit, although it should be positioned near the bottom ("cold") end of the coil.

For higher power, a huskier coil and transmitting-type capacitors with a greater air gap should be used.

Construction Hints. It's a good idea to use reduction dials on the tuner. Tuning is quite sharp and interlocking. I used vernier dials from a BC-375 surplus tuning unit. Other vernier drive dials would probably work just as well (**Photo 7-D**).

The circuit is high-C, and there is high circulating current in the coil. At 150 watts, the coil I used ran warm. It was wound with no. 18 tinned wire. I would

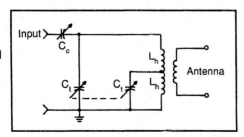

Figure 7-11. The single-coil Z-Match as described in NZART *Break-In*, March 1992.

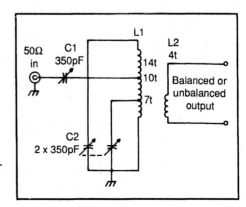

Figure 7-12. Up-to-date Z-match (150 watts).

Photo 7-E. Link coil L2 is slip-fit over the main coil and may be moved up and down about 1/2 inch to adjust coupling.

suggest using no. 12 enamel-coated wire to reduce coil loss.

It's easy to set the tuning ranges of the Z-match with a dip meter. My first Z-match tuned down to 2.8 MHz, but wouldn't tune to 10 MHz. Using the dip meter, I trimmed the top end of the coil until the lowest frequency of the circuit was about 3.4 MHz. That permitted the unit to resonate on the 10-MHz band near minimum capacitor setting.

Keep all leads short and heavy for the greatest possible tuning range. After a little diddling around, my Z-match covered the 3.5 to 29.7 MHz range. My test antenna was an off-center-fed, 7-MHz flat-top with balun and coax feed. I could tune it up for near-unity SWR on all bands, including 80 meters.

I never modified the 4-turn pick-up coil. There may be merit in trying more or fewer turns in a difficult loading situation.

Construction is very simple. My unit is made on a piece of plywood, 8 × 8 inches. The panel is a piece of Masonite, 4 inches high and 1/8 inch thick (**Photo 7-E**). Vernier drives are most helpful, as tuning is interlocking and quite sharp. The following are construction and operation suggestions that will aid you in duplicating this device.

1. Components are mounted directly to the board. The two capacitors have small metal brackets that permit them to be screwed securely to the surface. The vernier drive for the "Load" control (C1) is insulated from the dial by a ceramic coupling. This decreases hand capacity effect. For appearance, the "Tune" dial for C2 is a similar unit. The dial mechanisms are bolted to the rear of the panel.

2. The fiberglass coil form is mounted in the clear, in a vertical position. The coil is "hot," so keep it clear of the capacitors. It is bolted to the baseboard with two small right-angle brackets.

3. The 4-turn pickup coil (L2) is a loose slip-fit over the main coil. I used high-voltage hookup wire wound by hand into a coil. Five plastic cable ties are used to hold the coil in shape. The pickup coil is positioned around the two bottom turns of the main coil. If coupling is too loose, the main tuning capacitor (C2) may spark over. In my case, the dual capacitor is a well-made broadcast type with 0.02-inch spacing. Since the plates are stamped out and the edges aren't rounded or buffed, the RF breakdown voltage is only about 800 volts. When the link coupling is correct, the capacitor won't spark over at power levels up to 125 watts.

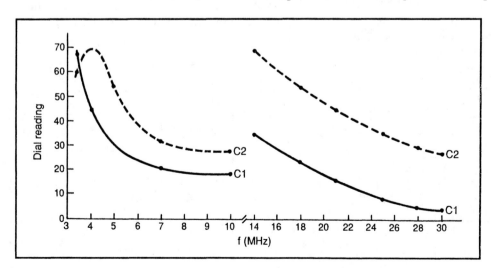

Figure 7-13. Frequency ranges versus dial settings (approximate).

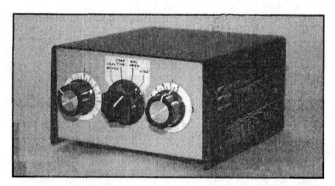

Photo 7-F. A compact Z-match tuner that was built by Roy Gregson, W6EMT. Vernier drives are used on both of the variable capacitors.

Photo 7-G. An oblique view of the W6EMT tuner. The ceramic switch is centered on the panel, flanked by "Tune" and "Load" capacitors.

(That was the maximum power my transceiver would develop for the tests.) No sparking was ever noticed in the single-section input capacitor, which also has 0.02-inch spacing.

4. Tuning is sharp and interlocking. A dual-needle SWR meter that registers forward and reverse power, plus SWR, will simplify adjustment. Tune for minimum reflected power at the same time the maximum power output is obtained. One eye on the ATU dials and the other on the SWR meter does the trick! Once you've found the correct dial settings, log them for future use.

5. To tune up from scratch, place the SWR meter between the Z-match and your transceiver. Set the loading capacitance to about half-range and tune the resonating capacitor (C2) until you notice a "kick" in the SWR meter forward reading. Vary the loading capacitor (C1) back and forth until the reading is enhanced. Now retune C2 to peak the reading, and follow this with a second adjustment of capacitor C1. Continue tuning and loading until you "waltz" the controls to provide maximum power output with an SWR indication of less that 1.2:1. That's it!

6. With the values given, the unit tunes from 3.5 to 11 MHz and 13 to 30 MHz. A tuning gap exists between 11 and 13 MHz. The frequency range versus dial readings are shown in **Figure 7-13**. Note that the setting of capacitor C2 apparently drops in value across the 80-meter band. Why? I don't know. I've checked this apparent contradiction many times and it really exists. It could be an idiosyncrasy of the particular antenna system under test. One of these days, I may investigate further.

7. I used Formvar insulated wire for my coil, and it is a devil of a job to scrape the insulation off in order to make taps on the coil. I wound the coil on the form, marked the tap points with the sharp blade of a knife,

and then unwound the coil so I could attack the tap points—cleaning about 1/2 inch of insulation completely around the wire. These two spots were then tinned.

8. The coil turns are spaced a little more than the wire diameter. Even so, care must be taken when making the tap points. I took a long, thin soldering lug and wrapped the arm around the wire, leaving the main body of the lug free so I could bolt a connection to it. The arm soldered easily to the coil wire, and the lug provided a rigid, reliable mounting point for a connecting wire. I used 4-40 hardware to make the connection at this point. (A friend of mine said that my approach was the hard way. He suggested I merely hammer flat the end of the connecting wire and wrap the flat portion around the coil wire. A nifty idea! All that's needed is a hammer and a bench vise, and it's easy to flatten the copper wire.)

9. You can substitute a two-terminal connector for ladder line in place of the coax plug. In normal use, the coaxial-connector frame is grounded to the ground wire of the tuner. For the balanced line, the connector need not be used, and the 4-turn coil "floats" with respect to ground.

Photos 7-F and **7-G** show a compact Z-match tuner built by Roy Gregson, W6EMT.

The Z-Match ATU for 160 Meters

In the last two sections, I discussed the Z-match antenna tuning unit (ATU). This clever little device provides a balanced or unbalanced match for the 3.5 to 30 MHz range—with only two controls and no band-switching! The basic circuit, shown in **Figure 7-12**, achieves this result through the use of a parallel-tuned circuit that covers two frequencies simultaneously. The matching range is computed to be from 10 to

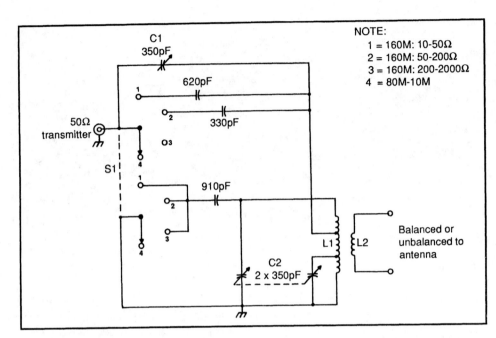

NOTE:
1 = 160M: 10-50Ω
2 = 160M: 50-200Ω
3 = 160M: 200-2000Ω
4 = 80M-10M

Figure 7-14. A modified Z-match for 160–10 meters. S1 is a two-pole, 4-position ceramic switch.

2,000 ohms resistive on most bands. In actual practice, it will match a wide range of complex impedances exhibited by various antennas.

An article by Lloyd Butler, VK5BR, in *Amateur Radio*, discusses the coil assembly of the Z-match and provides data to make the unit cover the 160-meter band. The following material is excerpted from that article.

"One version of the Z-match was built with the main coil wound on a form cut from a length of PVC tubing. The unit performed in a satisfactory manner, but the PVC material increased the distributed capacitance of the coil, resulting in settings of 10 to 15 pF less than normal in the dual tuning capacitor. The result was that on 7 MHz, with a load resistance around 100 ohms, the capacitor resonance occurred very near to the zero setting of the capacitor. The same minimum was also observed at the high end of the 10-meter band.

"My coil form was a very thin one of unknown plastic material right out of the junk box. If I were to rebuild the unit, I would choose an air-wound coil, such as the Barker & Williamson 3061 or the Air-Dux 1604T. These coils are wound of no. 12 AWG wire, 4 turns per inch. This assures a minimum distributed capacitance."

The VK5BR Z-Match

Lloyd Butler also discussed a modified Z-match in the same article. This circuit is shown in **Figure 7-14**. The tuner covers 1.8 to 30 MHz. The extended low-frequency range is achieved by adding capacitance to

the two tuning components. A four-position switch does the job.

Position 1 of the switch covers 160 meters for loads ranging from 10 to 50 ohms. Position 2 allows loads in the range of 50 to 200 ohms. Position 3 covers loads between 200 and 2,000 ohms. Position 4 covers the 3.5 to 30 MHz range. If you only require the lower impedance range on 160 meters, two fixed capacitors and a two-position switch will do the job.

VK5BR used 350-volt mica ceramic capacitors that stood up under a power level of 200 watts. However, it might be a good idea to use higher voltage capacitors for an additional safety factor.

The Gamma Match for Your Yagi

When the 88 to 108 MHz FM broadcast band was authorized shortly after World War II, a VHF transmitting antenna using an off-center feed system was introduced. Adapted for amateur use, the system was termed the "gamma match" and was featured in *QST*, September 1949. The builder, H. Washburn, W3MTE, remarked that the device worked well, permitting him to achieve an SWR value as low as 1.75:1. His arrangement is shown in **Figure 7-15**.

Several other antenna experimenters and I worked with the W3MTE gamma match. We soon determined that to lower the SWR appreciably below 2:1, a variable capacitor had to be placed in series with the gamma rod (**Figure 7-16**).

Little information was available on optimum rod-to-antenna spacing, rod length, or rod diameter. It was strictly a cut-and-try situation. Some amateurs had

Figure 7-15. The early gamma match described by W3MTE (*QST,* September 1948).

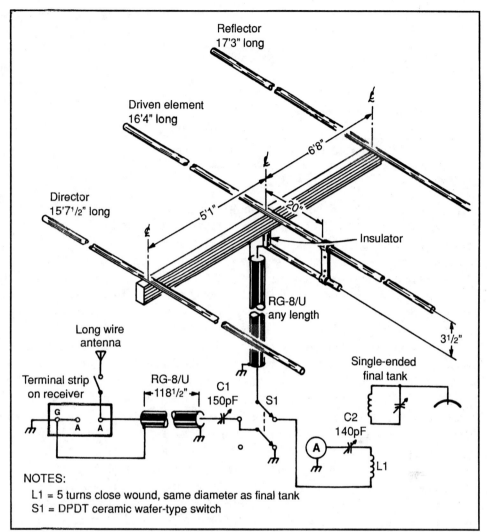

good luck with the device; others couldn't get it to work. The gamma match acquired a reputation as a tricky device that was hard to adjust. In time, it became apparent that the gamma rod had to be small in diameter compared with the driven element, and that the spacing of the gamma rod to the element had to be quite large compared with rod diameter in order to make the system work properly.

Some attempts were made to analyze the gamma match using transmission-line equations. But it wasn't until Harold Tolles, W7ITB, derived a computer program that would predict gamma dimensions accurately for a particular antenna that this was accomplished.

The Gamma-Match Program. The gamma program, written in BASIC by Richard Nelson, WBØIKN, is based upon W7ITB's analysis and is designed for the Apple II+. It can be modified to work equally well with DOS-driven computers.

I put the program to use designing a gamma match for a three-element, 10-meter Yagi. I took beam dimensions from my *Beam Antenna Handbook.* The design frequency was 28.5 MHz. I planned to use a 1-inch diameter element, a 1/4-inch diameter gamma rod, 3-inch center-to-center spacing, and a 100-pF

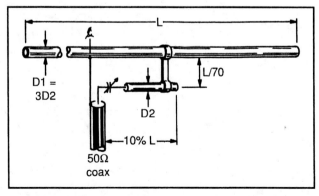

Figure 7-16. Early *Radio Handbook* shows series gamma capacitor and approximate dimensions for gamma match.

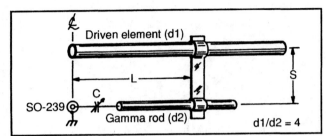

Figure 7-17. W6SAI's 10-meter gamma match. Diameter d1 = 1 inch, d2 = 1/4 inch. Center-to-center spacing = 3 inches.

series capacitor (**Figure 7-17**). Feedpoint impedance was estimated to be 18 ohms and I wanted to match a 50-ohm line. When I plugged these values into the computer program, it indicated a gamma rod length of 22 inches and a series capacitance of 180 pF.

These results immediately rang an alarm bell. Our experiments had indicated that the series gamma capacitor should be about six times the operating frequency in meters and the gamma rod should be about 0.04 wavelength long. For the 10-meter band, this works out to a capacitor of 60 pF and a rod length of about 16 inches. To back up my assumption, I found a commercially produced 10-meter beam with substantially the same dimensions as my design using a 19-inch rod and a 45-pF capacitor—not too close, but a lot closer than the answer ground out by the computer program!

Obviously, there was some factor I hadn't taken into account that influenced gamma dimensions. There was more to the gamma match than met the eye!

Gamma-Match Computation. I found the answer to the puzzle in a short remark (almost an afterthought) in the text of the W7ITB computer-program article. Harold worked out gamma dimensions for a sample antenna and then mentioned that if the drive-point impedance of the antenna had capacitive reactance, the value of the gamma capacitor would decrease, as would the length of the gamma rod. Armed with this morsel of information, I read the WBØIKN computer program again. At the end of the article, the author mentioned that a smaller gamma capacitor may be used if radiator reactance is made capacitive (negative) by reducing its overall length. Aha! Here was the missing clue. With a given value of drive-point resistance and a given gamma-to-driven-element spacing, what would happen to the rod length and series-capacitance values when different amounts of negative reactance were introduced into the driven element?

Varying the Driven-Element Reactance. For a given frequency, an antenna element may exhibit either positive or negative reactance at its drive point when the antenna simply is made longer or shorter than the resonant length. Shortening the element produces negative reactance; that's what I was interested in! I reran the WBØIKN program, plugging in various values of negative reactance from j = Ø to j = –50 (see **Figure 7-18**).

The plot shows that the series-capacitance value peaks at the element resonant frequency (j = Ø) and decreases in value either side of resonance. The length

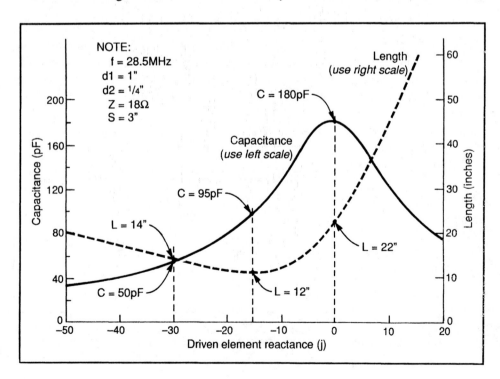

Figure 7-18. Graph for determining design lengths of the gamma match.

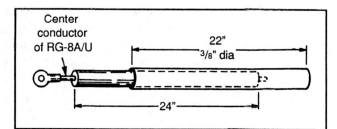

Figure 7-19. Coaxial gamma-rod capacitor for 10-meter beam. Maximum capacitance is about 55 pF.

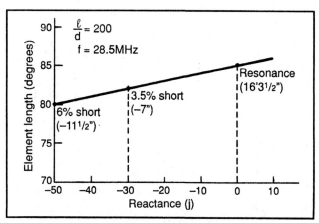

Figure 7-20. Tip-to-tip shortening required for various values of driven-element reactance for 1-inch diameter element.

of the gamma rod, however, follows a different curve. It exhibits the shortest length when the antenna exhibits negative reactance (–j15).

A practical gamma-match system (one that can be built cheaply and adjusted easily) calls for the shortest gamma rod and the least amount of capacitance. It's no fun to hang from the top of a tower and try to adjust a gamma rod the shorting bar of which isn't quite within reach!

You can build a small gamma capacitor inexpensively with a coaxial gamma rod that has the inner conductor serving as one capacitance element as shown in **Figure 7-19**.

In my case, a 22-inch adjustable gamma rod works over a range of antenna reactance from j∅ to –j5∅. However, as the antenna element approached resonance, the value of the gamma capacitance rose sharply, and the coaxial rod length didn't provide sufficient capacitance. From the plot, it was obvious that the designer of the manufactured antenna had cut his driven element shorter than resonance to provide a negative value of reactance (about –j30 ohms) in order to have reasonable gamma dimensions.

Gamma-Rod Spacing. My next question was: what is the effect on gamma dimensions when element-to-rod spacing is varied? I used the computer program for the 10-meter beam element diameters; the results are summarized in **Table 7-1**. Rod length compared with spacing is given for four values of antenna reactance: j = ∅ (resonance), j = –15, j = –30, and j = –50 ohms.

Larger values of element-to-gamma spacing require a shorter rod length, but greater gamma capacitance. The shortest rod length is achieved when the driven element has a reactive value between –j15 and –j30, with an element-to-gamma spacing of 3 to 4 inches.

Gamma capacitance increases with element-to-gamma spacing, and decreases as the driven element exhibits greater values of negative reactance. Practical (small) values of capacitance are reached in the reactive region between –j30 and –j50.

Because shortening the driven element has minimal effect on beam performance, it would be helpful to choose a length providing a negative reactance of 30 to 50 ohms.

Element Shortening. How much physical shortening is required to provide a reactance of –30 to –50 ohms? It depends upon the ratio of element length to diameter. Such ratios have been computed and measured, and a simplified plot for a length-to-diameter ratio of 200 is shown in **Figure 7-20**. This corresponds to a 1-inch diameter element at 28.5 MHz. To achieve a reactance value of –j30, you must shorten the driven element about 7 inches (tip to tip). For a reactance of –j50, you'll need to shorten it 11.5 inches.

Drive-Point Impedance and Element Length. What happens to the 18-ohm figure if the driven element has a drive-point value of 18 ohms at resonance and is shortened to provide a negative reactance? It decreases in value. The reduction depends upon the

j	Spacing (inches)	Rod Length (inches)	Capacitance (pF)
j∅	1	39	83
	2	25	145
	3	23	180
	4	22	212
–j15	1	33.5	57
	2	15	80
	3	12	95
	4	11	105
–j30	1	36	24
	2	18	31
	3	13	52
	4	12	58
–j50	1	36	22
	2	22	31
	3	20.5	32
	4	17	35

Table 7-1. Various gamma and series capacitance values for different length driven elements.

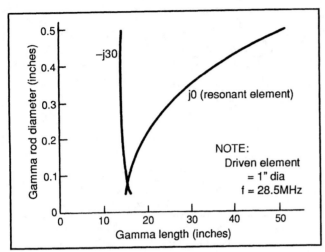

Figure 7-21. The length of the gamma rod with a shorter than resonant driven element (–j30) is nearly independent of gamma-rod diameter.

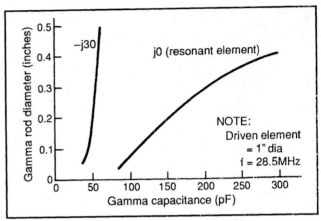

Figure 7-22. Gamma capacitance is nearly independent of gamma length when a shorter than resonant driven element (–j30) is used.

amount of shortening and the element diameter, as discussed previously. Assuming that the new resistance value is 15 ohms at a reactance value of –j50, a computer run shows that gamma-rod length increases by an inch, and the series capacitance decreases by 3 pF from the values determined for a feedpoint value of 18 ohms. This indicates that the actual feedpoint resistance isn't critical, and the feedpoint values given in the literature for multi-element Yagi beams hold well for use in the gamma computer program.

Gamma-Rod Diameter. The computer program provides interesting information about gamma-rod diameters (see **Figures 7-21** and **7-22**). The curves show the importance of having a shorter than resonant driven element. With the –j30 element length, gamma-rod length changes less than 2 inches as the rod diameter is varied from 0.05 to 0.5 inches. The gamma capacitor, given the same rod diameters, varies from 36 to 65 pF. When the driven element is resonant, the values of rod length and series capacitance vary greatly. This gives further proof that adjustment of driven-element length is of paramount importance in making the gamma match work.

Frequency Scaling. If all the dimensions of a 28.5-MHz beam and gamma-match system are doubled, the computed results will be identical at half the frequency—or 14.25 MHz. This scaling isn't practical for my 10-meter beam; it would result in a 20-meter driven-element diameter of 2 inches. I prefer a diameter of about 1.25 inches, all else being equal. I'd probably also build a tapered element. The gamma-match computer program doesn't consider this style of element, but there are programs that compute an equiva-

lent element length for a tapered element. This equivalent can then be used with the gamma program once its length is readjusted to provide a reactive termination. Someday, a Yagi computer program will be modified for frequency scaling. It will also accommodate the gamma match, as well as other matching systems requiring adjustment of the driven-element length.

Is There Pattern Distortion with the Gamma Match? The gamma match feeds only half the driven element. What happens to voltages and currents in the other half? Does the unbalanced feed system upset the beam pattern? Tests run by Katashi Nose, KH6IJ (SK), show that voltage at the driven-element tips of a 20-meter Yagi isn't equal when a gamma match is used. Even so, the azimuth pattern seemed balanced. Nose concluded that the voltage imbalance wasn't important.

Later tests run by Bob Sutherland, W6PO, a VHF "moonbounce" enthusiast, on a large array of 220-MHz gamma-fed Yagis showed that the array's pattern was normal with no noticeable "squint" or distortion that could be attributed to the gamma matches.

Gamma-Match Summary. The gamma match provides a mechanically simple and easily adjusted network for matching a Yagi to a coaxial transmission line, provided the driven element of the array is somewhat shorter than the resonant length. This point has often been overlooked or not emphasized in the literature, leading to puzzling results.

For the best mechanical arrangement, make the capacitor part of the gamma rod, as shown in **Figure 7-19.** As they say in the world of computers, the gamma match is "user friendly." Information provided here, along with the computer program, should make life easier for those contemplating using this simple match system.

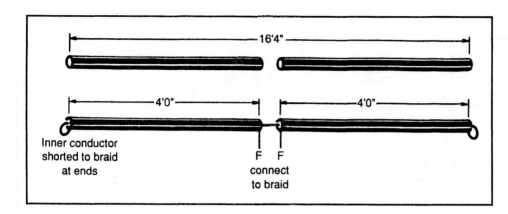

Figure 7-23. The W6GKM feed system. The matching coax is taped to the element. The feedline is connected to the braid at F–F.

Interesting Antenna Feed Systems

I've discussed the gamma match—a convenient and easily adjustable device for matching a coax line to the driven element of a Yagi beam. Many commercial beams use this system. Other interesting but less well-known matching systems exist; I'll cover a few the homebrewer can use. Some of the matches will function with a multiband antenna, while others are single-band devices. All of them deserve consideration for your next antenna project.

The W6GKM Matching System

Back in 1950, Dale Frink, W6GKM, devised a match for his 10-meter beam. The arrangement is shown in **Figure 7-23**. The driven element is split with a 2-inch gap at the center, and excited by a length of 50-ohm coax. The inner and outer conductors are shorted together at each end of the coax, and the shield braid is broken and fed with the transmission line at the center. The "matching coax" is about one-quarter wavelength long.

Dale taped the matching coax to the driven element. He found the SWR was low over the entire 10-meter band. Dale told me that he'd also placed the matching coax inside the driven element, instead of taping it to the outside. It seemed to work equally well either way.

How does this device function? The driven element is split and there are no electrical connections to either half. The simplest explanation is that the capacitance between the matching coax and the dipole halves does the job.

The Mosely "Classic" Match System

The Mosely "Classic" series of antennas use a similar device, shown in **Figure 7-24**. The Mosley advertisement calls it a "balanced capacitive match." The Classic match resembles the system used in W6GKM's design. Even though Dale uses coax in his match, the only meaningful part of the match is the outer shield of the coax; the inner conductor contributes nothing. By substituting a single insulated wire for the coax, you have the Classic system instead of the W6GKM match.

With the Classic-33 tribander, the match conductor is about a quarter wave long on 20 meters. It's placed inside the split driven element. I'll accept that, but how does the match function on the 15- and 10-meter bands, where the match wire is longer than a quarter wavelength? Is the length of the match wire unimportant, or does it bear a specific relationship to the operating frequency? I know the match works because I have a Classic-33 beam. It has a good front-to-back ratio, has a good operating bandwidth, and exhibits a low SWR value at resonance on each of the three HF bands (10, 15, and 20 meters). Those are the principal attributes of a good matching system. Is it purely a capacitive match, or do the match wire and the split element form some kind of a coaxial matching transformer?

The Clemens Match

In 1951 John Clemens, W9ERN, proposed a novel match system he had adapted from a television-antenna matching scheme. He applied the match to a 3-ele-

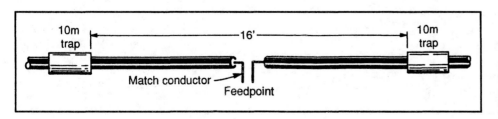

Figure 7-24. "Classic" feed system consists of coaxial wire placed in each half of the trapped driven element.

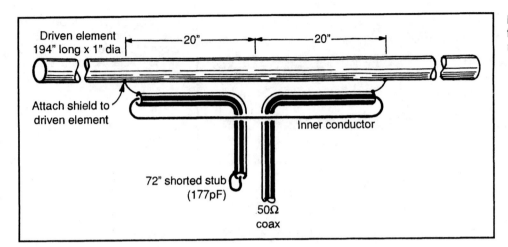

Figure 7-25. "Clemens match" for 29 MHz. Two gamma matches back-to-back?

ment 10-meter beam (**Figure 7-25**). This device taps the outer conductor of the coax on the driven element at a point that provides a good impedance match. The inner conductor is brought back along the driven element to an equivalent point on the opposite side of the element. It's connected to the element at this point through a series capacitor. The capacitance is made up of a section of coax line. The tap points and capacitance value are varied until unity SWR is obtained at the design frequency.

If you use your imagination, you can think of this device as two back-to-back gamma matches. The gamma capacitor is moved from the base of one gamma to the antenna end of the gamma conductor. The gamma "rod" is a 40-inch length of coax conductor running from one tap point to the other. What an interesting idea!

The Clemens match sank into oblivion for decades. I forgot about it completely until I worked Tony, ZL2ANT. He had taken the 1951 design and modernized it (**Figure 7-26**). Tony jettisoned the coax and substituted an aluminum tube. He fed the tube and one side of the driven element with the coax feedline taped along the driven element. With the dimensions shown, his series capacitor was 15 pF, as opposed to the 177 pF of the W9ERN design. He feels the 6-inch separation between the matching tube and the driven

element accounts for this difference. Tony says the match is very broad and he can work the dipole on both the 10- and 12-meter bands, with low SWR on each band.

All of these designs show the promise of multiband operation. In fact, multiband operation is proven with the Mosley Classic match. Perhaps one of these ideas is the one for you!

The Weinschel Matching System

In 1972, *QST* published data on a triband beam that uses a trapped 20/15-meter driven element connected in parallel with a 10-meter element placed about 18 inches away (**Figure 7-27**). The elements are connected by double wires, and the combination is fed at the center of the 10-meter element. The product review reported very low SWR on all bands, and the antenna exhibited good front-to-back ratio. I don't know of anyone who has tried this multiband matching system. I'm eagerly awaiting a missive that will inform me of the actual operating results achieved with this simple design.

The Open-Sleeve Dipole System

An unusual dual-frequency antenna was developed at Stanford Research Institute in 1950. Its operation was described in a paper by H. B. Barkley. Roger Cox,

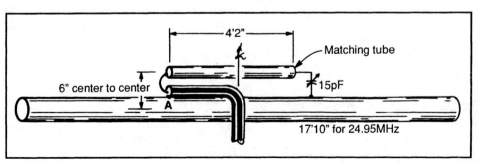

Figure 7-26. The ZL2ANT version of the Clemens match. Coax is taped to the driven element. The shield is attached to the driven element at A and the center conductor is attached to the matching tube. Tony says the system works best when both tubes are the same diameter.

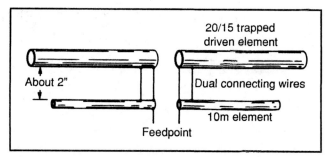

Figure 7-27. The Weinschel match. A coax balun is used at F–F. A later model beam used a "hairpin" match at the feedpoint in addition to a balun.

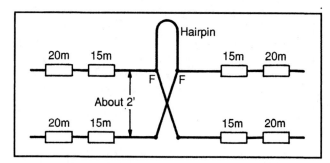

Figure 7-29. Telex/Hy-Gain triband match system using two trapped elements.

WBØGDF, gave a good description of the device in amateur terms in *CQ* magazine.

The device is called an "open-sleeve dipole." It consists of a conventional center-fed dipole with two parasitic elements spaced close together on each side. The parasitics are cut to a half-wavelength at some higher frequency (**Figure 7-28**). The ratio of high to low frequency can't exceed about 2 to 1.

You can make a practical open-sleeve dipole for 20/17, 20/15, 15/12, 20/10 meters, or other combinations of frequencies between 14 and 29.7 MHz. The drawing gives dimensions for a 20/10 dipole.

This scheme looks like a quick and painless way to add second-band capability to an existing beam. In addition to the "sleeves," you can interlace the parasitic elements for the higher band between the existing elements. It's worth a try!

The Telex/Hy-Gain Parasleeve Matching System

Here's a triband antenna that uses the open-sleeve dipole concept. The driven element of the Explorer 14 beam consists of three elements insulated from the boom. The longer element is trapped for 20- and 15-meter operation. The two short sections spaced close to the driven element act as an open-sleeve dipole for 10 meters. The short elements are optimized to provide the best SWR across the 10-meter band. The 15/20-meter element is fed with a "hairpin match," balun, and 50-ohm line. The SWR is quite low at design resonance and the front-to-back ratio is good on each band.

The Telex/Hy-Gain TH7DX Drive System

This top-of-the-line triband beam has two trapped, driven elements for 20, 15, and 10 meters. **Figure 7-29** shows the feed arrangement. The elements are cross-connected at the centers, and the rear element is fed with a hairpin match, balun, and 50-ohm line. The TH7DX antenna has very low SWR and good front-to-back ratio at design resonance on each band.

This matching idea resembles the Weinshel system, but uses a cross-over connection instead of a parallel connection between the elements. I wonder about the significance of this difference in connections. The cross-over scheme reminds me of the feed system used on a log-periodic array. Hopefully, someone will come up with a computer program that analyzes these interesting matching systems.

"Hairpin" Antenna Matching Systems

A simple matching system is an adaptation of the L-network, commonly called the "Beta" or "hairpin" match. It's an easily constructed matching device that any home builder can use with his beam antenna.

Generally speaking, the feedpoint impedance of a Yagi (regardless of the number of elements) falls between 15 and 25 ohms. The problem is to reach a reasonable match between these impedances and a 50-ohm coax line. The picture is complicated by the fact that when matching is achieved at the design frequency of the antenna, it deteriorates when the antenna is operated off frequency. The L-network, however, is "user friendly" (low Q) and provides a good match

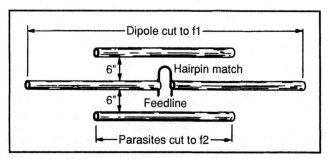

Figure 7-28. An "open-sleeve" two-frequency dipole. Spacing between the driven element and the parasitic element is about 6 inches.

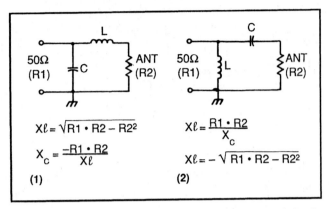

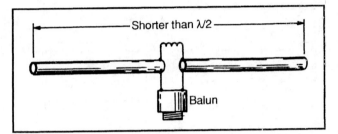

Figure 7-31. The balanced driven element is matched to the coax by shortening it and using a parallel inductor at the feedpoint. A balun is used to match the antenna to the unbalanced coax.

Figure 7-30. Basic single-ended L-networks to match feed-line (R1) to antenna (R2) when line impedance is greater.

across the HF amateur bands, in spite of the impedance gyrations of the driven element. Some matching schemes won't do that.

When the line impedance is greater than the feedpoint impedance of the antenna (as is the general case), the L-network takes the forms shown in **Figure 7-30**. Only two components are required—an inductor and a capacitor. It's possible to eliminate the series-connected component by making the driven element take its place. This is accomplished by detuning it slightly to introduce a value of series reactance equal to that of the missing network component. If the driven element is longer than the resonant length, its feedpoint reactance will be inductive (positive). If it's shorter than resonance, the reactance will be capacitive (negative). In this case, the shortened element will be used.

Because the feedpoint of the Yagi is balanced with respect to ground, it's necessary to use a balun with the matching network, as shown in **Figure 7-31**.

Using the Reactance Match. In most cases, the driven element of the Yagi is shortened to exhibit a series capacitive reactance. A shunt inductor can be a coil, or it may be a "hairpin" of wire (**Figures 7-32A and 7-32B**). Most commercial beams using this matching scheme prefer the hairpin over the inductor because the inductance (length) of the hairpin can be adjusted easily. The approaches are equally effective.

The homebrewer, on the other hand, may find the coil inductor easier to build than the hairpin. I prefer the coil because it's cheap, easy to wind, and can be adjusted at the center of the element, which is within easy reach from the top of the tower. (I don't like the idea of hanging out over open space to adjust the shorting bar on a hairpin match!)

In any event, the only adjustments you need to make in either system are to the length of the driven element and the inductance of the coil, or hairpin.

A Practical Matching Circuit. The L-network parameters are summarized in **Figure 7-33**. The X-axis of the graph represents the feedpoint impedance of the Yagi driven element, and the Y-axis represents the value of shunt reactance necessary to achieve a match to the 50-ohm line.

For example, assume a Yagi has a feedpoint of 20 ohms. The corresponding value of shunt reactance, as shown by the dashed lines, is 40 ohms. The actual inductance of the coil is determined by the formula. The driven element must be shortened, or "equalized," to provide the capacitive portion of the network.

Equalizing the Driven Element. To make this matching system work, the driven element must be slightly detuned (equalized) to provide the necessary reactance at the feedpoint. What does this mean in practice?

By definition, when an antenna is detuned from one frequency it becomes resonant at another. For example, assume the driven element of a Yagi is resonant at

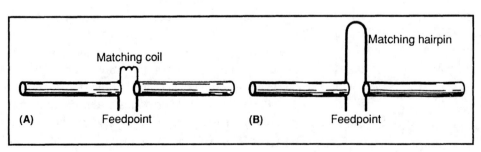

Figure 7-32. The shunt inductor may be either a coil or "hairpin."

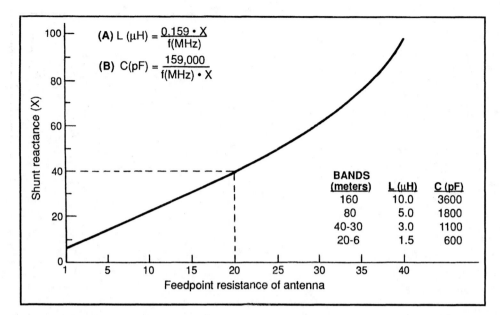

(A) $L\ (\mu H) = \dfrac{0.159 \cdot X}{f(MHz)}$

(B) $C(pF) = \dfrac{159,000}{f(MHz) \cdot X}$

BANDS (meters)	L (μH)	C (pF)
160	10.0	3600
80	5.0	1800
40-30	3.0	1100
20-6	1.5	600

Figure 7-33. The shunt reactance values required for various values of feedpoint resistance. Typical baluns are listed in the chart.

14.2 MHz and has a feedpoint resistance of 20 ohms, and you want to match it to a 50-ohm coax line. A frequency run of the antenna will resemble the SWR curve of **Figure 7-34**. At the resonant frequency, the minimum SWR value is 50/20, or 2.5:1. The SWR gradually increases as the antenna is operated off frequency (curve A).

A coil match is to be used at the feedpoint to reduce the SWR. The correct value of inductance is determined from the table and an appropriate coil is placed across the feedpoint. An SWR plot of the antenna is run across the 20-meter band and compared with the plot run without the coil. The driven element and inductor combination are now resonant at 13.8 MHz instead of 14.2 MHz and minimum SWR is about 1.5:1 (**Figure 7-34**, curve B). Addition of the matching inductor has lowered the indicated resonant frequency of the driven element by 400 kHz. Resonance is now outside the 20-meter band! The final step is to shorten the driven element to restore resonance at 14.2 MHz. Once you've done this, the minimum SWR at the resonant frequency will be very close to unity (**Figure 7-34**, curve C). Squeezing or expanding the coil turns a bit will drop the SWR curve "in the slot."

This procedure determines the correct length of the driven element indirectly, providing the required value of negative reactance at 14.2 MHz in order to make the matching system work as it should.

Is Equalization Necessary? Equalization is necessary, especially with regard to solid-state transmitters that don't like to load into a transmission line having a high value of SWR. The proper amount of equalization required for the matching system depends on the

ratio of antenna feedpoint resistance to the coax-line impedance. The greater the ratio, the more equalization (less coil inductance) required.

The problem is to determine the degree of shortening required to equalize the driven element. Very little information exists about the reactance change per unit of length for a Yagi driven element of a certain diameter. The reactance change is a function of frequency, element diameter, and taper. It generally amounts to a foot or more at 14 MHz, and correspondingly lesser amounts for the higher frequency bands.

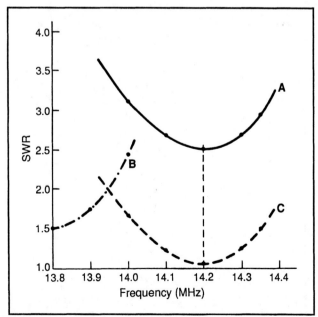

Figure 7-34. Curve A shows SWR with a feedpoint resistance of 20 ohms. Curve B shows the SWR with parallel inductance added. Curve C shows the SWR with the driven element equalized.

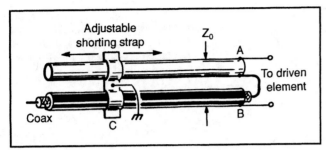

Figure 7-35. Matching balun is constructed by passing coax down the inside of one leg. The inner conductor is cross-connected to the other leg at the balanced feedpoint.

The Adjustable Beta Match

This relative of the hairpin match combines an adjustable impedance transformer with a balun. It's usable with antenna feedpoint impedances between 10 and 40 ohms. Basic operation follows that outlined for the hairpin match. The device is the parallel reactance portion of the L-network (**Figure 7-35**). The series reactance is attained by shortening the driven element.

The network is converted to a balun as shown in the drawing. Points A and B of the linear balun are balanced to ground. The unbalanced coax line is brought into the balun through one of the balun tubes, with the center conductor of the coax crossing over at the antenna end of the balun to contact the opposite balun tube. This device provides both excellent balance and transformer action when you adjust the shorting bar at the opposite end of the balun and the length of the driven element.

Balance is achieved by permitting the outer shield of the coax line to assume the potential of the balun tube as it passes from the grounded end (C) to the ter-

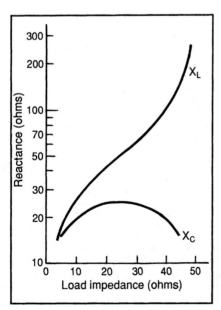

Figure 7-36. Inductive and capacitive values for antenna equalization when 50-ohm coax line is used.

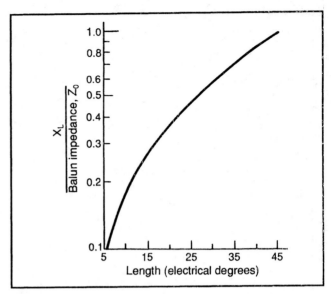

Figure 7-37. The electrical length of a balun in degrees as a function of inductive shunt element (X_L) to balun impedance (Z_0).

minal end (B). Cross-connecting the center conductor to the opposite balun leg at A ensures the desired 180-degree phase reversal is achieved.

Once the transformation ratio and the values of the series and parallel reactance have been determined, the balun is designed from transmission-line formulas. The relationship between the balun parameters and the driven element is given in **Figures 7-36** and **7-37**. A plot of the ratio X_L/Z_0 in terms of line length for 20 meters is provided in **Figure 7-38**.

You can build a practical balun of 3/8-inch diameter thin-wall copper tubing. A center conductor of RG-8 or RG-213 coax will just pass through the tubing when the braid and vinyl jacket have been removed. Using a center-to-center spacing of 3 inches for the tubes, you'll form a balanced line having a characteristic impedance of about 325 ohms.

Designing the Beta Match. Assume the coax is 50 ohms and the Yagi feedpoint resistance at resonance is 20 ohms. In **Figure 7-36**, the value of X_c is −24.5 ohms and the value of X_L is 41.5 ohms. **Figure 7-37** shows that the ratio of X_L to balun impedance is 41.5/325 = 0.127, as read on the Y-axis. The balun length, as read on the X-axis, is about 7.5 electrical degrees. To obtain the answer directly in feet, use **Figure 7-38** for the 20-meter band. In this example, the balun length is about 1.4 feet, or 17 inches, for a ratio of 0.127 (read on the Y-axis).

The series reactance value (X_c) of −24.5 ohms is achieved by shortening the driven element. It would be nice if the value could be computed, rather than

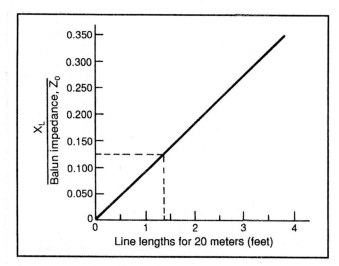

Figure 7-38. A balun conversion chart for 20 meters. Balun length in feet may be determined if feedpoint resistance, shunt reactance, and balun impedance are known.

determined by the heuristic (cut-and-try) technique. As I mentioned before, it's about a foot for 20 meters.

A Cheap and Effective Center Insulator

Do you need an inexpensive center insulator for a Field Day dipole? You can buy several different makes, but here's a design you can build yourself for just a few pennies. The idea originated with Lloyd Bensen, W9YCB. The device is light, waterproof, and made of easily obtainable materials (**Figure 7-39**). Lloyd uses his insulator on a beam because he had problems with water entering the line.

The heart of the assembly is a 4-1/2 inch length of 1/2-inch (inner diameter) automotive hose. Taper one end of the hose with a razor or sharp knife, and slot the other end to receive the wires of the coax cable. Slide the hose over the cable as shown, with the slotted end facing the end of the cable.

Prepare the cable by fanning out the braid and unbraiding about 2 inches with a pointed tool. Twist this portion of the cable into a tight pigtail. Now remove the inner insulation, leaving only a protective collar about 1/8 inch long between the inner conductor and the outer, braided pigtail.

Bend the coax conductors into the shape shown in the drawing and tin them. Extend the tinning back to the insulating material. Tin the exposed portion of the outer braid all around the cable. Finally, cut the con-

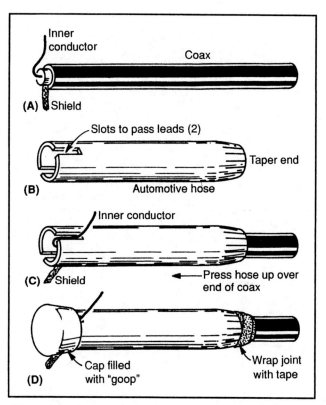

Figure 7-39. Making the coax center insulator. (See text for instructions.)

ductors back, leaving leads about 3/4 inch long. Press the hose up so the tinned conductors drop into the slots you cut. Taper the slots slightly for a tight fit.

Now weatherproof the end of the cable. Lloyd recommends using a plastic cap from a hardware store or home service center. A cap with about a 5/8-inch inner diameter slips nicely over the hose. Cover the end of the cable and the inside of the cap with semi-liquid insulation before attaching the cap. Lloyd used "Sportsman's Goop" from a sporting-goods shop. (You could fill the cap with quick-setting epoxy instead.) Press the cap over the hose and the end of the cable and carefully wipe away any excess goop or epoxy around the conductors.

Wrap the tapered end of the hose with vinyl tape. Extend the tape an inch or two down the coax line. This prevents moisture from entering the end of the hose and being drawn up into the coax by capillary action.

It takes almost as long to read this as it does to make the joint. Try out one of these simple devices on your next Field Day antenna!

Chapter 8

Antenna Analysis Programs and How They Work

In 1935 Marshall Mims, W5BDB, described a startling new beam antenna concept in *QST* magazine.[1] It was a two-element Yagi made of aluminum tubing elements. The antenna had remote-control rotation and a direction-indicating system. Nothing like it had ever been seen before in amateur radio!

The Mims beam took over a year to perfect; four designs were built and discarded. Number five worked, after a fashion. Number six seemed better. By the seventh model, the beam was ready for action. It had quarter-wave spacing between the driven element and the reflector, and provided about 2.7 dBd gain and a front-to-back ratio of 10 dB—or so Mims thought. Running his 1935 design through a modern computer program, we see that the pioneering ham-band Yagi provided 4.3 dBd gain and a front-to-back ratio of about 12 dB. Mims designed a pretty good beam and made an excellent guess about its characteristics. His data was based upon measurements made by interested hams using their receivers' S-meters. *(Editor's note: Actually, "R-meters" were used in those days.)*

Antenna design and measurement techniques had a crude and shaky beginning, but were refined over the decades. What was once thought to be a rather routine field measurement proved quite tricky and complicated if reproducible results were desired. Over the years, military and commercial manufacturers built some large and expensive antenna ranges to measure the characteristics of HF and VHF antennas, but amateur antenna measurements were rough-and-ready.

The Computer Enters the Picture

The arrival of the powerful digital computer soon provided a new insight into antenna operation. In 1968, an analysis technique known as "moment methods" was publicized.[2] This scheme dealt with the investigation of electromagnetic fields using computer techniques. Those who remember their high-school integral calculus will no doubt recognize the concept. But the new idea didn't catch fire until computer power was generally available at low cost.

The moment method gave antenna designers the know-how to translate theory into practice. The job at hand was to create a good computer analysis program for transmitting antennas.

The birth of the home computer brought a new level of antenna analysis. Some computerized methods for calculating antenna properties were based on FORTRAN programs that used simple approximations for mutual and self-impedance to calculate element currents in arrays. The magnitude and phase of the element currents were then combined to produce moderately accurate radiation patterns. One of the most popular and well known of these programs was outlined and used by James Lawson, W2PV, in his article series[3] and his book.[4] Stanley Jaffin, WB3BGU, was another contributor to this field.[5]

About the same time, the Lawrence Livermore Laboratory at Livermore, California was manipulating a different, more powerful antenna analysis program, Numerical Electromagnetic Code (NEC), a mainframe program used to analyze electromagnetic fields.[6] A derivation of the program (MININEC) was refined at the Naval Ocean Systems Center, Point Loma, California. It applied specifically to antenna analysis using IBM PCs. Unfortunately, it wasn't user friendly and was too complex for everyday amateur use. Even so, it was a gigantic step in the right direction.

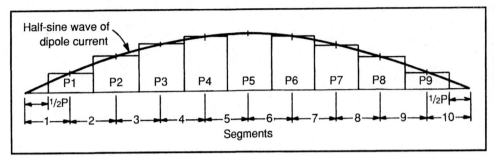

Half-sine wave of dipole current

Figure 8-1. A plot of current in a dipole. The dipole is divided into ten segments, with nine full pulses centered on the segments. Half-pulses exist at ends of the dipole. The feedpoint is between segments 5 and 6 (pulse no. 5).

A Representative Antenna Analysis Program

Brian Beezley, K6STI, took the MININEC program and modified it for general amateur work (MN). He retained the original antenna-modeling algorithm, but optimized the code for higher performance. He then massaged the program to make it more applicable to the amateur service. The original MN program, discussed here, has been superceded by a more powerful program, AO (Antenna Optimizer), but the principle remains the same.

The MN approach to antenna analysis can be illustrated by considering a straight conductor, such as the dipole shown in **Figure 8-1**. The dipole is broken into segments for examination. The number of segments depends on the complexity of the antenna and may be chosen by the user. In this case, ten segments are used. More segments would increase the accuracy of the computations, but would also increase computer time.

Each pair of wire segments defines a rectangular current pulse. As shown in the illustration, the current is modeled as uniform within each pulse. The current pulses are centered on segment boundaries and are the same length as the segments. The amplitude of the pulse closely approximates the amplitude of the current in the dipole at that point, as long as enough current pulses are used. The collection of pulses approximates the dipole current, which in this case is the classic half sine wave. A half pulse of zero current is placed at each end of the dipole; thus, there are ten segments and nine full pulses along the wire.

Certain restrictions apply. The wire is always straight. A bent wire is modeled by connecting two straight wires. Wires that cross or terminate at midpoints of other wires are modeled by defining separate wires which join. Connections are allowed only at wire end points.

The antenna feedpoint must be defined at a pulse. You can place the feedpoint where desired by specifying the correct number of segments in the wire. After doing it once or twice, you can almost make this placement by intuition.

Once all the data for an antenna is entered into an antenna file for the MN program, you can quickly determine antenna gain, front-to-back ratio, side-lobe level, beamwidth, feedpoint impedance, and vertical angle of radiation. These parameters once took hours of calculation or tedious field-strength measurements to characterize.

To illustrate the program, let's run an exercise with MN on a 3-element, 20-meter Yagi beam.

The Antenna Design Program. You must define the antenna in terms that the MN program understands. Those who studied descriptive geometry in high school will grasp the idea immediately. Even if you didn't, you'll have no trouble picking up the procedure.

An X-Y-Z Cartesian coordinate system is used to refer to points in space (see **Figure 8-2**). The antenna is placed in this system. X and Y are the coordinates in the horizontal plane; Z is in the vertical plane. Think of the dimensions as X = length, Y = width, and Z = height. An antenna may be placed in the coordinate system in any position, but a directional antenna, such as a Yagi, should be "aimed" in the +X direction. For convenience, the center point of the driven element is sometimes placed at the center of the coordinate system (X = 0, Y = 0, Z = 0).

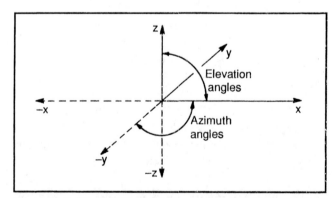

Figure 8-2. The X-Y-Z coordinate system. Three dimensions are shown. X-Y is the horizontal plane. Scale drawing of the antenna may be placed anywhere in this frame of reference.

20-meter Yagi Conventional Dimensions	
Boom	21.4 feet
Reflector	34.64 feet
Driven Element	33.2 feet
Director Element	31.34 feet
Element Diameter	1 inch

Table 8-1. Conventional dimensions of a 20-meter Yagi.

The sample antenna is a Yagi of conventional dimensions as listed in **Table 8-1**. The Yagi is placed in the coordinate system shown in **Figure 8-2**. It's analyzed in free space so only the X-Y plane is required. The boom extends along the X axis and the elements fall along the Y axis (**Figure 8-3**).

Now that you've established the reference frame, you must describe the specific end points of the elements. The Yagi dimensions (in feet) are known, as are the end points of the elements. The midpoint of each element falls on the X axis and the end points fall in the +Y and −Y areas of the plot. For example, the reflector falls at a distance of X = −10.7 feet from the center point of the plot, the driven element is placed at X = −1.28 feet from the center point, and the director is placed at X = +10.7 feet from the center point. This adds up to a 21.4-foot boom.

The reflector is 34.64 feet long; each half is 17.32 feet long. One end point of the reflector, which falls in the +Y quadrant, is labeled Y = +17.32 feet; the other end point, which falls in the −Y quadrant, is labeled Y = −17.32 feet.

Element	End point no. 1 Coordinates			End point no. 2 Coordinates		
	X	Y	Z	X	Y	Z
Reflector	−10.7	−17.32	0	−10.7	17.32	0
Driven	−1.28	−16.6	0	−1.28	16.6	0
Director	10.7	−15.67	0	10.7	15.67	0

Table 8-2. The X-Y coordinates of element ends.

The same sequence is followed by the end points of the driven element and the director. All the resulting end-point plots are shown in the illustration.

All that remains is to tabulate the end points and choose the tubing diameter of the elements. One-inch tubing was chosen here for simplicity, although tapered telescoping elements may be modeled as well. The end points converted to our coordinate system are shown in **Table 8-2**. MN next needs to know the number and locations of feedpoints (sources), and the number of segments in each element.

Ten segments are chosen for each element. This determines the number of pulses per element. The number of full pulses per element is the number of segments minus one. Thus, there are nine pulses in the reflector. There are also nine pulses each in the driven element and in the director. The source is located by counting the pulses, starting at one end of the first element of the antenna. In this case pulses are counted starting with the reflector, followed by the driven element. That is, nine reflector pulses plus one-half the number of driven element pulses specify the source. This falls at pulse 14 (nine reflector pulses plus five driven-element pulses). Half pulses aren't counted. (If an odd number of pulses were chosen for the driven element, the feedpoint would be off center.)

Thus, the antenna has one source and the feedpoint is at pulse number 14. There are no loads in the antenna (inductors, capacitors, or resistors), so this portion of the MN file may be left out. It would be used if a triband Yagi with traps were being modeled.

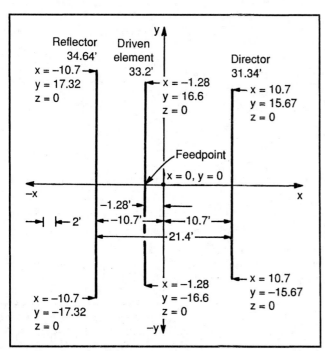

Figure 8-3. The 20-meter beam laid out in X-Y coordinates.

1	3 element 20-meter Yagi
2	Free space
3	14.175 MHz
4	Three wires, feet
5	10 −10.7, −17.32, 0 −10.7, 17.32, 0 0.083
6	10 −1.28, −16.6, 0 −1.28, 16.6, 0 0.083
7	10 10.7, 15.67, 0 10.7, 15.67, 0 0.083
8	1 source
9	14
10	0 loads

Table 8-3. Antenna data file for input to MN. Line numbers are for reference only and shouldn't be in the final file.

The Antenna File. Now that we have the information in hand, all that remains is to use an ASCII text editor or word processor to place it in a computer file in the stylized form shown in **Table 8-3**. Line numbers have been added for reference, but they shouldn't be in the final file.

Line 1 specifies a title for the antenna. This one is "3-element 20-Meter Yagi." Line 2 tells whether the antenna is in free space or modeled over the ground. I've chosen free space for this example, so MN looks for those words. If I had specified a Z dimension (such as +45) to all elements, it would indicate that the antenna is 45 feet in the air.

Line 3 specifies the analysis frequency. In this case it will be 14.175 MHz—the center of the 20-meter band. Line 4 tells the number of "wires," or elements, and the unit of measurement. I'm using three elements measured in feet. This completes the introductory phase.

Now to the element specifics. Three computer lines are required (lines 5, 6, and 7), as there are three elements in the antenna. Each line (starting with the reflector) specifies the number of segments; the X, Y, Z coordinates of the wire (element) tips; and the wire diameter (chosen as 1 inch, or 0.083 feet).

Line 5 lists the number of segments (10), the coordinates of the left- and right-hand tips of the reflector, and the element diameter in feet. Lines 6 and 7 list the same for the driven element and director. Line 8 specifies the number of sources (1), and line 9 gives the drive-pulse number (14). Line 9 can also set the applied voltage and current. However, these values are optional and, if not entered, the computer picks a nominal default value to make things work out. Be-

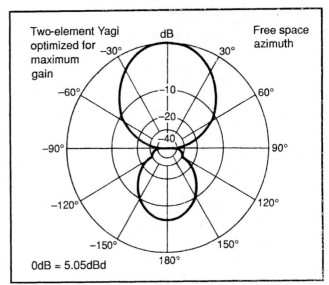

Figure 8-5. MN plot of a two-element Yagi shows good gain but poor front-to-back ratio. In comparing Figures 8-4 and 8-5, note that the gains for 0 dB (shown in the lower left) are different.

cause there are no loads, line 10 is omitted.

The MN program allows dimensions in feet, inches, millimeters, etc., and permits wire gauges to be used for element diameter. We needn't concern ourselves with these items now.

The completed antenna file is entered into the MN program, which is ready to run.

Antenna Comparison with MN. MN can come up with some surprising answers. It's interesting to observe the power gain and field plot of a popular 20-meter four-element Yagi on a 26-foot boom. DXers favor this antenna. MN shows that the power gain of this array is 5.93 dBd with a front-to-back ratio of 27.17 dB at the design frequency. The field plot is shown in **Figure 8-4**.

A two-element 20-meter Yagi on an 8-foot boom is shown in **Figure 8-5** for comparison. The power gain at the design frequency is 5.05 dBd and the front-to-back ratio is 6.37 dB.

Consider that the boom of the 4-element array is 18 feet longer than that of the little 2-element beam. What did the extra 18 feet achieve? The big beam has a gain of only 0.88 dB over the small one. The real advantage is in front-to-back ratio—a whopping increase of 20.8 dB!

If you're only interested in power gain, it's a waste of space, time, and money to put up the big array. But if you need front-to-back ratio, there's no doubt as to which antenna is the logical choice.

After running various antenna designs on the MN program, I find it has proven decisively what I had

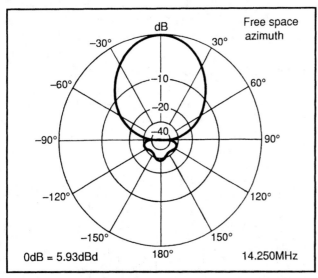

Figure 8-4. Azimuth plot of a four-element Yagi by representative MN program.

known intuitively for many years—there is no free lunch. Bigger antennas are generally better in most respects than small ones. When you optimize a design for one characteristic (say, maximum gain), it will suffer in another area (poorer front-to-back ratio or bandwidth). The "optimum" design depends on your definition of optimum.

The Yagi Optimizer (YO)

Is a 4-element beam a better performer than a 3-element beam? What is the optimum boom length for a given number of elements? What is the effect of element taper? Is it better to lengthen the boom when adding an extra element, or to drop an extra element into an existing array in order to achieve a little more gain? What is the relationship between gain and front-to-back ratio? Is it necessary to sacrifice one to enhance the other? Do maximum gain and highest front-to-back ratio occur at the same frequency? These are good questions, and ones that finally can be answered with the Yagi Optimizer (YO) program for the home computer.

YO analyzes and optimizes a given Yagi antenna. It will model arrays of up to 50 elements. The model is examined in free space and the accuracy is typically within 0.1 dB for forward gain, a few dB for front-to-back, and within a couple of ohms for input impedance.

Optimization may be done at a spot frequency within a band, or at the low, middle, and high frequencies of the band of interest. You may choose the parameters, aiming for maximum gain, best front-to-back ratio, a given value of input impedance, or a combination of these parameters.

Is There a Maximum Gain Yagi? Before discussing program details, it's interesting to contemplate the possibility of achieving a maximum gain Yagi. A popular question among HF and VHF operators is: How much gain can be achieved for a given number of elements or a given boom length? YO provides interesting answers to such questions.

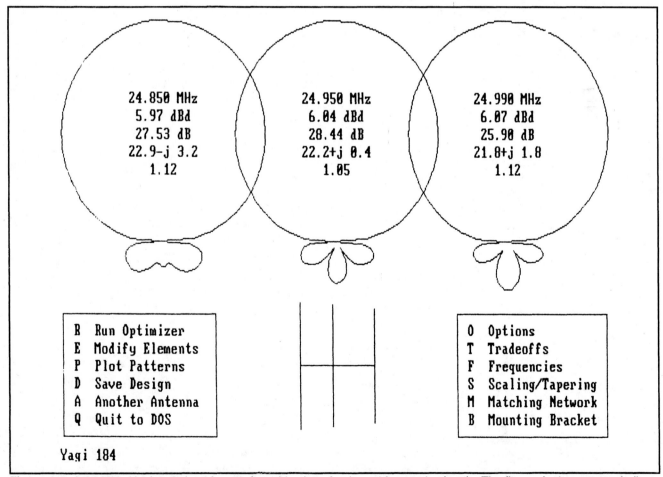

Figure 8-6. A 24-MHz Yagi optimized for good combination of gain and front-to-back ratio. The figures in the patterns indicate frequency, gain, front-to-back ratio, input impedance, and SWR. Beam is optimized at three frequencies. Below the patterns you see a representation of the Yagi. Monotaper dimensions are (length and position in inches): reflector 118.25/−72.96; driven element 112.75/−9.23; director 105.8/72.96. Boom length is 12 feet 2 inches.

Yes, Virginia, there is a maximum gain Yagi. YO will find it for you by crunching through variations in element length and spacing that would be impossible to compute a decade ago. For example, I entered typical dimensions for a 24-MHz, 3-element Yagi built on a 12-foot boom. Starting with these basics, I directed the program to search for a maximum gain Yagi that retained a good front-to-back ratio while maintaining the same boom length. The results are shown in **Figure 8-6**. The program examined 184 length/spacing combinations to arrive at the optimized design. The array has 6.04 dBd gain at the design frequency of 24.95 MHz, and a front-to-back ratio of over 28 dB. Input impedance is about 22 ohms.

This is a good compromise design. Can the gain be increased by holding the boom length constant, but allowing element length and spacing to be varied? Yes. Setting YO in action again, I found that the program quickly examined 262 designs in sequence and arrived at the maximum gain design shown in **Figure 8-7**. This Yagi provides 7.82 dBd gain with a front-to-back ratio of only 7.55 dB. Input impedance is about 1.7 ohms. And look at the spacing!

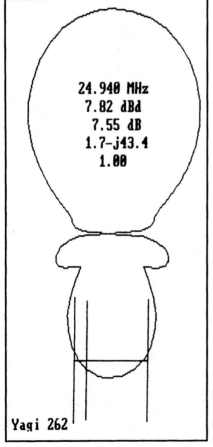

```
24.948 MHz
7.82 dBd
7.55 dB
1.7-j43.4
1.00
```

Yagi 262

Figure 8-7. The same Yagi as in Figure 8-6 optimized for maximum gain without regard to front-to-back ratio. The beam is optimized at only one frequency. Monotaper dimensions are (length and position in inches): reflector 115.251/0; driven element 108.008/23.663; director 111.006/142. Boom length is 11 feet 10 inches.

A beam of this design is a theoretical concept. The radiation resistance is so low that substantial ohmic losses exist in the array, and it's difficult to design a network that would match the low-impedance load to a coax line. The real-life gain of such an oddball design is questionable. Front-to-back ratio is poor, and wind vibration would upset antenna parameters unless the driven element and reflector were suitably braced.

What's the upshot of this optimization? The design has gained 1.78 dB at the loss of nearly 21 dB of front-to-back ratio. At the same time, the feedpoint impedance has become impossibly low. Exotic results, but the beam is impractical. Optimization has been carried to an extreme.

Practical Results with the YO Program. Running the YO program quickly shows the folly of being too eager to achieve forward gain at the expense of other important antenna parameters. The YO program emphasizes that maximizing forward gain results in poor front-to-back ratio, low input impedance, possible sidelobes, and small SWR bandwidth. However, because of the tradeoff capability, the program lets you automatically optimize a combination of gain, front-to-back, and either input impedance or SWR. The combination of parameters to be optimized and their relative importance are determined using a Tradeoff Menu.

The Tradeoff Menu. In most cases, maximizing forward gain at the expense of other parameters isn't practical. To obtain a good combination of parameters, set a ratio of forward gain to front-to-back of 9:1. This means that YO will weigh front-to-back by 10 percent and forward gain by 90 percent. (Other ratios may be chosen at your discretion.) This ratio, however, places 1 dB of gain equal to 9 dB of front-to-back ratio. If YO can change the design in such a way that the front-to-back ratio increases more than nine times as much as the forward gain decreases, it will do so.

Experience has shown that this ratio yields a very practical design. Once this optimization has been completed, you can then optimize the design for input impedance and bandwidth tradeoffs. Your strategy is to obtain the most uniform antenna performance across the band. Obviously, the final design depends considerably on the width of the amateur band; a 10-meter optimized design is quite different from a design optimized for the narrow 12-meter band.

The Optimization Method. The Yagi Optimizer uses a modified "Method of Steepest Descent." Parameters of each element are changed by a small amount, while other antenna dimensions are held un-

K7HYR's maximum gain Yagi 24.890 24.940 24.990 MHz 4 elements, inches				
	1.617	1.250	1.125	0.875
0.000	2.938	15.062	66.000	33.305
124.000	2.938	15.062	66.000	28.248
248.000	2.938	15.062	66.000	26.815
372.000	2.938	15.062	66.000	28.313

Table 8-4. YO format for 4-element beam.

changed. The program calculates the sensitivity of the objective to each variable. The collection of the element sensitivities leads to an iteration where all the variables are updated, each in proportion to its respective sensitivity. The process is repetitive, and terminates either at user command or when no further improvement in the objective is possible.

This technique doesn't guarantee the very best set of antenna dimensions out of all possible dimensions. That nirvana can be accomplished only by an exhaustive and impractical search of all possible dimensions. The definition of "best" is user determined. As an analogy, imagine that you're climbing to the very top of a mountain range of multiple peaks in a dense fog. You might arrive at a peak, but it might not be the highest one. Familiarization with the program and

examination of various antennas in the program library will quickly guide you into a comfortable relationship with program tradeoffs. The program lets you change element lengths and positions by keyboard entry. This is a great way to get the "feel" for how each element affects the overall antenna performance. Common sense is a great help in Yagi optimization.

YO Matching Networks. YO contains models for several matching systems, including the Gamma Match, the T-match, the "Hairpin" Match, and the Beta Match. The program allows you to determine the effects of element taper and mounting brackets. It's also possible to quickly scale any Yagi design to a new frequency, while maintaining essentially the same performance characteristics.

The YO File Format. The initial antenna configuration must be entered in a Yagi file in a specific format. The elements are specified in order, beginning with the reflector (see **Table 8-4**). One-half of each element, from the center of the boom to the element tip, normally is required. For monotaper elements, you may use the entire element length.

Place a title for the antenna on the first line. One or three analysis frequencies go on the second line. The program assumes you are using megaHertz if you

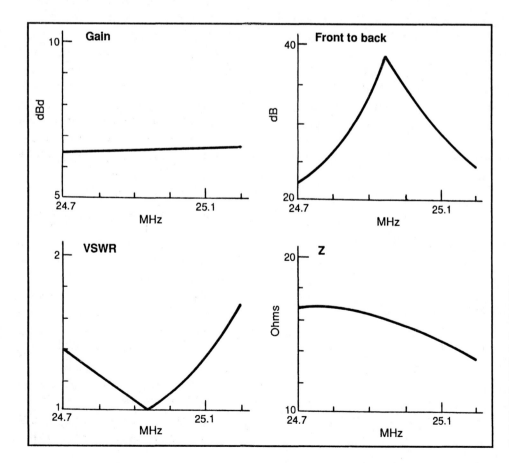

Figure 8-8. Parameters of a four-element, 12-meter Yagi are provided in four illustrations. The graph on the upper left shows gain is relatively constant at 6.5 dBd across the band. The graph on the upper right shows that front-to-back ratio peaks at about 37 dB at 24.95 MHz. The lower graphs illustrate VSWR match to a 50-ohm line (left) and feedpoint impedance versus frequency (right).

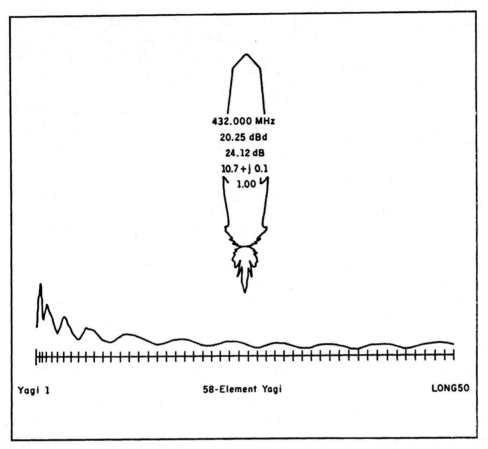

Figure 8-9. Element current along a 50-element Yagi varies in a cyclic manner. At one time, it was thought that current in parasitic elements decreased with increasing distance from the driven element. This analysis shows that this is not necessarily the case—at least not with this Long John Yagi!

don't specify frequency units. On the third line, enter the number of elements and the dimension units. In this example, inches are used.

The next line asks that you list the taper diameters, starting with those closest to the boom. The maximum number of taper sections you can use is seven. The first taper section in this example represents the element mounting plates. On the remaining lines list the element positions followed by the length of the taper sections, beginning with the section closest to the boom. (As an alternative, you may use element spacings.)

It's possible to accommodate different taper schedules for different elements. Various examples are given in the documentation that accompanies the program.

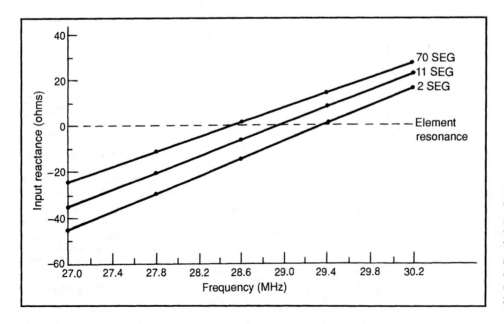

Figure 8-10. The input reactance of a tapered element analyzed by NEC varies with the number of segments used. This representative element is self-resonant near 28.6 MHz. If only 11 segments are used, element resonance falls about 300 kHz higher in frequency.

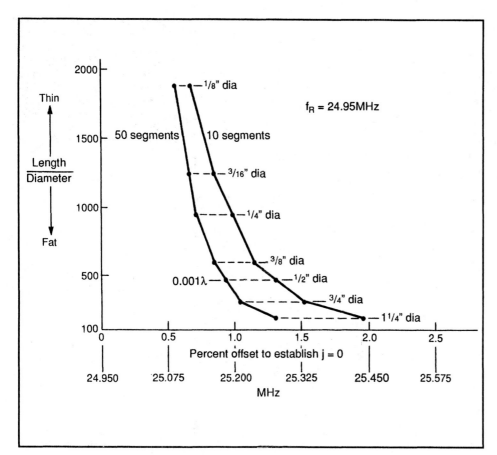

Figure 8-11. Representative frequency offset of a test dipole when examined in a MININEC-derived program. Percentage offset is least when many segments are used and element diameter is small compared to length (less than 0.001 wavelength). Once the offset is known, it may be factored into the final antenna analysis to provide accurate dimensions.

The parameters versus frequency graphs shown in **Figure 8-8** are a helpful addition to YO. Gain, front-to-back ratio, VSWR, and impedance curves versus frequency are displayed and may be printed. A quick overview of a complete Yagi design is given at a glance. Operator-introduced changes in antenna design are reflected in these graphs to provide visual evidence of antenna performance.

Element Current Profile. YO can draw a profile of element-current magnitudes along the boom of the Yagi (see **Figure 8-9**). The profile is normalized so the curve height for the largest current remains constant. This option can be used to spot grossly mistuned elements on long-boom Yagis by identifying elements with abnormally high or low current.

No doubt quicker, newer, more advanced, and increasingly accurate antenna modeling programs will surface. Even so, today's programs do the job and are a lot more satisfying to use than earlier cut-and-try and hope-for-the-best methods!

Problems with NEC and MININEC

A comparison of NEC results on a tapered element with antenna-range measurements on the same element showed that the NEC program introduced a frequency offset and considerable changes in current ratios and phasing. Correct values are essential for an accurate computer model, but once this tapered-element frequency offset is recognized (**Figure 8-10**), it may be accounted for. The programs of K6STI and W7EL compensate for this unwanted effect.

MININEC, on the other hand, also introduces a frequency offset. The shift is a function of the element length/diameter ratio and the number of segments used in the design program (**Figure 8-11**). This gave rise to the thought that some of the "stripping down" done to NEC to produce MININEC may have added built-in problems where large-diameter elements are involved. Both the K6STI and the W7EL programs have built-in compensation for this effect, provided a sufficient number of pulses are used. As one investigator put it, "Segments should not be as fat as a tuna fish can, nor as long as a clothes pole. Visualize the shape of a cigarette."

A final problem of frequency offset in the case of the quad antenna and other loops was also overcome by the two abovementioned programs. Other programs may also compensate for these peculiarities in computer analysis of antennas.

References

1. Marshall Mims, W5BDB, "The All-Around 14 Mc. Signal Squirter," *QST*, Dec. 1935, page 12.

2. R. F. Harrington, *Field Computation by Moment Methods*, MacMillan Company, New York, 1968.

3. James Lawson, W2PV, "Yagi Antenna Design," *Ham Radio*, Aug. 1979 to Dec. 1980.

4. James Lawson, W2PV, *Yagi Antenna Design*, American Radio Relay League, Newington, Connecticut, 1986.

5. Stanley Jaffin, WB3EGU, "Applied Yagi Antenna Design, part 6," *Ham Radio*, Oct. 1984, page 89.

6. Burke and Poggio, "Numerical Electromagnetic Code (NEC)—Method of Moments," NOSC TD-116, Jan. 1981. Naval Ocean System Center, Point Loma, California.

Chapter 9

Inexpensive Beam Antennas You Can Build

A well-known DXer once said, "If you want a REALLY LOUD signal, you need dBs in the air and dBs on the desk!" It is also said that if your beam doesn't come down in a storm, it isn't big enough!

Well! It's nice to think big, and some lucky fellas can put up giant antennas. Most of us can't. Even so, the ionosphere is a great leveler of signals, and the prize doesn't always go to the most powerful signal. A small beam can perform wonders—especially if you are a DX-wise, smart operator.

Here are some small and some not-so-small beams. They aren't hard to build and you'll have a lot of fun if you try one of them. Building antennas is almost the last refuge for the avid experimenter, and armed with basic tools, some aluminum tubing, and other stuff, you'll enjoy building the projects in this chapter. Go for it!

How Big a Beam?

Sure, I'd like a 6-element job on a 60-foot boom, but let's be realistic! This is a daydream when one lives in a suburban area hemmed in by property lines, building restrictions, and suspicious neighbors who equate a big antenna with TVI and telephone interference.

There's a case to be made for the 2-element Yagi. First and foremost, it's small! It provides plenty of bang for the buck. It's light compared to a bigger array, and it's inexpensive to build. Only two elements and a very short boom are required. Best of all, it's very unassuming to the neighbor's eye.

Let's talk about gain first, because this is where the little 2-element job really shines. Before computer-aided antenna design programs were available, extravagant claims were made by aluminum benders whose Yagis were perfected in the advertising department,

rather than the engineering department. The computer programs removed the hocus-pocus from antenna design and provided straight answers about operating parameters.

The NEC and MININEC analysis programs show that the maximum gain of a 2-element Yagi is very close to 5.1 dBd. Practical designs run a little less than this: about 4.8 dBd power gain. It's possible to squeeze slightly more gain out of the 2-element design, but bandwidth, input impedance, and front-to-back ratio are sacrificed. One mustn't be too greedy about antenna gain!

The computer program quickly tells the designer that when one characteristic of a Yagi is emphasized, other attributes suffer. Thus, one cannot obtain maximum gain, maximum front-to-back ratio, high input impedance, and maximum bandwidth all at the same time. Something has to give!

Unfortunately, the 2-element design doesn't provide much front-to-back ratio. About the best that can be obtained—taking gain, bandwidth, and feedpoint impedance into consideration—is a paltry 10 dB. The only way to improve F/B ratio is to add extra elements (directors).

Bigger Yagi Antennas

Compared to a 2-element Yagi, a well-designed, computer-optimized 3-element beam runs about 6.4 dBd gain at the design frequency. However, the extra 1.6 dB increase in gain is achieved at the expense of a boom that's three to four times longer than that of the 2-element array.

The significant improvement of the 3-element model over a 2-element Yagi is in the front-to-back ratio. It's not difficult to obtain a ratio of over 20 dB. This is a great asset—especially if you live in the midwest, where you get QRM from both coasts. The addition of an extra element gives the computer program another variable to play with, and allows the designer extra headroom when trying to optimize an antenna for a certain band. Consider the tradeoffs involved in designing a beam for 10 meters that provides good gain and F/B ratio over the entire band. A difficult problem!

The 4-element Yagi is the next step up in antenna capability. W2PV's array, the highest gain design in this category, sacrifices bandwidth for gain. The gain of this Yagi is about 7.5 dBd—or about 1.1 dB over the 3-element antenna, and 2.7 dB over the little 2-element beam. (A narrowband design by K6STI for 50 MHz provides 8.8 dBd gain and 20 dB F/B ratio on a 13 foot 8 inch boom. That's equivalent to a 50-foot boom on 14 MHz.)

I think that as far as gain is concerned, going from two to three elements is a waste of time, money, and space. An increase of 1.1 dB, although very helpful in the VHF/UHF region, is marginal in the HF region because background atmospherics, QRM, and other factors wash out the extra decibel. However, upgrading from a 2-element design to the W2PV 4-element design provides a power gain of about 2.7 dB. In effect, you've nearly doubled your power. This increase may make the difference between capturing a contact or losing it. The extra decibels are especially helpful when digging a signal out of the background noise, provided the atmospherics don't increase in strength at the same rate as the signal you're looking for!

Now for the bad news. The W2PV design requires a 40-foot boom for a 14-MHz array. The 2-element antenna, on the other hand, can be built on a boom less than 8 feet long (one-fifth the size). The decision the would-be antenna builder must face with regard to the 4-element, 20-meter Yagi boils down to this: Is the extra 2.7 dB gain worth moving from an 8- to a 40-foot boom, or to the 50-foot boom required with the K6STI design?

The front-to-back ratio of the proposed Yagi antenna is a different matter. A 2-element Yagi will provide only about 10 dB F/B ratio at the design frequency, while a 3-element antenna will provide over 20 dB F/B ratio. That's a big difference! If F/B ratio is your most important parameter, the extra size of the 3-element beam is well worth the effort.

The W2PV 4-element design provides better than 20 dB F/B ratio only over a narrow frequency range—about plus or minus 140 kHz on the 20-meter band. The old Hy-Gain 204BA for 20 meters was an interesting compromise antenna. It sacrificed some forward gain for excellent F/B ratio, high input impedance, and good bandwidth. The forward gain wasn't much higher than an optimized 2-element beam; however, it was user friendly, and that means a lot!

Some amateurs have gone to a 5-element beam, particularly on 10 and 15 meters, where boom length is more modest. Telex/Hy-Gain's model 155CA is a popular design. Built on a 26-foot boom, this antenna provides a power gain of 7.55 dBd at the design frequency. The F/B ratio is 25 dB. When this beam is adjusted for the 24-MHz band, the power gain at the design frequency is 7.75 dB and the F/B ratio is 28 dB. That's a little more gain than the W2PV 4-element design, but this Yagi has a much better F/B ratio.

So There You Are!

Antenna gain is a powerful example of the law of diminishing returns. If you want power gain, or F/B ratio, you pay for it! You can enjoy the luxury of indecision as you juggle size, cost, antenna gain, and F/B ratio against your desire to be the big signal on the band!

Power gain can be equated to boom length. Above two elements, power gain entails long booms, with just enough elements on the boom to provide adequate gain. Adding extra elements to a given boom length won't buy you a thing (except possibly bandwidth), provided you have the minimum required number.

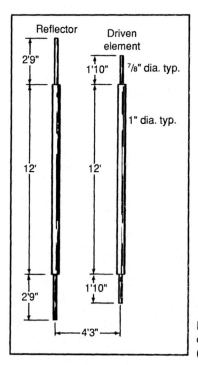

Figure 9-1. Dimensions of the 10-meter Yagi (top view).

If you want good F/B ratio, skip the 2-element beam and use a 3-element design. Adding extra elements above three helps the F/B ratio, but not as much as you might think.

Using the computer, any Yagi design can be jinked around to get a little more gain, a little more F/B, or a little more bandwidth. But beware, Murphy's Law is in effect! If you increase one parameter, you lose ground in others. Remember, there's no free lunch!

A Compact 2-Element Yagi for 10 Meters

There are plenty of good Yagi beams on the market, but it's possible to build one at home from scratch. The amateur with a lean purse will be interested in the simple beam described here. It's a 2-element design built on a boom that's only a little over 4 feet long! This gives you a low-profile installation that won't unduly excite the neighbors! If you have a Novice friend, you might want to build this antenna together. Because much of the assembly information is described in various handbooks, I'll just give you the basics.

The compact beam is shown in **Figure 9-1**. The design frequency is 28.4 MHz. The little antenna compares favorably with a conventional 3-element beam on a much longer boom. Power gain is about 4.2 dBd and the front-to-back ratio is about 11 dB. Those are very impressive figures for a beam of this size. The beam is light enough to mount above an existing beam. About 8 feet of separation between the arrays is recommended.

Beam Construction. The beam is built on a 4-foot 6-inch length of 2-inch OD aluminum tubing. The elements are composed of 12-foot center sections made of 1-inch aluminum tubing with a 0.058-inch wall. Tip sections of 7/8-inch diameter tubing slip nicely inside the center sections, which are slotted at each end. Hose clamps make a good mechanical joint. The overlapping section of the tips is coated with anti-oxidizing compound ("Penetrox," or equivalent) before the joint is clamped. The elements are mounted to the boom by aluminum plates measuring 8 by 2-1/2 inches. Galvanized U-bolts attach the elements to the plate

and the plate to the boom. This type of construction is described in detail in the *Beam Antenna Handbook*.

Overall element length is affected by element taper and mounting hardware. The elements must be extended about 1 inch to compensate. Final dimensions are shown in the drawing.

The Feed System. Use of a gamma-match system allows the driven element to be grounded to the boom. Details are shown in **Figure 9-2**. This match is a coaxial design. The 0.375-inch diameter gamma rod serves as the outer conductor of a capacitor made up of a length of RG-8A/U or RG-213/U coax. The outer jacket and braid are removed from the coax, and the insulated inner conductor is slipped within the aluminum tubing. Adjustment of the overlap determines the value of series capacitance the match requires. In this case, the capacitance is about 48 pF. High-quality coax runs about 29.5 pF per foot, so the overlap comes to about 20 inches. To make the match work properly, the driven element must be shorter than resonance, as shown in **Figure 9-1**.

Antenna Adjustment. Using the dimensions given, the antenna is very close to optimum. It may be necessary to touch up the gamma match a bit to obtain the lowest value of SWR at the design frequency. This can be done by placing the antenna atop the tower or atop a high stepladder. Using a ladder, the beam should be tilted so it points up at about 45 degrees to lessen the effect of the ground (driven element higher than the reflector). The length of the gamma rod and overlap of the coax capacitor are adjusted for lowest SWR when low power is applied to the antenna. If an acceptable minimum value of SWR isn't attained, the length of the driven element is adjusted slightly. A change in length is applied equally to each tip. The interlocking adjustments are element length, gamma-rod length, and gamma capacitance. You'll find that the antenna is probably on-the-nose and requires little, if any, tuning to achieve a good value of SWR at the design frequency.

A "Big Gun" Yagi for 10 Meters

So much for the little array. Now how about a big-

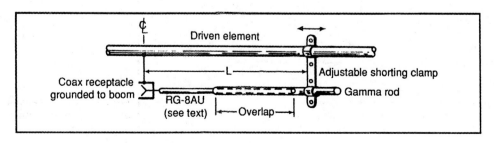

Figure 9-2. A coaxial gamma match. Center-to-center spacing of the rod to the antenna is 2 inches. Length L is about 23 inches. Seal the ends of the gamma rod against moisture.

gun design that will really bore a hole through a pile-up? Since Yagi computer-modeling programs became readily available, it's been possible to model antenna designs to fit specific applications. Tradeoffs among gain, front-to-back ratio, operating bandwidth, and input impedance are easily and quickly accomplished with these programs.

MININEC, the best-known antenna modeling program, was developed at the Naval Ocean Systems Command at Point Loma (San Diego), California. This antenna design is based on a modified (MN) program, using the K6STI version suitable for IBM PC-clone home computers. Contrary to a long-held belief, the program shows that when staggered director elements are used, improved results can be had in the areas of bandwidth and improved front-to-back ratio without a loss of gain. That is to say, the director lengths aren't constant, nor do the they decrease in an orderly manner with respect to distance from the driven element.

Antenna Characteristics. This beam provides a power gain of 9 dB over a dipole with a front-to-back ratio of 23 dB at the design frequency. SWR is less than 2:1 over the range of 28.0 to 28.8 MHz. Gain remains within 0.1 dB of the maximum figure over the operating range. For simplicity, the antenna is fed with a gamma matching system so all elements can be grounded to the boom.

The "big gun" is shown in **Figure 9-3**. Note that directors 1 and 3 are longer than directors 2 and 4.

Boom length of the array is 31 feet, and the elements are mounted on small plates above the boom. The center sections of the elements are 1-inch aluminum tubing with a 0.058-inch wall. The tip sections are 7/8-inch tubing with a 0.049 wall. This combination makes a light-rigid element.

The boom is made from 2-1/2 inch diameter tubing with a 0.083 wall. Sections of tubing are spliced together and supported by a top strut and bracing guys run to the boom tips. Each guy has a turnbuckle and is broken at two points by strain insulators. The turnbuckles place the boom under slight tension, which helps to keep the array from weaving around in a heavy wind.

A Lightweight 2-Element Yagi for 18 MHz

I've discussed the virtues and deficiencies of the 2-element Yagi beam. On the plus side, it's small, light-weight, and exhibits very high gain for the boom length. Deficiencies include a mediocre front-to-back ratio and a low feedpoint impedance. Moreover, the operational bandwidth defined by the allowable SWR and minimum front-to-back ratio is small compared to that of an optimized 3-element Yagi.

Having said that, I believe the virtues greatly outweigh the deficiencies of this little array. Take an 18-MHz design, for example. It can be built light enough to be mounted above an existing triband array and is (relatively) unobtrusive.

The 18-MHz band is narrow (18.068 to 18.168

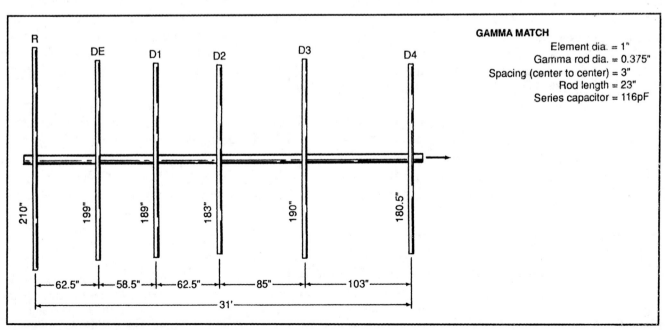

Figure 9-3. Assembly of the "big gun" Yagi (top view). See Figure 9-1 and its associated text for element assembly. Feedpoint resistance is about 30 ohms.

MHz), only 100 kHz, so operational bandwidth isn't a problem. And even though the feedpoint impedance is low (on the order of 12 ohms), the 2-element Yagi can be matched properly with either a gamma or a hairpin match. I think a 2-element Yagi is an ideal antenna for this band!

Average front-to-back (F/B) ratio of the little beam is about 10 dB. While this is nothing to get excited about, the relatively long skip on 18 MHz usually means that when the antenna is aimed in the direction of propagation, relatively little is coming in off the back of the beam. At least that's the way it's worked for me on the west coast!

During the morning hours, when the band is open to Europe and Africa, the Pacific area (off the back of the beam) is closed. During the afternoon, when the band is open to the Pacific, most of the signals to the east of me have faded out. Consequently, in my case F/B ratio is no big deal. If you have a similar propagation situation, the 2-element Yagi may be the right beam for you.

The Design. The Yagi lends itself to accurate computer-aided design. The beam described in this section was taken from a set of generic, untapered dimensions and placed in the Yagi Optimizer (YO) program of K6STI. YO analyzes and optimizes a Yagi array using performance criteria that the user specifies.

My specifications call for a short boom (not over 4 feet long), elements tapered from 0.75 inch down to 0.375 inch, and either a gamma or hairpin match. Elements are to be mounted directly by U-bolts to small plates attached to a 2-inch diameter boom. Feedpoint impedance is 50 ohms, unbalanced. Optimization frequencies are 18.068, 18.115, and 18.168 MHz. The antenna is designed in a "free space" environment.

The YO program permits tradeoffs in the areas of forward gain, F/B, and input impedance. The tradeoffs are expressed in percentages. To keep input impedance and F/B values reasonable, forward gain percentage of tradeoff was set at 60 percent. Input impedance and F/B ratio were set at 20 percent each. These choices were intuitive. If the gain tradeoff was too high, both SWR bandwidth and input impedance would suffer. One nice point about the YO program is that the tradeoffs can be modified quickly, if the results aren't to your liking.

The YO program iterates the generic design 482 times during the optimization process. Each element length and position is changed individually by a small amount to calculate the sensitivity of the objective to each variable. The **objective** is the combination of gain, F/B, and impedance defined with the tradeoffs. The set of sensitivities is called the **gradient**. The gradient points in the direction that maximizes the objective. Once the gradient is calculated, element lengths and position are upgraded, each in proportion to its sensitivity. The upgrade yields a new design with incrementally higher performance. The optimizer program runs until further improvement is no longer possible when additional small changes are made.

If the user decides additional investigation is worthwhile, he can modify antenna dimensions manually and continue automatic optimization. With the 2-element Yagi, there aren't many variables to manipulate. As far as gain and F/B ratio go, driven-element length is relatively unimportant. It is important, however, in determining impedance matching to the feedline.

This leaves director length and element spacing as variables to investigate. Experience, intuition, or data gleaned from handbooks and magazine articles will help determine the approximate spacing and director length to a rough degree. Director spacing falls in the 0.07- to 0.12-wavelength range. The forward-gain target is about 5 dBd. The F/B target is 10 dB. The feedpoint impedance (before matching) should be 10 ohms or more. As optimization progresses, these and other criteria are continually upgraded on the computer screen. With a keen eye and experience, a designer can guide the optimizer to produce the desired results.

Once the program has produced the design, tapering information is available for the tubing diameters specified. This information is important, as overall element length is a function of the taper. For a given element, the greater the taper, the greater the element length. The final computerized element dimensions for this Yagi antenna are given in **Figure 9-4**.

Note that if a gamma match is used for the driven element, the half-length dimension runs from the center of the element to the tip. If a hairpin match is used, the half-length dimension is from the attachment of the feedpoint of the element to the tip. Because a gap exists at the element center when the hairpin match is used, the overall physical length of the driven element is slightly longer than in the case of the gamma match.

Antenna Construction. A 4-foot length of 2-inch diameter aluminum tubing serves as the boom. Element spacing, center to center, is 44 inches. The center section of each element is 12 feet (144 inches) long and 0.75 inches in diameter. The next sections are 4 feet (48 inches) long, telescoped 2 inches into the center section ends. The short, middle C sections are 26-inch long segments of 0.625-inch diameter tub-

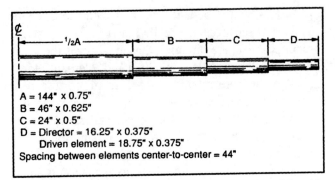

A = 144" x 0.75"
B = 46" x 0.625"
C = 24" x 0.5"
D = Director = 16.25" x 0.375"
    Driven element = 18.75" x 0.375"
Spacing between elements center-to-center = 44"

Figure 9-4. Dimensions for half-element lengths of the driven element and director.

ing, telescoped 2 inches into the larger section. The C sections are 0.5-inch diameter. The tip sections are 0.375-inch diameter tubing and their length is set according to **Figure 9-4**.

The outer end of each section is slotted, so the inner telescoping section can be grasped firmly by a stainless-steel hose clamp placed over the joint. All joints are coated with anti-oxidizing compound before assembly.

Elements are affixed to a small metal plate attached to the boom with U-bolts. The director is held to the plate by two smaller U-bolts. The driven element, with gamma match, can be bolted to a mounting plate in similar fashion. If a hairpin match is used, the driven element must be insulated from the boom. Methods of doing this are described in the *Beam Antenna Handbook*.

The usual anti-rust precautions should be observed. All hardware should be stainless steel, or in the case of nuts, bolts, and U-bolts, they should be plated. After assembly, it's a good idea to give each joint and connection a shot of rust-preventing paint from a spray can.

Antenna Operating Characteristics. The azimuth, free-space field plot of the antenna is shown in **Figure 9-5**. Beam width of the forward lobe (defined by the 3 dB down points) is about 70 degrees. The F/B ratio at the design frequency is about 12 dB. Forward gain is 4.98 dBd.

A summary of the operating characteristics appears in **Figure 9-6**. The upper-left-hand graph shows that the antenna gain varies around 5 dBd, and is greatest at the high-frequency end of the band.

The upper-right-hand graph illustrates the SWR, which is a minimum at 18.12 MHz, rising to about 1.4 at the band edges. I was unable to achieve this pristine curve, due no doubt to the fact the antenna had to contend with objects in the immediate vicinity (the house, ground, control cables, nearby TV antenna, etc.). However, I measured an SWR of 1.2 close to 18.115 MHz, with SWR less than 1.6 at band edges. I used a hairpin match and eventually lengthened the driven element 1 inch on each side to drop the antenna "in the slot." Adjustment was made when the telescoping tower was retracted to the 20-foot level. I noted the SWR changed slightly when the antenna was run up to its normal 45-foot elevation.

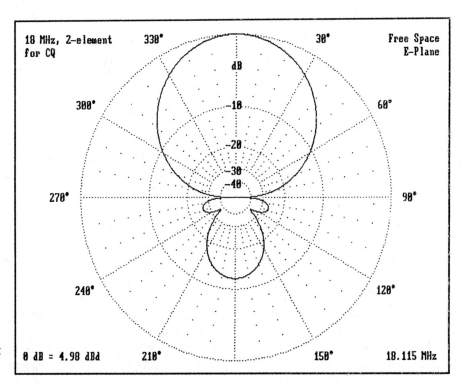

Figure 9-5. Polar plot of a 2-element beam.

Figure 9-6. Parameters of a 2-element beam. (See text for details.)

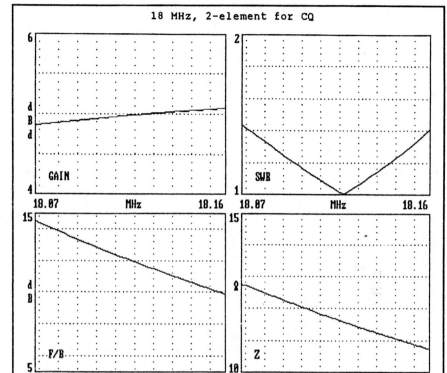

The lower-left-hand graph shows the antenna's F/B ratio. Note that F/B decreases rapidly, while power gain increases very slowly as the operating frequency is raised. That is characteristic of this type of simple Yagi. The F/B ratio is quite good at the low end of the band, approaching 15 dB.

The lower-right-hand graph shows the feedpoint impedance of the antenna. It runs from about 12.5 ohms to 10.5 ohms, within the limits of both the gamma and hairpin matching systems.

Antenna Matching. The antenna is ideal for stacking above a 20-meter beam. I didn't derive any stacking information, but I'd suggest a stacking distance of at least 6 feet for minimum interaction with a bigger array.

While the builder can hit the design frequency and minimum SWR values quite well, a purist may wish to adjust the match to provide unity SWR at the design frequency. To do so, it's necessary to be able to reach the matching system from a safe perch atop the tower. The short boom makes this job easy. **As with any antenna work, a safety belt is mandatory!**

With regard to the hairpin match, the length of the driven element is more critical than hairpin length. Enough overlap should be left at the first antenna joints so the driven element can be lengthened or shortened 3 or 4 inches. My preliminary hairpin match was made from two lengths of no. 10 copper

wire, plus a jumper made of back-to-back alligator clips. The length of the hairpin and that of the driven element can be varied by the experimenter, noting the SWR on the coax line for each adjustment. A notebook to log the dimensions and an assistant to turn on and off the transmitter are helpful.

The length of the matching rod and the value of the gamma capacitor are the variables in the gamma match. Information on building and adjusting both matching systems is given in the *Beam Antenna Handbook*.

A 3-Element Yagi for 20 Meters

The principal virtue of a 2-element beam is a high gain figure for a short boom. At the design frequency, gain is approximately 5 dBd. This is achieved with a boom length of less than 0.1 wavelength. Better performance is obtained with a director element than with a reflector.

The main disadvantage of the 2-element Yagi is poor front-to-back ratio. Typically, it will run from 10 to 12 dB. Input impedance is about 12 to 15 ohms, depending on parasitic element tuning. This value permits the use of a simple matching system, such as a gamma or hairpin match.

All things considered, the 2-element Yagi is a good performer for amateurs who desire a good gain figure,

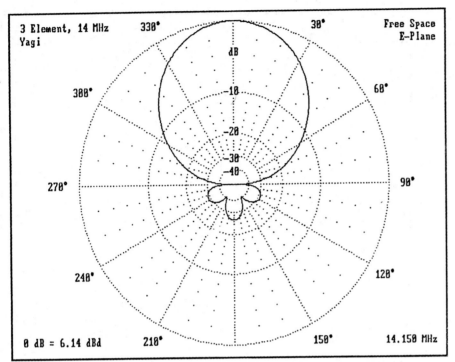

Figure 9-7. Polar plot of a 3-element Yagi.

but aren't worried about mediocre signal rejection from the rear of the antenna.

The 3-element Yagi is the antenna of choice on the HF bands. It provides a little more gain than the 2-element version, improved front-to-back ratio, and higher input impedance. The price paid for better performance is a longer boom and more aluminum up in the air.

Boom lengths for HF 3-element Yagis usually run from 0.2 to 0.4 wavelength. Short boom designs provide good gain and front-to-back ratio, but restricted bandwidth; that is, they cover only a narrow frequency range before the SWR rises over 2:1 on the feedline. Wider spaced arrays provide much improved bandwidth and good gain, but poorer front-to-back ratio.

As you may imagine, the process of designing a Yagi antenna consists largely of balancing the various attributes in a mix that's suitable for the user. Commercial antennas usually shoot for a user-friendly array, sacrificing a little gain for improved F/B ratio.

There's nothing wrong with this concept. It's easy for the user to check SWR and front-to-back, but it's difficult to check power gain. The antenna provides what the user wants to observe. And, he can work plenty of DX with the antenna, so the question of power gain is secondary.

Gain Figure of Merit

What are the factors that enter into antenna gain? The main factors are element lengths and spacing. If you assume the element lengths are optimized, maximum possible gain can be calculated from a gain Figure of Merit (FOM), based on antenna boom length.

One FOM study conducted by Tom Ring, WA2PHW, on an extensive collection of Yagi designs, yields this formula:

$$\text{Gain (dBd)} = 10 \text{ Log } (5.4075B + 4.25)$$

where B is boom length in wavelengths.

Another FOM is proposed by Rainer Bertelsmeier, DJ9BV:

$$\text{Gain (dBd)} = 7.773 \text{ Log } (B) + 9.28$$

The formula above was derived from the gain of DL6WU-design long-boom VHF/UHF Yagis.

A third gain formula comes from Bill Myers, K1GQ, for HF Yagis:

$$\text{Gain (dBd)} = 3 \text{ Ln } (B) + 9.85$$

The FOM doesn't represent the theoretical absolute-maximum gain figure; this leads to extremely low impedances and impractical designs. The formulas were derived from gains of practical near-maximum- gain Yagi designs with real-world losses and design compromises. The FOM isn't intended as an overall quality rating for Yagis, as it rates gain/boom length efficiency

Figure 9-8. Parameters of a 3-element, 14-MHz Yagi. At the top left is gain across passband. At the top right is SWR response. At the bottom left is front-to-back ratio, and at the bottom right is feedpoint impedance.

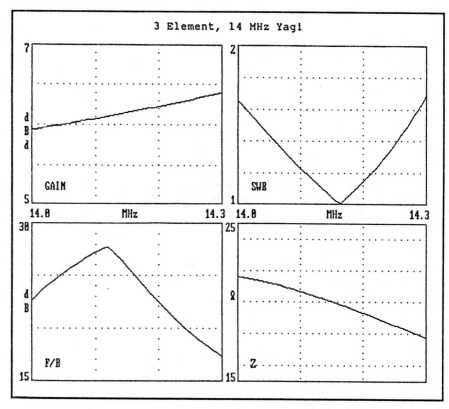

only. Most Yagi applications require good patterns, and this constraint always places a limit on forward gain. Nevertheless, gain FOM provides a valuable yardstick for showing at a glance how close a particular design comes to realizing maximum possible gain.

The FOM concept is particularly helpful when used in combination with a computer-driven antenna analysis or optimization program. With a given boom length, such programs can vary element length and spacing, while displaying an FOM for each variation in the antenna.

The 3-element, 14-MHz Yagi design shown here was derived using the Yagi Optimizer program of K6STI. The goal was to achieve maximum possible gain consistent with good front-to-back performance, adequate SWR bandwidth, and acceptable input impedance. The WA2PHW formula provides good results for any boom longer than 0.25 wavelength, and it's used in the optimizer program for the Yagi described here.

A Practical 3-Element Yagi for 14 MHz

Computer analysis of a Yagi antenna is an exercise in compromise. For example, when the designer shoots for maximum gain, he forfeits front-to-back ratio or bandwidth. The trick is to balance these attributes until he achieves his objective.

The target design provides 6 dBd forward gain, better than 20 dB front-to-back ratio over the design range, and an input impedance on the order of 15 ohms or better. The FOM should be better than –1.5 dB. Boom length should be 24 feet or less. (Boom length is chosen so two 12-foot sections of tubing are sufficient.)

The design includes tapered elements with diameters ranging from 1.25 inches at the center to 0.875 inches at the tip. The elements are mounted on small aluminum support plates attached to the metal boom with U-bolts. Either a gamma or hairpin match may be used with the antenna.

A polar plot of the computed horizontal pattern is given in **Figure 9-7**. At the design frequency the front-to-back pattern is excellent, with three minor lobes to the rear, all of them better than 24 dB down from the frontal lobe. The "3 dB" beamwidth is about 64 degrees.

Important parameters of the antenna are shown in **Figure 9-8**. Gain varies from about 5.9 dB at 14.0 MHz to 6.4 dB at 14.3 MHz. At the design frequency (14.15 MHz), it's 6.14 dBd. This is shown in the upper-left-hand graph. The upper-right-hand graph illustrates SWR response over the operating range. SWR is approximately 1.6 at the frequency extremities, falling to near-unity at the design frequency.

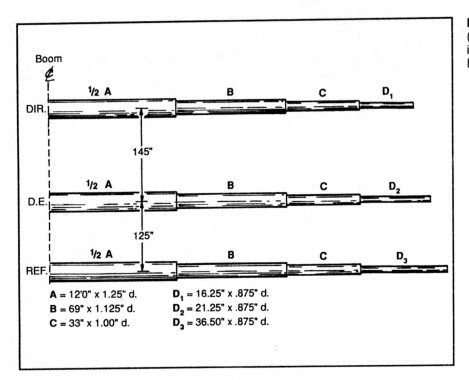

Figure 9-9. Half-element dimensions (with the exception of section A, which is full length, add 3 inches to B, C, and D for overlap when cutting the tubing).

A = 12'0" x 1.25" d.   D₁ = 16.25" x .875" d.
B = 69" x 1.125" d.   D₂ = 21.25" x .875" d.
C = 33" x 1.00" d.   D₃ = 36.50" x .875" d.

Front-to-back ratio is illustrated in the lower-left-hand plot. Maximum F/B is achieved near 14.12 MHz, where it peaks at 28 dB. Input impedance falls in the 20-ohm area (lower-right-hand graph), where a match may easily be achieved with either a gamma or hairpin type. Power gain is about 1.3 dB less than the maximum possible amount, and this falls within the FOM limit.

This beam represents a comfortable tradeoff regarding gain, front-to-back ratio, bandwidth, and input impedance. It's possible to squeeze more gain out of the 3-element beam, but front-to-back ratio and input impedance must be sacrificed.

Antenna dimensions are listed in **Figure 9-9**. The center section of each element is a 12-foot length of 1.25-inch tubing with a 0.058-inch wall thickness.

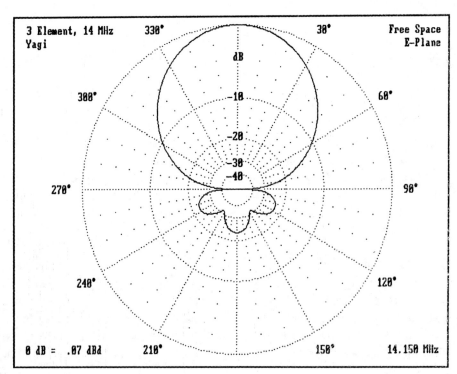

Figure 9-10. A short-boom (12 foot) Yagi provides 5.07 dB gain and 23 dB front-to-back ratio.

Figure 9-11. Top left: gain versus frequency. Top right: SWR versus frequency. Bottom left: front-to-back versus frequency. Bottom right: feedpoint impedance versus frequency.

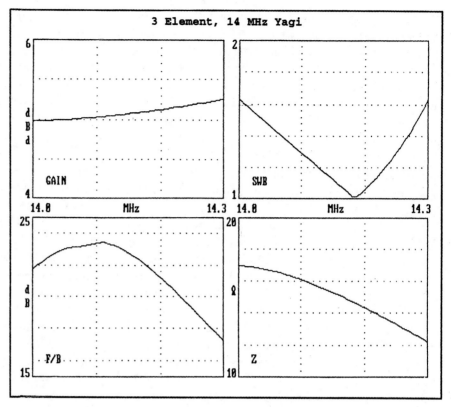

The next sections are cut from a 12-foot length of 1.125-inch wall tubing with a wall thickness of 0.058 inch. The sections with a diameter of 1.0 inch also have the same wall thickness. The tip sections have a wall thickness of 0.049 inch.

I haven't provided construction details here, as they are fully covered in the *Beam Antenna Handbook*.

A Short-Boom 3-Element Yagi for 20 Meters

A short-boom Yagi is an interesting antenna design that can be investigated by the Yagi Optimizer. A 3-element, 20-meter Yagi on a 12-foot boom sounds very attractive. A single section of 2 or 2-1/2 inch

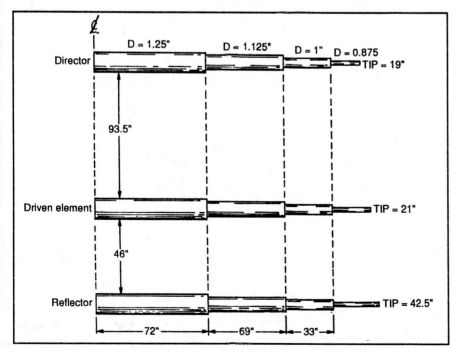

Figure 9-12. Half-element lengths, spacing, and diameters for a short-boom Yagi.

diameter tubing can be used for the boom, eliminating the boom splicing usually required for a longer boom.

Maximum element spacing (reflector to director) of 11 feet 8 inches was chosen, and element lengths and spacing were iterated by the optimizer program. After 803 iterations, the program provided a design that exhibited a gain of 5.07 dBd at the design frequency of 14.15 MHz, a front-to-back ratio of 23 dB, a feed-point impedance of about 15 ohms, and an SWR figure of better than 1.6:1 over a range of 300 kHz. The free-space polar plot of the short-boom array is shown in **Figure 9-10**. Not too shabby!

Antenna operating parameters are shown in **Figure 9-11**. The upper-left-hand plot shows power gain, which runs from 5 dBd at 14.0 MHz to 5.5 dBd at 14.3 MHz. The upper-right-hand plot illustrates the very reasonable value of SWR across the design range. The lower-left-hand plot shows that front-to-back ratio peaks at nearly 25 dB around 14.11 MHz. The lower-right-hand plot shows that feedpoint impedance is about 15 ohms at the resonance frequency; this value can easily be matched by any of the popular systems. Antenna dimensions are given in **Figure 9-12**.

All in all this is a good, practical design. However, reflector-to-driven-element spacing is tight, and movement and vibration of the elements may show up as slight SWR variations when the antenna flexes in a heavy wind.

Compared to the wide-spaced 3-element, 14-MHz array on a 24-foot boom, this little antenna has about 1.04 dB less forward gain, and sacrifices about 5 dB in front-to-back ratio.

It's interesting to compare this antenna with the 2-element Yagi. The big advantage of this little antenna over the 2-element type is not in gain, but vastly improved front-to-back ratio!

An Interesting 3-Element Yagi Design

The Yagi Optimizer user can spend many a rainy day exploring antenna parameters, playing with gain versus front-to-back versus bandwidth versus boom length versus input impedance. There are an infinite number of configurations. I ran across the interesting one shown in **Figure 9-13**. It's a 3-element design on a 20-foot boom. The beam provides 5.86 dBd gain and 26 dB front-to-back ratio near the design frequency of 14.2 MHz. This is a well-behaved, wide-bandwidth design, with a feedpoint impedance of about 20 ohms at the design frequency. Various operating parameters are shown in **Figure 9-14**.

Note that the element spacing isn't equal (**Figure 9-15**). The reflector/driven-element spacing is much less than the driven-element/director spacing. This uneven spacing has appeared so many times in modern Yagi designs that it seems to be an important factor in providing optimum performance.

Where did this particular design come from? It started with a design for a 3-element Yagi given in Chapter 8, Section 14, of *Yagi Antenna Design* (an

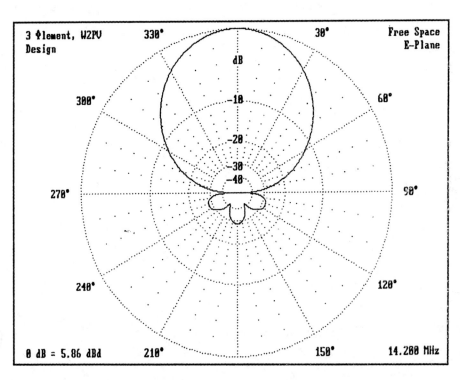

Figure 9-13. Polar plot of a modified W2PV-style 14-MHz Yagi on a 20-foot boom.

Figure 9-14. Top left: gain versus frequency. Top right: SWR versus frequency. Bottom left: front-to-back versus frequency. Bottom right: feedpoint impedance versus frequency.

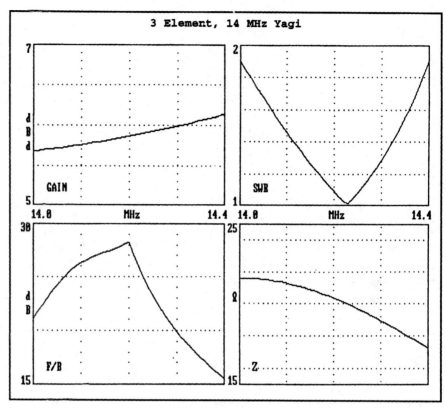

ARRL publication), by the late James Lawson, W2PV. Gain, front-to-back, SWR response, and input impedance derived by the optimizer program are very close to those values given in the original W2PV design. However, notice the difference in element spacings and length!

I started the program by inputting the W2PV data to the optimizer program. As the program ran, I could see on the monitor the driven element moving steadily closer to the reflector and the element lengths changing. Very interesting. The end results were the same as those derived by W2PV, but the optimizer provided a different set of element dimensions and spacing.

Well, that's what makes the ball game interesting.

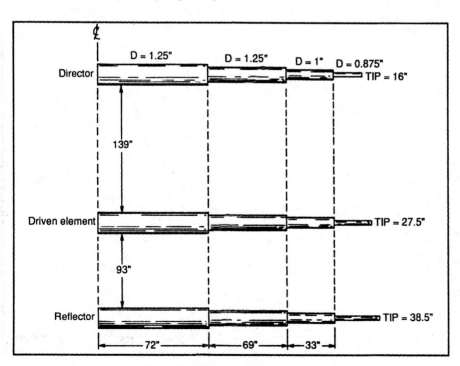

Figure 9-15. Half-element lengths, spacing, and diameters of a W2PV-type Yagi.

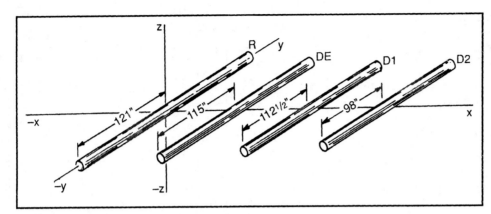

Figure 9-16. The W6SAI 4-element, 24-MHz beam in X-Y-Z coordinates. Element spacings are measured from the reflector, and half-element lengths are used.

The K6STI Yagi Optimizer is calibrated against NEC, the accurate antenna analysis program used by professionals. I believe the results obtained from K6STI's program are very close to real-life data obtained in the field on a well-calibrated antenna range.

A 4-Element Yagi for the 24-MHz Band

During the higher portions of the sunspot cycle, 24 MHz is an exciting band. Although its width is narrow, occupancy is less than either 28 or 21 MHz, and pleasant DX QSOs can be had without eager-beaver DXers breathing down your neck!

As always, a good beam pays big dividends. Fortunately, a 24-MHz, 4-element beam isn't big enough to excite the neighbors and is light enough for one

man to handle. This design is built on an 18-foot boom and provides about 6.3 dBd gain across the band. The F/B ratio is about 25 dB. Tweaking the beam on an optimizer program increases the gain only slightly, but it can provide an additional 7 dB in F/B ratio. This exercise is left for those fortunate owners of Optimizer software.

Beam dimensions are shown in **Figure 9-16** and the input for the file, in YO format, is provided in **Table 9-1**. Element half-lengths are used. Beam parameters are shown in **Figure 9-17**. Additional information on the Optimizer is given in Chapter 8.

Note that the driven element of the beam when measured in full from tip-to-tip is 230 inches. This dimension holds true even if the element is split at the

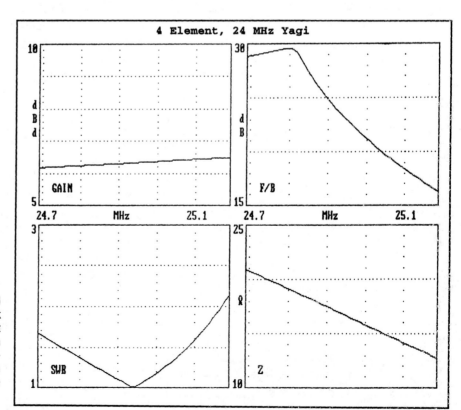

Figure 9-17. A look at the W6SAI beam. Gain is 6.33 dBd; front-to-back is 23.26 dB; input impedance is about 16.8 ohms, reactive. SWR when matched is 1.00. Gain is nearly constant across the band, but maximum front-to-back ratio occurs outside the low end of the band.

(1)	W6SAI Beam				
(2)	24.94 MHz				
(3)	4 elements, inches				
(4)		0.875	0.75	0.625	0.5
(5)	0	25	45	45	6
(6)	67.625	25	45	45	
(7)	115	25	45	42.5	
(8)	210	25	29	44	

Table 9-1. The input file for the W6SAI beam. The first vertical column lists element spacing, measured from reflector. Line 4 lists tubing diameters of element sections. Note that the reflector has a 6-inch tip, 1/2 inch in diameter. (Numbers shown to the left of the box are for reference only—see text—and do not appear.)

Driven Element	Position	Length
Reflector	0.00	105.75
Driven Element	37.50	100.75
Director #1	90.75	97.25
Director #2	174.00	94.50
Director #3	259.75	93.50
Director #4	369.00	94.75
Director #5	478.00	91.25

Boom Length = 40 ft. 0 in. = 480 in.
All elements = 12 ft. × 1 in. diameter
Plus .875 in. diameter tips

Table 9-2. Half-element dimensions of a 7-element Yagi on a 40-foot boom. Height above ground is 70 feet.

center and a few inches are removed for a hairpin match. If the element isn't split, and a gamma match is used, the full length dimension also applies.

A 2-inch diameter boom is recommended and elements are held in position with small mounting plates and U-bolts. Beam construction is covered in detail in the *Beam Antenna Handbook* and in the ARRL publication, *The ARRL Antenna Book*.

A Big Gun for 10-Meter DX

When 10 meters is open, it's an amazing band. DX signals are loud and strong, and there's plenty of competition in working the choice ones. A 7-element Yagi on a 40-foot boom is the answer!

Here is the design data for a nice 7-element Yagi on a 40-foot boom, optimized over the 28.0 to 28.6 MHz range by the K6STI's YO program. All data shown is for a height above ground of 70 feet. **Figure 9-18** and **Table 9-2** give a quick summary of the array. Nearly 10 dBd gain is achieved over the operating range, with an average front-to-back ratio of about 25 dB. Input impedance is about 23 ohms at the design frequency (28.3 MHz).

Figure 9-19 shows the parameters. Gain is close to 10 dBd, with a smooth front-to-back ratio curve. The SWR curve is very docile, running below 1.4:1 across the range. This permits quick QSY without time-consuming amplifier retuning. Front-to-back (upper right plot) is excellent.

Figure 9-20 shows the polar plot. The –3 dB points of the pattern are at plus and minus 25 degrees. The split back lobes are comfortably low. Looking back at **Figure 9-19**, you can see that this pattern is nearly constant across the operating range.

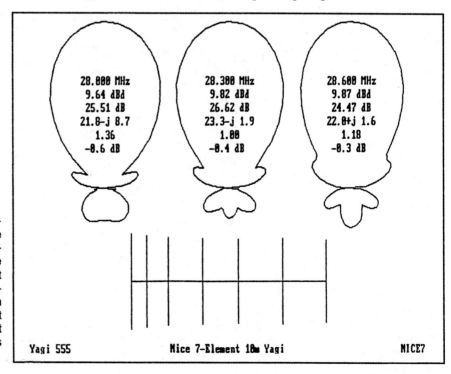

Figure 9-18. Parameters of a 7-element beam. Three frequencies are given with data for each. Line 1 is frequency, line 2 is gain over dipole, line 3 is front-to-back ratio, line 4 is input impedance, line 5 is SWR match to 50-ohm line, and line 6 is antenna gain compared to a theoretically perfect antenna, showing loss due to element resistance. Outline of the antenna is below the plots.

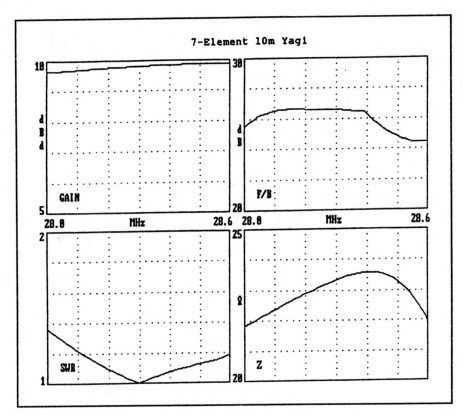

Figure 9-19. Plots of antenna performance. Upper left: gain over operating range. Upper right: front-to-back over operating range. Lower left: SWR response. Lower right: input impedance. Curves are derived from K6STI's Yagi Optimizer program.

The elevation pattern is shown in **Figure 9-21**. Note the main lobe of the array is at an angle of about 7 degrees. Nice! Over normal ground the nulls of the pattern will tend to fill in and it won't be quite as sharp as the computer indicates. In any event, the first lobe is right where you want it—just above the horizon!

I won't go into construction details; they're in the *Beam Antenna Handbook*. The design is for 1-inch diameter elements with 0.875-inch diameter tip sections. The boom is made of two 20-foot sections of aluminum irrigation pipe with two top guys to keep everything steady. Elements are mounted above the boom.

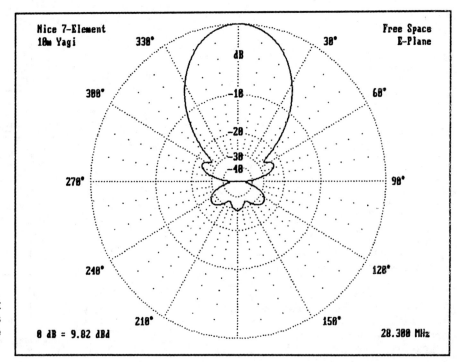

Figure 9-20. Polar plot of a 7-element Yagi. The beam is about 50 degrees wide at "–3 dB" points. Observe the good front-to-back ratio.

Figure 9-21. Elevation plot. The major lobe is 8 degrees above the horizon when the beam is 70 feet high.

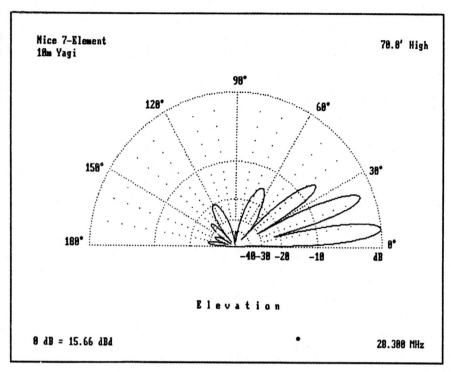

Matching the Beam

Either a hairpin or a gamma match may be used. For the hairpin, the driven element is broken at the center to make a 2-inch gap. The hairpin is placed across the gap (as is the 1:1 balun). The hairpin is made of a U-shaped piece of no. 10 A.W.G. copper wire. The U is 6-1/2 inches long, with 2-inch spacing.

For the gamma match, 0.125-inch diameter rod is placed parallel to the driven element, spaced 2 inches away. Length is about 14 inches. The series capacitor is about 63 pF, and should be adjustable.

The Yagi Over Ground

A while ago I spoke to a fella on 20 meters who had a 3-element Yagi on a 45-foot tower. There's nothing startling about that, but I found out during the QSO that he had laid out an elaborate copper ground

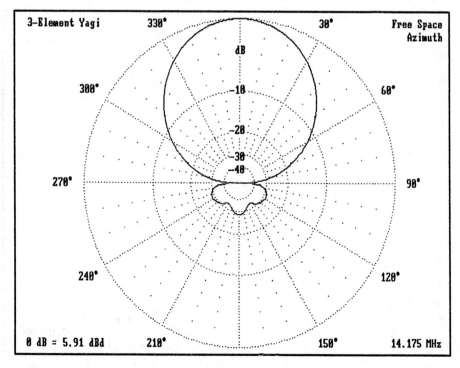

Figure 9-22. Classic plot of a Yagi in free space. Gain is 5.91 dBd.

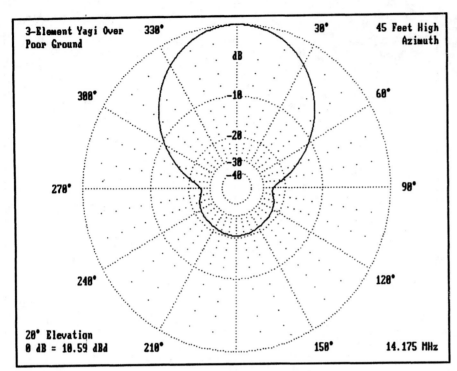

Figure 9-23. Plot of the same Yagi 45 feet above poor ground. Compare the front-to-back and front-to-side ratio with Figure 9-22. Gain figure includes ground-reflection gain.

screen, about 90 feet square, on the ground under the tower. He said the screen really improved his signal.

After the QSO, I began to think about that screen. Did it really improve his signal? He's in the midwest, where ground conductivity is pretty good. Has he wasted time and money in installing his elaborate ground?

The *ARRL Antenna Book* shows elevation patterns of horizontal half-wave antennas at various antenna heights above average earth (K = 13, G = 0.005 S/m) at 14 MHz. Taken as a whole, it looks as if there's a loss of about 2 dB in the plane of the main lobe as compared to the same pattern over perfectly conducting earth. Perhaps my friend does achieve something with his elaborate ground system.

The K6STI Antenna Analysis Program provides the means to check horizontal antenna azimuth and ele-

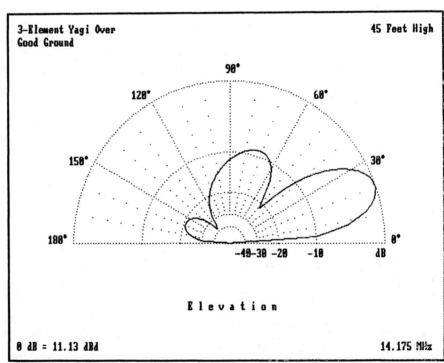

Figure 9-24. Elevation plot of a Yagi 45 feet over good ground.

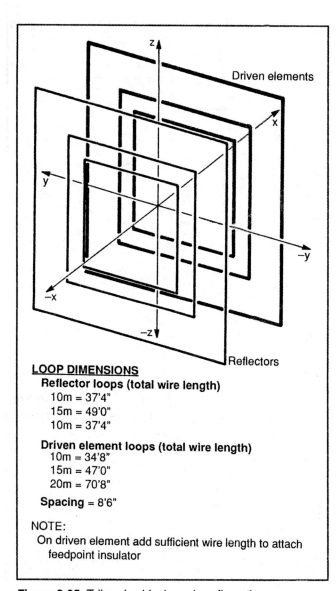

LOOP DIMENSIONS
  Reflector loops (total wire length)
    10m = 37'4"
    15m = 49'0"
    10m = 37'4"

  Driven element loops (total wire length)
    10m = 34'8"
    15m = 47'0"
    20m = 70'8"

  Spacing = 8'6"

NOTE:
  On driven element add sufficient wire length to attach
    feedpoint insulator

Figure 9-25. Triband cubical quad configuration.

vation pattern in free space, as well as over various grades of earth. I first configured the program to show the comparison in the azimuth pattern of a 3-element Yagi in free space, above good ground and above poor ground. The classic free-space polar pattern is shown in **Figure 9-22**. The patterns of the same Yagi over good and poor ground are nearly identical (**Figure 9-23**). The gain figure of the array over good ground is about 0.54 dB better than the figure for poor ground.

Note that the front-to-side and front-to-back ratios of the array are degraded for both cases of ground reflection, as compared to the free-space azimuth plots. Also note that ground reflection has added nearly 6 dB to lobe maxima in the elevation plane. This

gain occurs because the ground-reflected wave adds in-phase to the direct wave at this angle.

But what of the elevation plot? **Figure 9-24** shows the plot over good ground. The plot over poor ground is almost identical; the main difference is that the deep nulls apparent in the good ground pattern aren't as prominent in the poor ground pattern.

As far as a horizontally polarized HF antenna is concerned, there's no need to worry about ground conductivity. The horizontally polarized antenna is relatively immune to ground loss beneath it, provided it's reasonably high in the air. There's not much you can do about it, in any event!

A Practical Triband Quad for 20, 15, and 10 Meters

The quad is a popular antenna, particularly in those areas where it's difficult to obtain aluminum tubing, or where a multiband antenna with a small "wingspread" is desired. A lot of information is available on single-band quads, but there's not much specific data on multiband arrays.

Generally speaking, the quad is a tricky antenna to build. Side dimensions are critical, especially with regard to F/B ratio. A change in side dimension of one inch, for example, means a change in overall loop wire length of four inches. This can degrade the F/B ratio by up to 10 dB. Therefore, it's a good idea to hold wire length to a fraction of an inch. Prestretching the wire is suggested and the wire is most easily cut to length if it's under tension.

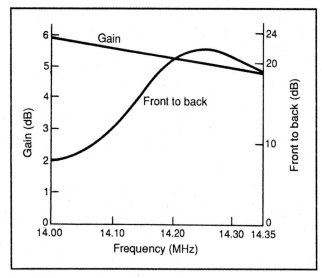

Figure 9-26. Response of 20-meter section of triband quad.

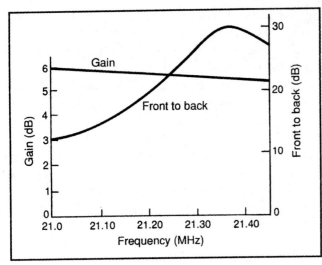

Figure 9-27. Response of 15-meter section of triband quad.

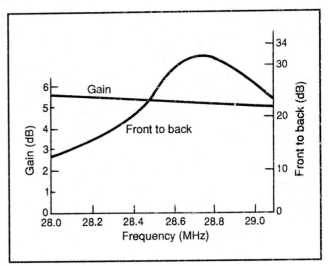

Figure 9-28. Response of 10-meter section of triband quad.

The finished loops should be held under tension so that the wires don't sag. This can be accomplished by adjusting the tie points of each quad loop so the wires are taut. Data on building a multiband quad and matching it to a single feedline are given in *All About Cubical Quad Antennas* (pages 75 to 80).

Quad Dimensions and Performance Data

Recent advances in computer programs for antennas have overcome the frequency offset and bent-wire problems inherent in MININEC-based programs. The new programs can compute side dimensions of the quad accurately and provide power gain and F/B ratio data at various chosen points in each ham band. It's up to the builder to duplicate the dimensions as closely as possible to obtain the best results.

Figure 9-25 gives dimensions for the triband quad. Wire size is critical; in this design it's no. 12 A.W.G. (2.053 millimeter diameter). A change in wire size will alter the electrical characteristics of the antenna.

Response of the quad in the various bands is shown

in the illustrations. On 20 meters (**Figure 9-26**), average gain across the band is 5.5 dBd, while F/B ratio varies between 8 dB at the low end of the band to about 22 dB near the high end.

Fifteen-meter response is shown in **Figure 9-27**. Average gain is 5.5 dBd, while F/B ranges from 12 dB at the low end of the band to about 30 dB near the high end. On 10 meters (**Figure 9-28**), average gain is maintained at 5.5 dB and F/B varies from 13 dB at the low end of the band to about 32 dB at the high end. Thus, all three quad sections have about the same gain figure and F/B ratio across the bands, with the F/B peaking near the high end of each band.

As with Yagi antennas, the F/B response of the quad can be seriously degraded by unwanted coupling between the transmission line and the antenna field. Use of a balun and correct placement of the coax with respect to the antenna are recommended for best results.

For additional information on the quad, refer to *The Quad Antenna*, by Bob Haviland, W4MB, published by CQ Communications, Inc., or *All About Cubical Quad Antennas*, by W6SAI and W2LX.

Chapter 10

Antenna Instrumentation

I was young once and knew everything. One of my beliefs was in the honest-to-gosh reading of an SWR meter. I believed that you merely put the meter in the line to the antenna and this magical instrument would tell you just what was happening inside the coax. It was all very simple. Fortunately, I learned rapidly, and in the process I amassed six or seven SWR meters. It was always amusing to make SWR measurements on an antenna with one meter and then to repeat the measurements with another. It was almost possible to hand-pick the SWR curve I wanted by choosing the correct instrument, as they provided widely different readings.

I'm not the only radio amateur who's been led down the daisy path by the SWR meter. The complications associated with this interesting device are more important today than ever before, because of the advent of the solid-state, high-frequency transceiver.

The More You Have the Less You Get

Most high-frequency transmitters with solid-state power amplifiers incorporate a protective circuit that gradually turns off the amplifier as the SWR on the antenna system rises. Because most antennas are single-frequency devices (that is, adjusted at one spot in a particular band), a low SWR value is obtainable at only one frequency. Operating the antenna off frequency causes the SWR on the feed system to rise, even though the antenna may work in excellent fashion across the whole band.

Tube-type amplifiers, with their adjustable output controls (TUNE and LOAD), can adapt themselves to wide variations in the SWR of the antenna system. The solid-state, wide-band amplifier, on the other hand, requires protection against SWR excesses—hence, the fail-safe shut-down design. When the SWR

starts to rise, the amplifier transistors are electrically derated for protection.

All well and good, I say, but the user of such equipment must pay attention to the SWR across his band of operation, or he'll find that he can get full power output from his rig only over a small portion of the band. This vexing problem is particularly true on 160, 80, and 10 meters, where the width of the band is large in proportion to the center frequency.

Enter the SWR Meter

As **Figure 10-1** shows, an SWR meter is commonly used to gain a picture of SWR versus frequency to determine just what's going on with regard to a particular antenna. Is this a true picture of what's happening? Possibly not. A knowledge of the workings of the SWR meter (sometimes called a "reflectometer") and its use are of utmost importance.

Many modern SWR meters are composed of two directional couplers built into one case. A single indi-

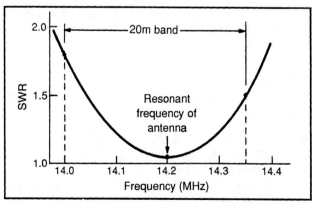

Figure 10-1. Idealized SWR curve of a 20-meter antenna. Resonant frequency is 14.2 MHz. The antenna is matched at this frequency and the SWR is very nearly 1:1, rising rapidly as the antenna is operated off frequency.

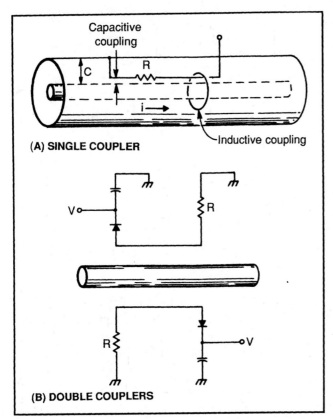

(A) SINGLE COUPLER

(B) DOUBLE COUPLERS

Figure 10-2. The directional coupler can sense either the forward or reflected wave components in a transmission line by taking advantage of the fact that the reflected components of voltage and current are 180 degrees out of phase, while the forward components of voltage and current are in phase. A short section of line coplanar with the inner conductor of the main transmission line (A) is formed into a loop through a series resistor. Voltage across the series-connected loop and resistor is measured, the combination constituting a short, terminated transmission line. The pickup device is sensitive to waves traveling in one direction by virtue of capacitive and magnetic coupling. The coupler may be rotated physically 180 degrees to pick up waves traveling in the reverse direction. An alternative is to use two couplers built in one unit, but oriented in the opposite direction (B). Ideally, both couplers should be identical in coupling to the coaxial line and in directivity.

cating meter is switched between the couplers, and the meter often is calibrated directly in terms of SWR (standing wave ratio). A directional coupler is a device that samples voltage flowing in one direction in a transmission line, but it is insensitive to reflected voltage flowing in the opposite direction.

If the antenna exactly matches the characteristic impedance of the transmission line and also matches the line with respect to balance, it will absorb all power transmitted down the line. If a mismatch exists at the antenna, a certain portion of RF power will be reflected back down the line toward the transmitter.

One form of directional coupler picks up energy from the line via both inductive and capacitive coupling. The induced voltage in the line flows according to the direction of the traveling wave producing it. Under SWR conditions, there can be direct and reflected waves passing through the coupler. The capacitive pickup, however, is independent of the direction of the traveling waves, and the sum of coupled voltages in the device produced from the waves of one direction will add in phase. Those produced from waves of the opposite direction will subtract in phase (**Figure 10-2A**).

The electrical balance of a coupler is such that the voltage induced from the reverse-traveling wave will cancel the other completely, or nearly so, resulting in a directivity factor in the coupler. This means the coupler is highly insensitive (nulled) to a wave traveling in the reverse direction. As a result, the device is sensitive to only one of the traveling waves, which produces standing waves by interference. To determine SWR, it's necessary to read forward and reverse (incident) voltages flowing in the line. Two couplers, reverse connected, can do the job (**Figure 10-2B**). In order to obtain accurate readings, both couplers must be identical. Each coupler should be insensitive to voltage that passes through it in the opposite direction.

The important coupler characteristic is the ratio of the measurement in the forward direction to that in the reverse direction. If the coupler is sensitive to the unwanted reading, coupler accuracy is seriously compromised. When two couplers are used to make up an SWR meter, the problem is compounded.

A good laboratory-type coupler will have a directivity of better than 25 dB, indicating that the coupler provides 25 dB of discrimination between opposite traveling waves. An SWR meter made up of two such couplers provides an indicated value of SWR differing from the true value, as shown in **Figure 10-3**. For example, a true value of SWR of 1.5:1 on a transmission line can provide an indicated value on the SWR meter that can vary between the extremes of 1.23:1 and 1.8:1. Most cheap CB-type SWR instruments aren't this accurate.

Added to the directivity limitation, most inexpensive SWR meters have a built-in error because of the nonlinearity of the diode used to provide voltage for the indicating meter. At low voltage levels, where the SWR reading is of the greatest importance, diode linearity is poorest.

Finally, all directional couplers are sensitive to second harmonic voltage that may exist in the antenna circuit. Because the antenna is mismatched at harmonics, it's possible for high SWR to exist at a harmonic frequency, and if the coupler is accidentally placed at a point in the line with high harmonic voltage, pickup of this voltage will adversely affect the reverse reading of the coupler.

You may scoff at this notion, and say that the second harmonic level of your transmitter or exciter is "down 35 dB," or some such number. This is all well and good, but just remember that with a high value of antenna mismatch reflection at a harmonic, the harmonic voltage passing through the coupler may be many times higher than you suppose. And don't forget that when a coupler is measuring the reflected wave in a line, it may be measuring as high as 40 to 50 dB below the fundamental signal level. That is to say, the unwanted harmonic voltage easily can be of the same order of magnitude as the measured reflected wave.

For best results, I suggest you buy the best SWR meter you can afford. Some SWR meters are made up of two directional couplers, back to back. Others have a single coupler with a reversible element. I prefer the latter. One coupler made in the United States has plug-in heads for various frequencies and power levels. It's useful for both HF and VHF antenna measurements. While I don't believe in "plugging" name brands, be assured this high-flying instrument is really a Bird!

Pitfalls in Making SWR Measurements

So now you have a good SWR meter! Congratulations. If you use it properly, you'll get meaningful information. But you just can't jam it into a coaxial line, and expect the instrument to do its job. It's up to you to make sure the meter reads what you're looking for (true SWR of the antenna) and not a jumble of information resulting from unwanted coupling between the transmission line and the antenna. Let me explain.

Any conductor in the field of an antenna is coupled to that antenna inductively. The degree of coupling depends upon the position of the conductor with respect to the antenna and the distance between antenna and conductor. A good example of such a conductor is a parasitic element in a beam antenna. It's closely coupled to the antenna and tuned closely to its frequency. Other conductors coupled to your transmitting antenna are overhead power lines, telephone lines, and your transmission line.

Yes! The outer shield of a coaxial line can be inductively coupled to the antenna if it runs parallel, or nearly so, to the antenna and is elevated above ground

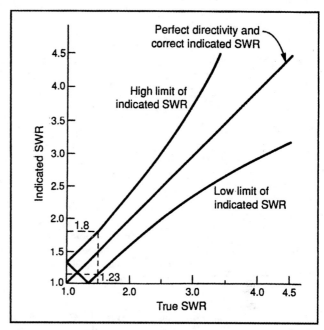

Figure 10-3. Extreme limits of indicated SWR versus actual SWR for a coupler having 25 dB of directivity. (Adapted from "Possible Errors in VSWR Measurement," Breetz, *QST*, November 1959.)

level. An example of this is shown in **Figure 10-4**, a typical antenna installation.

Antenna current induced on the outer shield of a transmission line will influence the SWR reading of voltages within the line, as the outer shield is no longer at ground potential, even though the SWR meter and transmitter are supposed to be near ground potential. The outside of the coax line has become part of the antenna system (due to inductive coupling to the antenna) and thus becomes part of the load on the line, in addition to the antenna load. The SWR on the line is now determined by the composite load of the antenna and the outside of the transmission line. *This is one reason why changing the length of the*

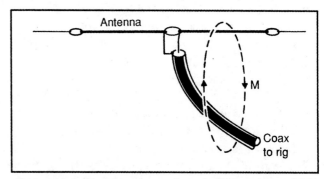

Figure 10-4. "Antenna currents" can be induced into shield of the transmission line by inductive coupling (M) between the line and the antenna, and also by lack of a balun at the antenna.

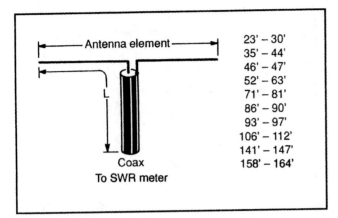

Figure 10-5. Recommended nonresonant transmission-line lengths (L) for the high-frequency amateur bands. The lengths indicated include the distance between one tip of the driven element and the feed point, plus the coaxial line length. (Adapted from the *ARRL Antenna Book*.)

transmission line changes the SWR reading. The portion of the load caused by unwanted line coupling is being changed!

How to Reduce Unwanted Line Currents

To achieve an accurate SWR reading on your transmission line it's necessary to detune and decouple the line from the antenna. Certain lengths of transmission line as measured between one tip of the antenna and the SWR meter (L) aren't resonant in the amateur bands (**Figure 10-5**). Cutting the transmission line to recommended lengths helps, but it isn't a total cure for the problem.

It's equally important to remember that the transmission line should not run parallel to the antenna elements. It should be positioned close to the ground, not suspended above it. This is a tall order when a rotary beam is used because at some beam headings the antenna elements probably will run parallel with the transmission line. The best solution is to run the coaxial line along the ground from the antenna tower to the station, or bury it beneath the ground in a section of water hose. The worst thing is to run the coaxial line a long distance above the ground from tower to station (along the rooftop, for example). This places the coax line up in the air and closer to the active antenna.

What do you do when it's impossible to cut line length to a recommended value, and the line must run along the rooftop in the vicinity of the antenna? Obviously, induced antenna currents are going to flow in the outer conductor of the line. How can SWR measurements made under these conditions be trusted?

Decoupling the Transmission Line

Let's assume that your situation is this: You have a triband beam for 20-15-10 meters atop a 40-foot tower. The coax feedline runs down the tower to the 10-foot level, then runs along your roof for about 20 feet to the station, drops down to near ground level, and enters a window near the transmitter. You make SWR measurements across each band and obtain a reassuring set of curves that bear little resemblance to the "typical" curves supplied by the manufacturer. How can you determine if your curves are valid?

The easiest and quickest check is to add four or five feet of coaxial line between the SWR meter and the antenna and rerun the SWR curves. If the shape or amplitude of the SWR curves changes, it's a good bet that you have unwanted coupling between the antenna and transmission line. Of course, when this experiment is performed, it's understood that the unbalanced, coaxial line is properly terminated at the antenna in a balun or other device that provides a match between the unbalanced line and the balanced driven element of the beam. (Note: Such a test is valid *only* if you have a good SWR meter.)

If you find there's interaction between line and antenna, and it's impractical to move or otherwise change position of either the line or the antenna, what's to be done?

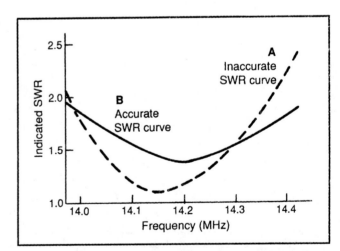

Figure 10-6. (A) Measured SWR curve with unwanted antenna currents flowing in the outer conductor of the coaxial line. The curve indicates antenna system resonance near 14.15 MHz with very low SWR. The more accurate curve run with antenna currents on line suppressed shows a flatter response, with higher value of minimum SWR at 14.225 MHz. The classic curve of measurement (A) may lull an amateur into thinking he has a perfect match, whereas the correct curve (B) shows match is not quite as good.

Figure 10-7. Three identical SWR meters placed at random spots along a transmission line should give the same indication regardless of the SWR on the line. Does this happen in real life? Probably not. The ability of the SWR meter to discriminate against the reverse-traveling wave determines to a large extent the accuracy of the readings. (By this I mean the ability of the "forward" indication to discriminate against the "reverse" indication, and the ability of the "reverse" indication to discriminate against the "forward" indication.) This discrimination is termed *directivity*.

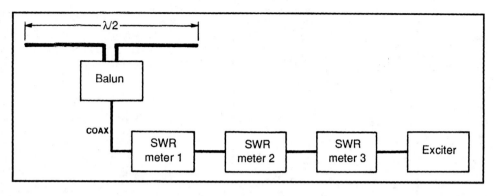

One helpful and easy thing to do is to coil the line into a simple RF choke at the foot of the tower. Four or five turns about a foot in diameter, held together with electrical tape, will help to "cool off" the line at the tower.

At the station end of the line, a second, similar coil may help solve the problem. The coil can be made by splicing an extra length of line into the system with coaxial adapters. After the coils are in place, make new SWR runs, with and without the extra spliced-in line section. Do the two sets of measurements agree within reason? If they do, your transmission line is reasonably well decoupled from the antenna (**Figure 10-6**). Don't expect the curves to match exactly; a degree of line coupling may still exist, particularly if the transmitter or exciter is enclosed in a "leaky" cabinet that permits RF to pass from the transmitter circuits to the outside of the cabinet (most of today's modern transmitters fall into this regrettable category).

SWR Meters: Good and Bad

The name of the game is to keep all the RF bottled up inside the transmission line up to the antenna and let none of it escape along the outside of the coaxial line. This will provide the most reliable SWR indication. But all your good efforts may go for naught, if you choose a poor SWR meter! Look at **Photo 10-A**. It compares the directional element of a Bird coupler with an inexpensive, imported "CB-type" SWR meter. Note that the coupling element of the cheap device is an open trough, with one side exposed, providing excellent coupling between the wanted measurements and any induced waves traveling along the outside of the coaxial line. The break in the line shield inside the SWR meter provides a perfect place for transmission line currents and unwanted induced currents to join—right at the point the measurement is being taken.

You don't have to throw out your cheap SWR meter, but don't put too much trust in it either. Borrow a good directional coupler and place it in series with your SWR meter. See how the two compare in readings across your antenna's span of operation. Decouple your transmission line by keeping it close to ground level and winding it up into RF chokes at the station and tower ends of the line. Make sure you use a good balun at the antenna, if one is required. You'll be doing OK!

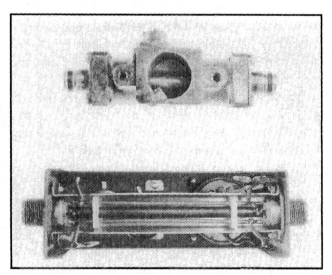

Photo 10-A. Bird coupler (top) is machined from solid-brass casting. The coupling element is plugged into the hole at the center of the structure. The center conductor of the coaxial line can be seen running through the center of the coupler. Voltage pickup is taken from the fitting on the side of the casting. The inexpensive "CB-type" SWR meter (bottom) has two directional couplers made up of wires placed parallel to the center conductor of the open coaxial line section. The open trough with one side exposed permits antenna currents flowing on the outside of the coaxial line to enter the measuring section of the line where the coupling elements are located.

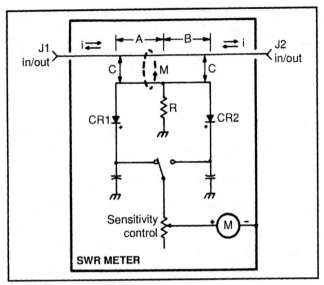

Figure 10-8. A simple SWR meter uses two direction couplers (A and B) to sense forward and reflected wave components in a transmission line. Reflected components of voltage and current are 180 degrees out of phase while the forward components of voltage and current are in phase. Inductive (M) and capacitive (C) pickup between transmission line and pickup line provide voltage that is rectified by diodes (CR1, CR2) to provide "forward" and "reflected" readings on meter M. Couplers are terminated in a common resistor, R.

More on the SWR Meter

How can the owner of an SWR meter determine if the readings he gets are meaningful? Fortunately, there's a simple and inexpensive test procedure that will determine the quality of any SWR meter. You can run the test in a few hours' time.

Consider the situation in **Figure 10-7**. Three SWR meters are placed at random spots along a transmission line to an antenna. At any given value of SWR,

the three devices should provide the same indicated reading. Does this happen in real life? Probably not. In addition to inherent error mechanisms such as meter movement and the linearity of the diodes in the SWR indicators, the directivity of the individual couplers in each SWR meter enters the picture. By directivity, I mean the ability of the coupler to discriminate between opposite directions of RF power flow. Because many mid-price-range SWR meters have both a "forward" and "reverse" coupler built into them, the directivity factor assumes great importance.

A sketch of a representative SWR meter showing the two couplers is given in **Figure 10-8**.

The SWR Meter Test

The technique shown in **Figure 10-7** provides a good check for an SWR meter. Move the meter along the transmission line and note any change in indicated SWR. However, this is cumbersome and hard to accomplish in most cases. Also, the results may not be reproducible due to the interaction between the field of the antenna and the outer shield of the transmission line.

A more practical test for the SWR meter is shown in **Figure 10-9**. A deliberate mismatch is measured through various lengths of transmission line. A dummy load is used to eliminate the interaction between antenna field and the line. The degree of mismatch SWR is known and repeatable. Best of all, the test is easy to run and inexpensive to set up. Note that a second harmonic filter is required between the signal generator (your transmitter or exciter) and the test setup. This is because the second harmonic energy, small though it may be, is sufficient to disrupt the results of the investigation (see **Figure 10-10**).

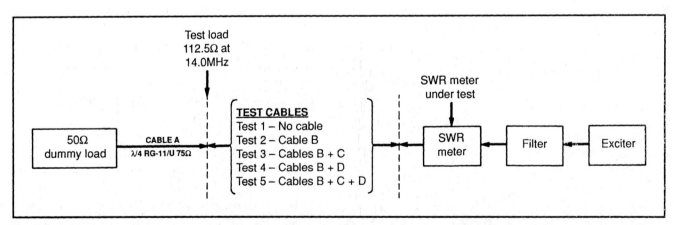

Figure 10-9. A representation of the test procedure. At the left is the 112.5-ohm dummy load made up of a 50-ohm load and a quarter-wave section of transmission line acting as an impedance transformer. At the right is the test setup for the SWR meter. See Figure 10-10 for filter data. The test arena is the area between the vertical dashed lines. Five tests are conducted: One test requires no interconnecting lines; the other four tests require line sections representing 1/8-, 1/4-, 3/8-, and 1/2-wave line sections.

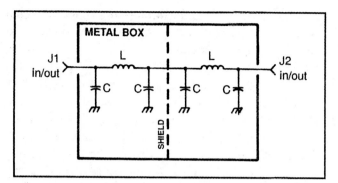

Figure 10-10. A harmonic filter for 14 MHz. An attenuation of about 30 dB is provided for the second harmonic. Each capacitor (C) is 220 pF. Each inductor (L) is 0.55 µH seven turns, no. 16 wire 1/2-inch diameter, 7/8-inch long. Suitable coaxial connectors are placed on the ends of the box (J1, J2) and the filter sections are separated by a shield plate placed across the middle of the box. Filter wire passes through a small hole drilled in the shield.

The mismatched load is made up of a 50-ohm dummy load and an electrical quarter-wave section of 75-ohm coaxial line. The line section serves as an impedance transformer, providing a terminal impedance of 112.5 ohms at the open end. If this value of load is measured through a 50-ohm SWR meter, the indicated SWR should be the ratio of the load to the line impedance, or:

$$\frac{112.5}{50} = 2.25\!:\!1$$

The test is conducted as shown in the illustration. The mismatch load is measured directly, and then remeasured through various lengths of 50-ohm line. If the SWR meter is perfect (and none of them are), the SWR reading will remain constant at each observation point. The amount of variation in the indicated SWR reading from the true reading determines the reliability of the SWR meter. Accuracy of the test depends upon the exact length of each line section, so cut them carefully and check your results with a dip-meter.

Preparing for the Test

The test is run at 14.0 MHz in this example. The 75-ohm mismatch line section is made from an 11-foot 7-inch section of either RG-59B/U or RG-11/U. (Other versions of RG-59 coax aren't suitable, as their impedances may be as low as 73 ohms.)

Suitable connectors are placed on each end of the line and line length is measured from tip to tip of the center conductor. Next, three sections of 50-ohm line are made up. Two are 1/8-wavelength long (5 feet

9-1/2 inches) and the third is 1/4-wavelength long (11 feet 7 inches). Again, suitable plugs are placed on the line and length is measured from tip to tip of the center conductor. An accuracy of plus-or-minus 1/2 inch is satisfactory. Suggested cable types are RG-8A/U, RG-213/U, RG-58/U, or RG-58C/U. Don't use the old cable designation of RG-8/U or "RG-8-type" cable. That stuff usually runs close to 52 ohms impedance.

When the cables are complete, label the 75-ohm cable A, the two short 50-ohm cables B and C, and the long 50-ohm cable D. You can make up paper labels and tape them directly over the jacket of the lines with transparent tape.

The last step is to make up the second harmonic filter. A suitable filter is shown in **Figure 10-10**. It's constructed from air-wound coils and mica capacitors and built in a small metal box. A shield is placed between the filter sections, as shown, and suitable coaxial receptacles are placed on the ends of the box. The filter is rated for a power level of about 150 watts.

Running the Test

Test 1 involves measuring the SWR directly at the end of cable A. Make up a suitable chart and record all your readings. Later a graph can be drawn from the chart data (**Table 10-1**).

For Test 2, cable B is added between the SWR meter and cable A, and an SWR reading is taken and logged. In Test 3, cables B and C are used in series. In Test 4, cables B and D are measured in series. Finally, Test 5 involves using cables B, C, and D in series. The numbers in **Table 10-1** were derived by testing a cheap, imported SWR meter.

What you have just finished doing, in effect, is to add 1/8-wavelength sections of coax line between the "mismatch" line section and the SWR meter. This is electrically equivalent to placing the SWR meter at different points along the line, as discussed in **Figure 10-7**.

Test Number	Cables	Length (λ)	Indicated SWR
1	0	0	3.35
2	B	1/8	2.00
3	B + C	1/4	1.50
4	B + D	3/8	2.75
5	B + C + D	1/2	3.35

Table 10-1. Representative SWR readings recorded with a "Brand X" SWR meter as various cable lengths are added between the meter and an unmatched load, as shown in Figure 10-9. Actual value of SWR in each case is 2.25:1.

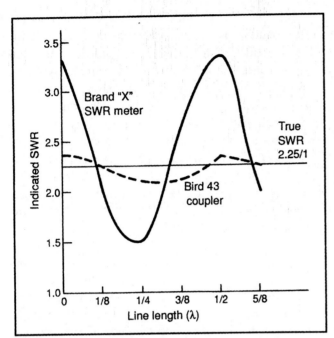

Figure 10-11. Using the data in Table 10-1, plus a second test run on a Bird 43 coupler, produces the chart shown. The indicated SWR measurements (Y-axis) are plotted against cable length (X-axis). An additional section of cable was used to extend the plot to 5/8 wavelength. Note that the plot is not symmetrical about the true SWR value.

Results of the Test

A representative test on two SWR meters is charted in **Figure 10-11**. The second instrument is a Bird 43 coupler. The variations of the indicated reading from the true SWR values are obvious and startling!

This graph explains one of the reasons why the indicated SWR will vary with the placement of the instrument in the line. It also gives lie to the popular but incorrect belief that changing line lengths alters the SWR on the line! Varying the line length changes the indicated SWR reading to a degree, depending upon the accuracy of the SWR meter, but the actual SWR on the line remains the same. (It's true that actual SWR will decrease with line length due to line attenuation, but this is another matter and may be ignored in the high-frequency spectrum. Most amateur handbooks provide tables of line attenuation for those interested in pursuing the subject further.)

Interpreting the Results

The graph in **Figure 10-11** shows that even an excellent SWR coupler such as the Bird provides a reading that varies with line length to a small degree. The inexpensive "Brand-X" SWR meter, however, is not to be trusted. The indicated reading varies between a

low value of 1.5:1 and a high value of 3.35:1 for a true SWR value of 2.25:1. You can get almost any reading you wish merely by moving the instrument back and forth along the line!

The test results are based upon a single frequency measurement (14.0 MHz) and the variations in SWR reading change with frequency, growing worse as the frequency of operation is raised. This is why most cheap SWR meters provide gibberish at 10 meters and higher. The Bird coupler, on the other hand, has frequency-rated, plug-in detectors that provide good accuracy in the HF, VHF, and UHF regions.

The indicated SWR excursions determined by the just-completed tests can be used to determine the directivity factor of the SWR meter (directional coupler), with the aid of **Figure 10-12**. (This drawing is reproduced with thanks from the November 1959 issue of *QST*. It appeared in an article entitled "Possible Errors in V.S.W.R. Measurement" by Louis D. Breetz, W3KDZ/W8QLP.)

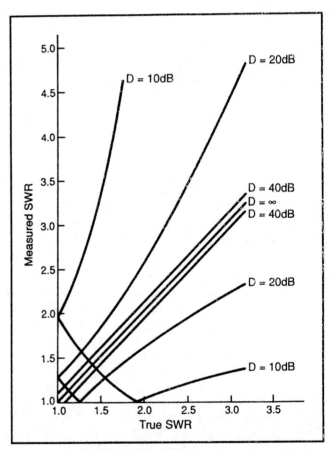

Figure 10-12. A reproduction of the chart in the November 1959 issue of *QST* showing the relationship between true SWR and measured SWR. A good directional coupler has a directivity figure of close to 40 dB. This is an expanded version of fig. 10-3. (Reprinted courtesy *QST* magazine).

The directivity is found by locating the maximum excursions of SWR on the graph you have made in **Figure 10-11** and finding them on the Y-axis (vertical) of **Figure 10-12**. For example, the Bird coupler has an SWR excursion of 2.35:1 to 2.1:1. Find the true value of SWR (2.25:1) on the X-axis (horizontal) and proceed upward until you cross the points you have located on the Y-axis. This indicates a directivity of almost 40 dB, which is excellent. On the other hand, the indicated maximum SWR excursions of the "Brand-X" SWR meter are 3.35:1 and 1.5:1. Locating these points on **Figure 10-12** indicates a directivity of about 15 dB, which is very poor!

As you can see from an inspection of your own graph, and also **Figure 10-12**, a directivity of nearly 40 dB is required to give a meaningful SWR reading, and even that degree of excellence allows an error of about 5 percent in the reading. Note, too, that the indicated SWR curve plotted for both instruments isn't symmetrical about the true SWR value, further complicating interpretation of data to a degree.

SWR Meter Wrap-up

This simple experiment illustrates that only a good SWR meter (or directional coupler, if you wish) will provide meaningful SWR numbers. Armed with this information, it should be possible for any amateur to make *meaningful* SWR measurements. (Thanks to Willy Sayer, WA6BAN, for deriving this test setup and for making the measurements on the two SWR meters.)

Beyond the SWR Meter— The Antenna Analyzer

Users of an SWR meter will quickly discover that the resonant frequency of an antenna system can be determined by varying the frequency of the exciter and watching the SWR change across the band. If your feedline is properly decoupled from the antenna, this check can be run in the station, and a curve such as the one shown in **Figure 10-1** can quickly be generated from a number of SWR readings.

The antenna experimenter can take this process one step further by using an SWR analyzer. The MFJ Model 259 (**Photo 10-B**) is an example of this helpful device. This hand-held instrument combines a variable frequency signal generator, a frequency counter, an SWR meter, and an RF resistance meter. The device can be run from internal batteries, or with an add-on AC supply.

Frequency coverage is 1.8 to 170 MHz and measurements are referenced to 50 ohms. Many resonant

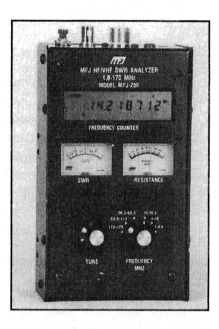

Photo 10-B. The MFJ Model 259 hand-held SWR analyzer.

circuits (besides an antenna)—such as amplifier input and output networks, stubs and traps, inductors, transmission lines and filters—can be analyzed.

With regard to antenna measurements, meaningful SWR and RF impedance can be made at the station end of the coax, providing the coax is not acting like part of the antenna by virtue of unwanted coupling. For example, to measure SWR on the coax to your antenna, the analyzer is connected to the line and the "Tune" and "Frequency" controls are adjusted to your test frequency—as read on the counter. The SWR is read from the meter. To find the lowest SWR, adjust the frequency until the meter reaches the lowest reading. Read the frequency from the counter. Is it the same as the test frequency, or is your antenna resonant at some other point in the band? Now you know the answer to this question.

If your SWR is unity, the resistance meter will give you the feedpoint resistance of the antenna. If the antenna is reactive (you are not at the resonant frequency), the reading you get won't be accurate. An SWR reading of 1:1 (unity) and a resistance reading of 50 ohms means you've hit the jackpot.

The beauty of the SWR analyzer is that you can vary your test frequency at will, find the resonant frequency of the antenna, and then determine the resistance at the input end of the coax line. With a little expertise, you can determine if your antenna is too long or too short, if your gamma match is set correctly, and if the bandwidth is between the 2:1 (or 3:1) SWR points. All of these tests, and more, can be performed with an antenna analyzer.

The Antenna Analyst

The AEA (Advanced Electronic Applications, Inc.) Antenna Analyst is a more sophisticated (and more expensive) antenna instrument than the Analyzer. The AEA SWR-121 HF is a representative version of this device (**Photo 10-C**). Basically, it consists of a micro-processor-controlled frequency synthesizer, an SWR bridge, and an LCD display that shows the SWR response of the antenna under test. Frequency coverage is 1 to 32 MHz. In addition to the SWR plot on the screen, a digital SWR readout is provided. An RS-232 interface allows remote control of the device, remote display, and the saving of plots.

The Analyst provides the SWR response over an entire range, selected by the user. It also has the ability to measure antenna reactance positive and negative, so meaningful results can be obtained at off-resonance frequencies.

As with the SWR analyzer, measurements may be made at the station end of the coax, which reduces the amount of running back and forth between the antenna and the station equipment. You can run a frequency sweep of your antenna, make adjustments to the antenna, and repeat the sweep. By making comparisons between the sweeps, you quickly determine if your adjustments are taking you in the right direction.

For instance, assume you wish an SWR plot of your antenna between the 2:1 SWR points. The center frequency of the instrument is set near the resonant frequency of the antenna, and the display width is selected. A 100-ohm resistor is temporarily placed across the antenna terminals to establish the 2:1 axis on the screen. The antenna is reconnected, the plot started, and in a few seconds the SWR response appears on the screen.

All in all, the SWR meter plus the new MFJ Analyzer and AEA Analyst provide a picture of antenna operation that was available only in well-equipped laboratories a few years ago. Ham radio has come a long way from the flashlight bulb on a loop of wire that the early experimenters used to try to puzzle out the bewildering operation of the early antennas.

A Final Word . . .

Congratulations! You have plowed through this handbook to the very end. I hope you have enjoyed reading it as much as I enjoyed writing it. There is a lot of practical data on the preceding pages, and I hope you'll try one of the many antennas described in this

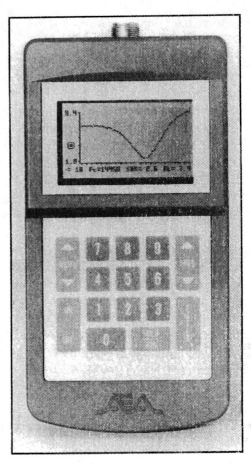

Photo 10-C. The AEA SWR-121 HF Antenna Analyst.

work. If you have success with it, tell a friend and encourage him to put one up, too. After all, building and testing antennas is just about one of the last areas of experimentation open to the average ham. All that is needed are some simple tools and the urge to experiment and learn something new. Gone are the days when you could build a complete station on breadboards with a hammer, screwdriver, and Boy Scout knife.

In addition, make up some original antenna designs yourself. It isn't hard to take an existing design and modify it to create something new and novel. How about building a half-wave dipole antenna in a space a quarter wavelength long? Or a loaded mini-loop antenna for 10 meters that your neighbors will think is a TV antenna? You might think about two 15-meter Yagis, on the same boom, crossed at right angles to each other and fed 90 degrees out of phase.

If you have one of the many fine antenna analysis programs on the market, your computer will assist you in the design of your next antenna project. The sky's the limit! Have fun, and let me know about your new knock-out design.

Index